CHEMISTRY TEACHER'S GUIDE

CHEMISTRY TEACHER'S GUIDE

Michael P. Olmsted

Parker Publishing Company, Inc. West Nyack, N. Y.

LIBRARY OF CONGRESS
CATALOG CARD NUMBER: 70-169596

PRINTED IN THE UNITED STATES OF AMERICA

ISBN-0-13-128900-4
B & P

To my students

Also by the Author:

Enrichment Experiments in Basic Chemistry

How to Use This Book

This book was written to help the experienced chemistry teacher present the important concepts of chemistry in an effective, meaningful way. It does not choose sides between such approaches as CHEM Study, and the more traditional courses, since you will select the type of course based on your training, experience, personal preference, and last but not least, the needs and abilities of the students you teach. This book will help guide you in designing the type of material best suited for you and your students by covering key questions and presenting suggestions.

Most of the book is devoted to important topics which should be covered in a one-year, college preparatory course in chemistry. No recommendations regarding depth of treatment are made, since this will vary with your purpose and ability as well as the students' needs. Practical ways of presenting most of the topics discussed are included. Demonstrations and laboratory experiments which relate chemical principles to descriptive chemistry are mentioned, and cross references are included. There is a broad spectrum of opinions regarding the sequence of topics. Historical material is included, since some teachers will present a liberal arts-oriented approach, exploring the growth of scientific ideas.

A meaningful chemistry course might best be held together by a few unifying concepts. Coulomb's law, for example, is used in developing atomic structure, chemical bonding, ionic reactions, and physical and chemical properties of substances, including acid-base properties. Much mileage can be obtained from this idea, which will recur many times throughout the book.

The concept of concentration will be applied to density, pressure, temperature, charge density, rates of physical and chemical processes, molarity and normality. Most of the chemical problems involving stoichiometry and the general gas equation are unified under the mole concept. Chemical behavior of the elements and their compounds are best treated by using the concept of chemical periodicity, which is in turn related to Coulomb's law and atomic structure. All of these underlying ideas can be used to great advantage in presenting a meaningful, coherent course in modern chemistry. Descriptive chemistry can be used as illustrations of the principles to help the student associate different ideas and apply principles. The principles represent the skeletion and the descriptive material the flesh on the body which we call "Chemistry."

The basic concepts of chemistry include the kinetic theory and states of matter, atomic structure, bonding, chemical periodicity, chemical calculations, solutions and ionization theory, acid-base chemistry, redox and electrochemistry. Colloid chemistry and nuclear chemistry are also discussed. You, as the teacher, can determine how much of this material should be emphasized and how to use descriptive chemistry to best advantage. Most college teachers prefer to have students who have been well grounded in understanding the basic principles, even though the syllabus may be only partially covered.

Science teaching is not static, and the study of science itself is a self-correcting approach to new knowledge and understanding. Although interpretations may change, the facts do not, and I hope this book will help you develop some of the basic methods and attitudes toward the quest for truth and excellence in chemistry.

Michael P. Olmsted

Table of Contents

How to Use This Book **7**

1 Introducing the Basic Concepts of Chemistry **17**

1. Explaining the Methods of Science — *17*
2. Solving Problems by Dimensional Analysis — *18*
3. Calculating Errors — *20*
4. Developing the Fundamental Concepts of Concentration, Coulomb's Law, Rate of Change in System, Equilibrium, Energy, Entropy — *22*
5. Distinguishing Between Different Kinds of Matter, Physical and Chemical Changes — *26*
6. Obtaining Information from Chemical Formulas — *29*
7. Writing and Balancing Equations — *30*

2 Interpreting States of Matter Using Kinetic-Molecular Theory **33**

1. Explaining the Gas Laws — *33*
2. Developing the Concept of Temperature — *37*
3. Applying Avogadro's Hypothesis — *39*
4. Deriving the General Gas Equation — *40*
5. Distinguishing Between Real and Ideal Gases — *41*

2 Interpreting States of Matter Using Kinetic-Molecular Theory .... continued

6. Accounting for the Physical Properties of Liquids and Solids and Changes in State — *42*
7. Explaining Vapor Pressure and Vapor Pressure Diagrams — *44*

3 Explaining Atomic Structure and the Periodic Law 49

1. Developing the Concept of Atomic Weight — *49*
2. Using Experimental Results to Develop a Model of the Atom — *50*
3. Approaching the Development of Atomic Structure Historically — *53*
4. Accounting for Radioactivity, Isotopes, and Other Phenomena — *54*
5. Developing the Ideas of Quantum Mechanics and the Quantum Atom — *56*
6. Developing the Electronic Distribution in Atoms, Shapes and Orientations of Orbitals — *59*
7. Relating Coulomb's Law to Ionization Energy, Electron Affinity, Atomic Radius, Nuclear Charge, Shielding Effect and Periodic Properties — *61*
8. Development of Periodic Law from Mendeleeff to Moseley — *64*
9. Correlating Periodic Properties of Metals and Non-Metals with Atomic Structure — *66*

4 Correlating Chemical Bonding and Properties of Compounds 69

1. Developing the Concept of Valence — *69*
2. Explaining Covalent, Coordinate-Covalent, and Ionic Bonding — *70*
3. Using Electronegativity Scale to Predict Types of Bonding and Oxidation Numbers — *75*

4 Correlating Chemical Bonding and Properties of Compounds .... continued

4. Predicting Properties from Molecular Geometry and Type of Bonding, Including Hybridization of Orbitals — *77*
5. Using Types of Attractive Forces to Explain Properties of Substances — *83*
6. Using Resonance Concept and Charge Density to Interpret Properties — *85*
7. Correlating Ionic Radius and Charge with Lattice Energy and Hydration Energy, Hydrogen Bonding — *87*

5 Teaching Chemical Calculations Using the Mole Concept 91

1. Developing the Mole Concept — *91*
2. Explaining the Concept of Equivalents — *93*
3. Using Experimental Data to Determine Atomic and Molecular Weights — *95*
4. Applying the Mole Concept to Per Cent Composition, Determination of Empirical Formulas, Problems in Stoichiometry — *98*
5. Using Molar and Normal Solutions — *102*
6. Using the General Gas Equation and Avogadro's Hypothesis — *104*
7. Correcting Pressure for Gases Collected over Water — *107*
8. Solving Problems in Electrochemistry, and Using the Oxidation Potential Concept — *108*
9. Calculating pH and Simple Problems Involving Equilibrium Constants — *110*

6 Interpreting the Properties of Solutions and Colloids 115

1. Explaining the General Properties of Solutions — *115*

6 Interpreting the Properties of Solutions and Colloids .... continued

2. Exploring Factors Which Influence Solubility — *116*
3. Unsaturated, Saturated, and Supersaturated Solutions — *119*
4. Determining Solubility and Interpreting Solubility Curves: Crystallization — *120*
5. Solutions of Gases in Liquids — *121*
6. Explaining Colligative Properties of Solutions — *122*
7. Interpreting Differences Between Solutions of Electrolytes and Non-Electrolytes — *125*
8. Distinguishing Between Colloids, Solutions and Suspensions — *125*
9. Explaining Adsorption, Light-Scattering, and Other Properties of Colloids — *126*

7 Developing Acid-Base Concepts and Ionization Theory 129

1. How Arrhenius Interpreted Properties of Solutions and Electrolytes — *129*
2. Accounting for Properties of Solutions of Electrolytes in Modern Terms — *131*
3. Developing the Bronsted Acid-Base Concept — *132*
4. Relating Structure and Electronic Effects to Strengths of Acids and Bases — *136*
5. Correlating Acid-Base Properties with Chemical Periodicity — *140*
6. Using the Lewis Acid-Base Concept — *141*
7. Teaching the Writing of Ionic Equations — *143*
8. Predicting Electrode Reactions in Electrolysis Cells — *146*
9. Use of Ionization Constants, pH, Acid-Base Indicators — *148*

8 Explaining the Concepts of Kinetics and Equilibrium **151**

1. Interpreting the Factors Which Influence Rates of Reactions — *151*
2. How We Recognize and Explain Equilibrium — *151*
3. Using the Concepts of Activation Energy, Collision Theory, and Reaction Coordinates — *152*
4. Determining Rate Laws Experimentally — *155*
5. Using the Law of Mass Action to Write Equilibrium Constants — *159*
6. Using Le Chatelier's Principle and Equilibrium Constants — *161*
7. Relating Situations of Ionic Equilibrium to Principles — *162*
8. Applying Principles to Interpret Non-Ionic Equilibrium — *166*

9 Developing the Concept of Energy **171**

1. Explaining the Different Varieties of Energy — *171*
2. Developing the Concept of Chemical Energy — *172*
3. Explaining Heat Content, Entropy, Free Energy — *175*
4. Teaching Energy Calculations — *178*
5. Relating Free Energy to Electrical Energy in Electrochemical Reactions — *180*
6. The Use of Energy Diagrams and the Born-Haber Cycle — *182*
7. Use of Free Energy As Criterion for Feasibility of a Reaction — *185*
8. Relation of Free Energy to Equilibrium — *186*

10 Teaching Oxidation—Reduction and Electrochemistry . . **189**

1. Developing the Concept of Redox — *189*

10 Teaching Oxidation—Reduction and Electrochemistry .... **continued**

2. Determining Oxidation Numbers from a Formula — *192*
3. Use of Half Reactions — *194*
4. Balancing Redox Equations — *196*
5. How to Use the E° Concept and Its Relation to Equilibrium — *200*
6. Predicting Electrochemical Reactions — *204*
7. Interpreting the Corrosion of Metals — *207*

11 Teaching Organic Chemistry **211**

1. Explaining the Variety and Properties of Organic Compounds — *211*
2. Classifying and Naming Organic Compounds — *212*
3. Interpreting the Properties of Compounds from Structure and Electronic Effects — *220*
4. Exploring the Types of Isomerism — *226*
5. Exploring a Few Organic Reactions — *229*
6. Some Compounds of Biological Interest — *233*

12 Explaining Nuclear Phenomena **237**

1. Explaining Radioactivity, α and β Decay — *237*
2. Explaining the Concepts of Half-Life, Binding Energy, Fission, Fusion — *240*
3. Exploring Some Applications of Nuclear Reactions — *244*
4. Interpreting Energy Sources of Stars — *247*
5. Use of Radioactive Isotopes in Research and Medicine — *248*

13 Using Descriptive Chemistry **251**

1. Use of Demonstrations and Laboratory Experiments — *251*

13 Using Descriptive Chemistry .... continued

2. Relating Principles to Practical Situations — *252*
3. Getting Mileage from the Periodic Table — *257*
4. Some Examples of Creative Chemistry — *260*
5. How to Strike a Balance Between Descriptive Chemistry and Chemical Principles — *264*

Index 269

1

Introducing the Basic Concepts of Chemistry

1. EXPLAINING THE METHODS OF SCIENCE

Hopefully your students will have taken a previous course in physical science, such as Introductory Physical Science (IPS), in order to prepare them for chemistry. A chemistry student should know the metric system and be familiar with such terms as mass, weight, density, force, pressure, system, scientific law, hypothesis, and theory.

Give a brief review of the scientific method, and during the course you can point out the various steps involved in the formulation of laws, hypothesizing, developing concepts and theories. Point out that a *law* is empirical and results from *inductive reasoning,* based on experiment and observation. A *hypothesis* is an educated guess, or *model,* designed to account for experimental observations and is useful in generating new experiments to test the hypothesis. A *theory* is a set of assumptions which are used to interpret natural phenomena and lasts only as long as it is useful. It must be modified or even discarded if new experimental evidence is discovered which contradicts the mental pictures we have constructed. Emphasize that science is a dynamic process.

Experimentation is a method used for obtaining information: answers to questions asked of nature. In *qualitative* experiments the investigator is interested primarily in how something behaves under a certain set of conditions, and in *quantitative* experiments he is interested in *how much* is involved in a process. Chemistry began to flourish only after the advent of the quantitative approach, as is true in all science. The discovery of most scientific laws resulted from measurement. It was not until Lavoisier weighed materials entering and produced in a chemical reaction that the nature of burning was elucidated. The phlogiston theory had to be abandoned in favor of the new idea of reaction with oxygen.

Example Let us consider a burning candle. The system consists of wax, a piece of string, air, and a flame. If we isolate the system by placing a large beaker over the burning candle, the flame is seen to grow smaller and eventually disappear. The candle is still there, as is the wick. Did the air change? We could analyze the remaining air and find that it is different from ordinary air: the oxygen content has decreased markedly. From this experiment we might hypothesize that oxygen is necessary for burning. This would suggest more experiments in which different amounts of oxygen could be used to determine the effect of burning. We would find that the candle burns much more brightly and faster in pure oxygen than in ordinary air. This would suggest that the rate of burning is related to the concentration of oxygen in the system. An excellent illustration of the scientific method is found on page 3 of the 1963 edition of the CHEM Study text.

You should acquaint your students with the process of *deductive reasoning* as opposed to *inductive reasoning*. Aristotle used deductive reasoning without experimentation, inhibiting scientific progress for nearly two thousand years. He made certain *a priori* statements not based on experiment, and a host of logical consequences followed from these unproven premises, via deductive reasoning. Predictions based on theory involve deductive reasoning, too; but since theory is based on experiment, such predictions have some validity. Emphasize that experiment is the final arbiter of scientific thought.

Spend some time developing the idea of *concepts* and *operational* and *conceptual definitions*. An example such as acids should be used to point out the difference between these terms. Experimentally you may recognize an acid as something which has a sour taste and turns litmus red. An operational definition (based on behavior) of an acid can be made on this basis. A conceptual definition of an acid, on the other hand, is based on the explanation of behavior and evolved as the science of chemistry developed. The generalized definition of an acid, given by Lewis, is: an acid is an electron pair acceptor. Section 1.19 of the 1964 edition of the CBA text contains a good discussion of conceptual and operational definitions.

2. SOLVING PROBLEMS BY DIMENSIONAL ANALYSIS

Dimensional analysis (factor-label method) is a powerful tool used for setting up and solving problems, and you will find that time spent on teaching this method is well spent. Hopefully your students will know how to do simple algebra. If they are weak in math, they will have a difficult time with chemistry. Review the fundamental units of mass, length and time, as well as the use of scientific notation (powers of ten) before proceeding any further, and make sure they understand the idea of significant figures and rounding off numbers.

Illustrative examples, using experimental data, are helpful in demonstrating the use of dimensional analysis, scientific notation, and the use of significant figures. *Examples:*

1) Calculate the mass of the electron from its charge and charge-to-mass ratio:

Given: electronic charge = 1.60×10^{-19} coulomb electron^{-1}
charge-to-mass ratio = 1.76×10^{8} coulomb gram^{-1}

The problem consists of multiplying or dividing these numbers in such a way that we are left with units having the dimensions of gram electron^{-1}. If we divide coulomb gram^{-1} by coulomb electron^{-1}, we cancel and end up with electron gram^{-1}:

$$\frac{\text{coulomb gram}^{-1}}{\text{coulomb electron}^{-1}} = \text{electron gram}^{-1}$$

Therefore we must perform the operation in this fashion:

$$\frac{1.60 \times 10^{-19} \text{ coulomb electron}^{-1}}{1.76 \times 10^{8} \text{ coulomb gram}^{-1}} = 0.909 \times 10^{-27} \text{ gram electron}^{-1}$$

Since it is better form to write a digit followed by a decimal point in scientific notation, rewrite the answer in the form 9.09×10^{-28} gram electron^{-1}. Emphasize that a result may be no more accurate than the least accurate measurement used to calculate the result.

2) How many minutes are required to completely fill a rectangular tank 31.0 cm $\times$ 60.6 cm $\times$ 27.2 cm with water, if the rate of flow into the tank is 25.0 cm^3 sec^{-1}?

If we divide the volume (cm^3) by the rate (cm^3 sec^{-1}), the answer will come out in sec. This must be divided by a conversion factor of sec min^{-1} in order to obtain the answer in minutes. Setting up the problem on this basis, we have

$$\frac{(31.0)\,(60.6)\,(27.2)\text{ cm}^3}{(25.0\text{ cm}^3\text{ sec}^{-1})\,(60\text{ sec min}^{-1})} = 34.7\text{ min}$$

The answer is accurate to three significant figures.

3) If 1.5 hens lay 1.5 eggs in 1.5 days, calculate the number of eggs laid by 3 hens in 3 days.

$$\frac{(3\text{ hens})\,(3\text{ days})\,(1.5\text{ eggs})}{(1.5\text{ hens})\,(1.5\text{ days})} = 6\text{ eggs}$$

Remind your students that including units in calculations serves as a good check on procedure; if the wrong units appear in the final result, the student probably made an error in setting up the problem.

3. CALCULATING ERRORS

Scientists use the concept of uncertainty (experimental error) to judge the precision of their measurements and to establish the validity of results in making determinations not previously made. For example, a research scientist determines the rate of a chemical reaction using a certain procedure. He will make several determinations and calculate the error. If the results agree within experimental uncertainty, he has confidence in his method. If the results do not agree, the procedure may need changing, since it does not yield reproducible results. Analysis of errors tells the scientist whether or not to have confidence in his results.

Emphasize that there is a limit of accuracy in all measurements. Have the students examine a ruler and ask them to what degree of accuracy they can measure the length of a line.

Students develop a feeling for the concept of uncertainty and accuracy of measurement slowly and only through experience with making measurements. Relate the idea of significant figures to accuracy of measurement by using concrete illustrations and quantitative experiments. Distinguish between absolute error (uncertainty) and relative (per cent) error and show them how to calculate these quantities. A measurement, absolute error, and relative error are related in this way:

$$\frac{\text{absolute error}}{\text{measurement}} \times 100 = \text{per cent error}$$

When calculating results from experimentally-derived measurements, use the following rules:

(1) When adding or subtracting quantities, add the absolute errors of the quantities to find the absolute error of the result.
(2) When multiplying or dividing quantities, add the relative errors of the quantities to find the relative error of the result.
(3) The number of significant figures in a result should be no greater than that in the least precise measurement.
(4) The larger the sample or quantity, the smaller the relative error.

Examples such as the following will illustrate the calculation of errors and degree of accuracy in experimental results.

1) Determine the density of a rectangular block of wood using a platform balance and a ruler. The mass was found to be 239.3 ± 0.1 g, and the dimensions were found to be 3.7 ± 0.1 cm $\times$ 7.8 ± 0.1 cm $\times$ 10.1 ± 0.1 cm. Since we must divide the mass by the volume in order to find the density, apply rule (2). Use the same rule to determine the relative error of the volume. Since the establishment of the degree of uncertainty in a measurement is an arbitrary judgment on the part of the investigator, the error in the result is

only an approximation at best. Therefore, it is permissible to round off measurements for the purpose of estimating errors. We must calculate the relative errors for the mass and volume, add these to get the relative error of the density, then convert the relative error of the density to absolute error.

$$\text{Volume error:} \frac{0.1}{4} \times 100 = 2.5\%$$

$$\frac{0.1}{8} \times 100 = 1.3\%$$

$$\frac{0.1}{10} \times 100 = \underline{1.0\%}$$

$$\text{volume error} = 4.8\%$$

$$\text{Mass error} \quad \frac{0.1}{240} \times 100 = \underline{0.04\%}$$

$$\text{relative error for density} \simeq 4.8\%$$

$$\text{Density} = \frac{239.3 \text{ g}}{(3.7)\,(7.8)\,(10.1) \text{ cm}^3} = 0.82 \text{ g cm}^{-3}$$

Absolute error for density:

$$\text{absolute error} = \frac{(\text{per cent error})\,(\text{measurement})}{100} = \frac{(4.8)\,(0.82)}{100} \simeq 0.04 \text{ g cm}^{-3}$$

Since the final result is 0.82 ± 0.04 g cm^{-3}, we are justified in expressing the result to two significant figures, as predicted by rule (3). Point out that the larger the dimension of length, the smaller the relative error, illustrating rule (4).

2) The density of isopropanol was determined by measuring 20 ml from a buret and weighing to the nearest 0.01 gram.

Volume:		
	final reading:	22.4 ± 0.05 ml
	initial reading:	2.4 ± 0.05 ml
	volume taken:	20.0 ± 0.1 ml

Since the volume is determined by subtraction, apply rule (1).

Mass:		
	container + isopropanol:	63.43 ± 0.01 g
	tare weight:	47.72 ± 0.01 g
	mass of isopropanol:	15.71 ± 0.02 g

Since mass is determined by subtraction, apply rule (1).

Density: Rule (2) applies, so calculate the relative errors for mass and volume and add these to get the density error.

$$\text{Volume error:} \quad \frac{0.1}{100} \times 100 = 0.5\%$$

$$\text{Mass error:} \quad \frac{0.02}{16} \times 100 = \underline{0.1\%}$$

$$\text{Density error} = 0.6\%$$

$$\text{Density} = \frac{15.71 \text{ g}}{20.0 \text{ ml}} = 0.785 \text{ g ml}^{-1}$$

$$\text{Absolute error} = \frac{(0.6)\ (0.785)}{100} = \pm\ 0.005\ \text{g ml}^{-1}$$

We are justified in expressing the result to three significant figures, as predicted by rule (3).

4. DEVELOPING THE FUNDAMENTAL CONCEPTS OF CONCENTRATION, COULOMB'S LAW, RATE OF CHANGE IN SYSTEM, EQUILIBRIUM, ENERGY, ENTROPY

The concept of concentration is of vital importance to chemists. Convince your students that such diverse terms as density, pressure, molarity, normality, charge density, and population density are applications of the idea of how much stuff there is per unit volume or unit area. Point out that density is a measure of how much matter is crammed into a unit of volume. Lead (density 11.2 g cm^{-3}) is a more concentrated form of matter than wood (density less than 1 g cm^{-3}). Tokyo has a much higher population density than the Canadian Rockies. A diagram showing high and low concentration is helpful.

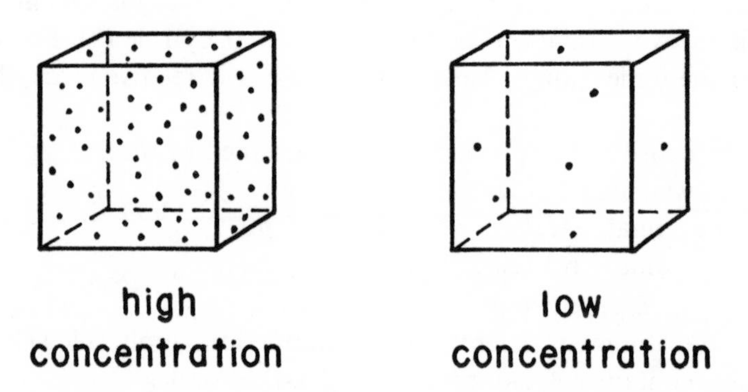

As you develop the concept of temperature, capitalize on the idea of concentration, pointing out that temperature is a measure of the concentration of heat energy. As you develop the idea of entropy, relate the increase of entropy to a decrease in concentration. For example, the fact that heat flows from a hot body to a cold body can be interpreted as heat flowing from a more concentrated to a less concentrated environment. This idea was embodied in the old caloric theory, which assumed that caloric was a self-repelling fluid. The fact that a compressed gas flows from a container to an environment having lower pressure is another example of increase in entropy (randomization). You can obtain a good deal of mileage from a unifying concept such as concentration.

Since electric charge is a fundamental cornerstone of modern chemistry, you should acquaint your students with Coulomb's law and its implications early in the course. A good way to do this is to show them the CHEM Study film "Electric Interactions in Chemistry," which shows qualitative and quantitative experiments using charged spheres, as well as the migration of colored ions in an electric field and the formation of precipitates as a result of interionic attraction. Once the students buy the idea that there are two kinds of charge, that opposites attract and likes repel, and that the force of interaction decreases as the distance between charges increases, they are ready to tackle atomic structure and a host of other applications of Coulomb's law.

A unifying concept from which you can obtain much mileage is the idea of *charge density* (charge per unit volume). When introducing this idea, it might be well to discuss the concept of energy sufficiently to drive home to the student the general principle that a system which contains more energy is less stable than one which contains less energy (relate this to concentration and entropy). There is a tendency for a system to achieve greater stability by losing excess energy. Consider a cloud which has accumulated an electric charge. It has, in effect, accumulated energy. The tendency of the charged particles in the cloud is to disperse, and when sufficient charge has accumulated, energy is released in the form of lightning. A cloud that is about to release a bolt of lightning has a high charge density and represents an unstable system. The tendency is to lower the charge density, thereby achieving greater stability. A condition of high charge density is something like a bull confined in a small pen. The bull would be much happier and less aggressive if he were in a larger pen (lower bull density, analogous to lower charge density). The concept of charge density can be applied successfully to lattice energy, hydration energy, acid-base chemistry, and other topics.

Perhaps one of the most useful generalizations in chemistry is the idea that rate is proportional to concentration. Introduce this early in the course and use plenty of examples. A good one involves burning substances in pure oxygen and relating the difference in rate of reaction to the concentration of oxygen in air as opposed to 99 per cent oxygen. Point out that the higher the temperature of a hot body, the more rapidly it dissipates heat to the cooler surroundings. This, too, can be interpreted in terms of rate being proportional to concentration. This idea becomes more developed in the study of reaction rates as being dependent upon temperature and molar concentration of reactants, since the frequency of collisions depends upon these two factors.

We can also sneak into the area of chemical equilibrium more easily and meaningfully once the idea of rate-concentration dependence has been introduced.

When introducing the notion of equilibrium, don't limit yourself to chemical examples. Start with everyday situations, such as stretching an elastic. It stretches until the tension becomes great enough to prevent further stretching, provided the force remains constant. If the force is increased, the elastic will stretch more. When the force tending to make the elastic contract is equal to the force causing it to stretch, we have a condition of balance, and the system no longer changes. We have reached equilibrium. A tug of war is another example of opposing forces and a condition of equilibrium when there is no change in the system. Show the CHEM Study film "Equilibrium," which effectively drives home to the student the criteria for recognizing equilibrium as opposing processes in balance.

Another familiar example of equilibrium is a leaking boat. The level of water in the boat rises unless you remove it fast enough. If the rate of bailing is the same as that of water entering, the water level does not change (equilibrium), but if the rate of bailing is faster than the rate of water entering, then we no longer have equilibrium, since the water level decreases.

Consider a room full of flies. If the window is open, some of the flies will leave the room. The rate at which they leave depends upon the fly concentration. As the flies leave the room, the concentration decreases, and the rate of exit decreases. If there are flies outside, some will in all probability fly through the window. The rate of entrance is small, since the concentration of flies outside is small. When the concentration of flies inside and outside is the same, the rates of exit and entrance will be the same, and no more change will occur in the average fly population in the room. We will have a condition of equilibrium, recognized by the constant concentration of flies in the room. The motion of the flies does not stop, however. Some flies are going through the window in both directions all the time, but the net change in the average fly population is zero (dynamic equilibrium).

If a box full of flies is released in the room, the fly concentration increases, disrupting the equilibrium. There is a net flow of flies exiting through the window until a new balance is established. Introducing more flies into the room consisted of subjecting the system at equilibrium to a stress, and the system adjusted itself to relieve the stress. Perhaps this is a sneaky way to introduce Le Chatelier's principle, but the use of familiar examples is quite effective for introducing abstract ideas. If you have introduced the concept of equilibrium early in the course, the treatment of numerous topics becomes more meaningful. The following diagrams may be helpful for illustrating equilibrium.

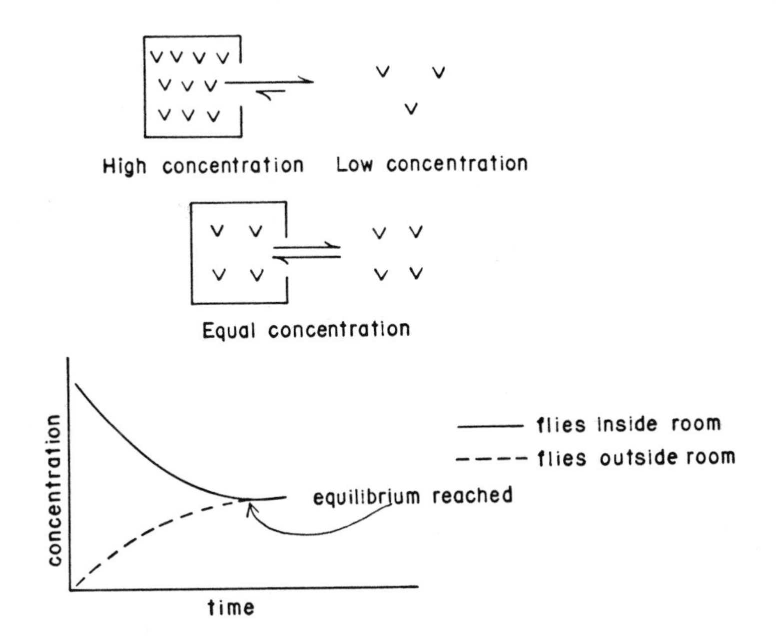

Before proceeding with the study of chemistry, make sure your students have some idea of the nature of forces and energy. In order to appreciate the meaning of *force,* the students should understand the terms *mass, inertia, acceleration, velocity,* and Newton's laws of motion. Point out that weight is merely a gravitational force. Distinguish between weak gravitational force, intermediate electromagnetic (coulombic) forces, and very strong nuclear forces.

Define *energy* as something which is *conserved,* can be transferred or transformed from one kind to another, and can do *work.* Emphasize that in chemistry and physics you can't get something for nothing (relate this idea to the conservation laws). The following table summarizes the different forms of energy and evidence for energy being transferred.

Type of Energy	*Evidence for Energy Transfer*
mechanical	change in motion
electrical	change in charge
heat, light	change in temperature
chemical	change in composition

The concept of energy is much more sophisticated than it appears on the surface, and you should make a conscious effort to develop this concept throughout the course. Chapter 9 is devoted to the concept of energy and its relation to chemistry. In order to predict the feasibility of a chemical reaction, one must consider not only the change in heat content (*enthalpy*) of the system but also the change in *entropy* (organizational energy). An effective way to approach the subject of energy change and the stability of systems is to use everyday examples.

A man sitting on top of a flag pole is in a precarious position. From the physical viewpoint, the man on top of the pole has more potential energy than a man on the ground. The man on the ground is a more stable system than the man on the pole. In general, a system which contains more energy is less stable than one which contains less energy.

Water has a natural tendency to flow downhill, losing potential energy. A coiled spring tends to unwind, losing potential energy. Most chemical reactions, such as burning, proceed with the release of energy. There seems to be a natural tendency for processes to proceed spontaneously with the release of energy (exothermic processes). But there are some natural processes which proceed spontaneously with the absorption of energy (endothermic processes) such as, ice melting, water evaporating, photosynthesis, and many others. There must be a factor other than energy release which acts as a driving force for natural processes.

What is the natural tendency if we start with a system consisting of a neat room and a boy? The odds are overwhelmingly in favor of the room becoming disorganized. When a jar containing alternate layers of black and white marbles is shaken, the marbles become disarranged. No matter how long we shake the jar, the chance of the marbles rearranging themselves into orderly alternating layers is virtually zero. There is a great scientific truth expressed in the story of Humpty Dumpty. The natural tendency seems to be for a system to proceed from a state of order to disorder, measured in terms of an increase in entropy, or tendency toward randomness. You will have an opportunity to develop the idea of entropy quite early in the course (see section 2.5) when discussing changes in state.

5. DISTINGUISHING BETWEEN DIFFERENT KINDS OF MATTER, PHYSICAL AND CHEMICAL CHANGES

Chemistry couldn't get off the ground until the distinction was made between different kinds of matter: elements, compounds, and mixtures. Before attempting to distinguish between these terms, make sure that the students understand the difference between *homogeneous* and *heterogeneous.* Classify matter according to its behavior, as shown in the follwing diagram:

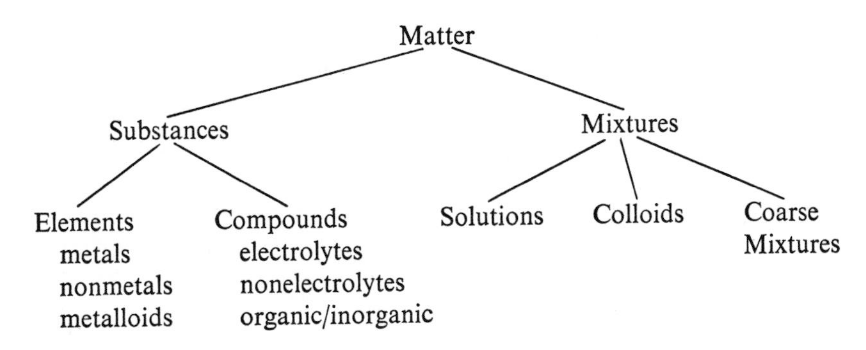

The CHEM Study film "Chemical Families" illustrates how elements can be classified experimentally into metals and non-metals as well as families. Substances are homogeneous materials, cannot be separated by physical means, and are not variable in composition. Mixtures, which are heterogeneous in composition, can be separated by physical means. Solutions present a problem, since they appear to be homogeneous in composition, and are sometimes classified separately from mixtures. These criteria are operational definitions, based on behavior. Robert Boyle's definition of an element earned him the name "Father of Chemistry" and can be paraphrased in modern English as follows: an element is a substance that cannot be decomposed into or synthesized from simpler substances by ordinary chemical means (operational definition). A conceptual definition: an element is a substance that is made up of only one kind of atom. Metals are shiny, not brittle, conduct electricity, but non-metals do not conduct electricity. Solid non-metals are brittle and have little or no metallic luster.

The classification of mixtures is made essentially on particle size. Heterogeneous materials whose particle size is less than about 10 Angstroms in diameter are solutions, those between about 10 and 10,000 Angstroms are colloids, and those of larger particle size are coarse mixtures, which tend to settle on standing. Chapter 6 discusses solutions and colloids.

A summary of the differences between compounds and mixtures is found in most textbooks, and an excellent discussion of the differences between elements and compounds is given in Chapter 1 of the CBA text. Show your students this table and comment on it.

Compounds	*Mixtures*
1. Homogeneous	1. Heterogeneous
2. Definite composition	2. Variable composition
3. Constituent elements lose their identities	3. Components retain their identities

4. Decomposed by chemical means	4. Separated by physical means
5. Prepared by chemical reaction	5. Preparation does not involve chemical reaction

Make sure your students know the difference between physical and chemical changes and give them some examples of these. The criterion is simple: in a chemical change new substances are produced, but in a physical change no new substances are produced.

Demonstrations and Examples

1) Mix approximately equal volumes of powdered potassium nitrate (carefully grind some crystals) and powdered charcoal, pointing out the physical changes. Place a small amount of the mixture in a dry test tube and heat carefully (take necessary safety precautions). Place about ten grams of the mixture in a large Pyrex test tube and add some distilled water. Stir well and heat to nearly boiling. Filter and evaporate some of the water from the filtrate. Cool the filtrate and obtain white crystals of potassium nitrate. Comment on the difference in behavior of the mixture at different temperatures and the role of the water.

2) Precipitate some mercuric iodide by mixing about two volumes of 0.1 M potassium iodide and one volume of 0.1 M mercuric nitrate. Filter the precipitate, using a filter flask and a small Buchner funnel. Smear some of the red powder on a piece of filter paper and carefully heat the reddened paper over a flame. (Use adequate ventilation, since mercuric iodide vapor is very toxic.) The red form of mercuric iodide changes to the yellow form by absorbing energy from the flame. Scratch the yellow material with a spatula or pointed object, producing the red material again. Comment on the physical changes involved in converting one allotrope to another. Show the students samples of mercury and iodine, pointing out the different properties of the compound. Gently heat some mercuric iodide with a small amount of concentrated nitric acid, pointing out the appearance of a new product (brown gas, NO_2). Add some water and carbon tetrachloride and shake, producing a violet color (free iodine) in the carbon tetrachloride. Show the students what happens when free iodine and mercuric iodide are shaken with carbon tetrachloride in separate test tubes. Relate the phenomena to the criteria for elements, compounds, mixtures, chemical and physical changes.

3) Place some ammonium dichromate crystals in a dry test tube and heat gently. Nitrogen, water vapor, and finely-divided green chromic oxide are produced, as well as heat and light.

6. OBTAINING INFORMATION FROM CHEMICAL FORMULAS

A formula describes the composition of a compound qualitatively as well as quantitatively. The quantitative aspects of formulas, including the mole concept and percentage composition, derivation of formulas from experimental data, empirical and molecular formulas, will be treated in Chapter 5 and section 2.3. Before the students can write formulas, they should know the meaning of *valence,* and it might be wise to begin with the historical meaning of this concept, which can be described as "combining capacity." Historically the valence of an element or radical is the number of hydrogen atoms which combine with or are replaced by one atom (radical). Relate the whole number aspect of valence to Dalton's assumption that only whole atoms combine to form compounds. If you are planning to include the concept of equivalents and normal solutions in your course, the historical definition of valence provides a good point of departure.

Give your students several key formulas, such as $NaCl$, H_2O, HCl, H_2SO_4, HNO_3, $CaCl_2$ $AlCl_3$. From the formulas containing hydrogen, have them determine the valences of O, Cl, SO_4, NO_3. Once these valences have been established, have them give the valences of Na, Ca, Al. Once they get the idea of applying the basic definition of valence, you can proceed with this type of game and expand their list of valences by giving them several formulas for compounds you name. Approaching formula writing in this fashion gives students some feeling for the idea of chemical equivalence.

Before proceeding very far, you should give your students the basic rules for writing formulas: (1) the metal or positive ion precedes the non-metal or negative ion (the less electronegative element first for covalent compounds), (2) a subscript applies to the term immediately preceding it, (3) enclose radicals in parentheses when a subscript applies and treat the radical as a single unit, (4) a large number (coefficient) in front of a formula applies to everything that follows in that formula. Give the students some examples and have them tell you how many atoms of each element are represented in the following: $2H_2O$, $Fe_2(SO_4)_3$, $5H_2SO_4$, $3(NH_4)_2$ HPO_4, $4CuSO_4 \cdot 5H_2O$, and other examples.

Introduction of the mole concept at this point is logical and will pay off later. (Chapter 5, section 1.) Sell your students on the need for using bundles of atoms instead of single atoms, since single atoms are too small to be measured or handled in the laboratory. Have the students give the number of moles of each kind of atom in the examples above.

After having developed the ideas of atomic structure, subatomic particles, and chemical bonding, the use of plus and minus valence (charge of ions) can be used meaningfully. Emphasize that a compound, whether it is ionic or covalent, is electrically neutral. Therefore, the sum of the charges must add up to zero. The charge of a complex ion is the sum of the charges of the ions that make up the complex.

Emphasize the difference between empirical and molecular formulas. A molecular formula tells us how many atoms of each element are in one molecule, but an empirical formula merely tells us the *ratio* of atoms which have combined to form the compound. The formula NaCl is empirical. NaCl is not a molecular compound but is made up of many Na^+ and Cl^- ions held together in a crystal lattice by coulombic forces. The ratio of sodium to chlorine atoms which have combined to produce sodium chloride is 1:1. The empirical formula for benzene and acetylene is CH, telling us that the ratio of carbon to hydrogen atoms is 1:1. The molecular formula for benzene is C_6H_6 and that of acetylene is C_2H_2. Different compounds may have the same empirical formula.

When you get to organic chemistry, emphasize the possibilities for different isomers, which have the same molecular formulas but different structures or arrangement of atoms in space. (See Chapter 11.) A simple example is ethanol versus dimethyl ether, which both have the molecular formula C_6H_6O but have different structures.

7. WRITING AND BALANCING EQUATIONS

A chemical equation is a quantitative statement as well as a qualitative description of a chemical reaction. Emphasize that all chemistry students must be able to write balanced chemical equations, not only because they are a shorthand description of the reactants and products, but also they are the basis for many calculations. Once a student can write formulas and understands the use of coefficients, he can learn to balance equations. Remind your students of the law of conservation of matter, since this is the reason an equation must be balanced. For some reason many students think that there has to be the same number of moles of reactants as products. Point out that moles of reactants and products do not have to be the same, but *atoms* must be conserved.

Give the students word equations, since these will not only provide practice in writing formulas but will also give them practice in balancing equations. Remind them that in order to write a balanced equation they must know what all the reactants and products are. Having written the formulas for these correctly, an equation should balance. Beginning students often tend to write the most absurd garbage imaginable, since they don't follow the rule about knowing the formulas for the reactants and products. Since they don't know much chemistry, some students will write an equation for the decomposition of calcium carbonate:

$$2\ CaCO_3 = 2\ Ca + 2\ C + 3\ O_2$$

As they learn about general types of reactions and something about acid-base reactions, behavior of metals and non-metals, and general descriptive chemistry (which is sadly neglected in some courses), they will gradually acquire the knack of writing equations correctly.

Start with simple molecular equations, which can be categorized into four general classes (see below). Later they can begin to write simple ionic equations and balance redox equations (see Chapter 10, section 4). Give them a summary of the four types of reactions and some examples of each, as shown in the following summary. When you discuss redox, point out that categories A, B, and C often involve redox, but metathesis does not involve redox.

A. *Combination:* A + B = C (reverse of decomposition)

1. Metal + non-metal = salt (ionic compound)

$$Na + \frac{1}{2}Cl_2 = NaCl$$

$$2\ Ca + O_2 = 2\ CaO$$

2. Non-metal + non-metal = covalent compound

$$2\ H_2 + O_2 = 2\ H_2O$$

$$P_4 + 6\ Br_2 = 4\ PBr_3$$

3. Metal oxide + non-metal oxide = salt

$$CaO + CO_2 = CaCO_3$$

$$CuO + SO_3 = CuSO_4$$

4. Salt + water = hydrate

$$CuSO_4 + 5\ H_2O = CuSO_4 \cdot 5\ H_2O \quad [\text{or } CuSO_4\,(H_2O)_5]$$

5. Normal salt + acid = acid salt

$$Na_2\ CO_3 + H_2CO_3 = 2\ NaHCO_3$$

6. Water + non-metal oxide = acid

$$H_2O + SO_3 = H_2SO_4$$

7. Water + metal oxide = metal hydroxide

$$CaO + H_2O = Ca(OH)_2$$

B. *Decomposition* (reverse of combination): A = B + C

1. Binary compound

$$H_2O = H_2 + \frac{1}{2}O_2$$

$$HgO = Hg + \frac{1}{2}O_2$$

2. Chlorate = chloride + oxygen

$$2\ KClO_3 = 2KCl + 3O_2$$

3. Nitrate (alkali metal) = nitrite + oxygen

$$NaNO_3 = NaNO_2 + \frac{1}{2}O_2$$

4. Nitrate (other than alkali metal) = oxide + oxygen + NO_2

$$2\,Pb(NO_3)_2 = 2\,PbO + 4\,NO_2 + O_2$$
$$4\,HNO_3 = 2\,H_2O + 4\,NO_2 + O_2$$

5. Carbonate = oxide + CO_2 (except alkali metals)

$$CaCO_3 = CaO + CO_2$$
$$CuCO_3 = CuO + CO_2$$

6. Acid salt = normal salt + acid

$$Ca(HCO_3)_2 = CaCO_3 + H_2O + CO_2$$

7. Metal hydroxide = oxide + water

$$Cu(OH)_2 = CuO + H_2O$$

8. Hydroxy acid = oxide + water

$$H_2SO_4 = H_2O + SO_3$$

C. *Displacement:* AB + C = AC + B

1. Reduction by metal

$$Na + HOH = NaOH + \frac{1}{2}H_2$$
$$Zn + H_2SO_4 = ZnSO_4 + H_2$$
$$Cu + 2\,AgNO_3 = 2\,Ag + Cu(NO_3)_2$$

2. Oxidation by non-metal

$$Cl_2 + 2\,NaBr = Br_2 + 2\,NaCl$$
$$I_2 + H_2S = S + 2\,HI$$

D. *Metathesis* (double displacement): AB + CD = AD + CB

1. Acid + hydroxide (neutralization)

$$HCl + NaOH = NaCl + H_2O$$

2. Formation of precipitate

$$BaCl_2 + K_2SO_4 = BaSO_2\downarrow + 2\,HCl$$

3. Gas evolution

$$H_2SO_4 + FeS = FeSO_4 + H_2S\uparrow$$

4. Hydrolysis* of organic compound

ester: $CH_3COOC_2H_5 + H_2O = CH_3COOH + C_2H_5OH$

peptide: $RC(=O)\text{—}NH\text{—}CH_2R' + H_2O = RCOOH + H_2NCH_2R'$

5. Hydrolysis* of covalent compound

$PCl_5 + 4\,H_2O = H_3PO_4 + 5\,HCl$

6. Hydrolysis* of salt (partial reaction)

$H_2O + CO_3^{-2} \rightleftharpoons HCO_3^- + OH^-$

$H_2O + NH_4^+ \rightleftharpoons H_3O^+ + NH_3$

* Hydrolysis: a reaction in which water is consumed (See Chapter 7).

2

Interpreting States of Matter Using Kinetic-Molecular Theory

1. EXPLAINING THE GAS LAWS

Summarize the characteristics of the three common states of matter as follows:

Fluids	*Solids*
Gases: have no definite shape, no definite volume, are without order *Liquids:* have no definite shape, occupy a definite volume, have more order than gases, less than solids	Have definite shape, occupy a definite volume, have highly-ordered structure

Point out that the word *gas* is derived from a Greek word meaning *chaos,* which is descriptive of their structure. The degree of order is related to the increase in entropy in going from solid to liquid to gas.

The easiest state of matter to understand and study is the gaseous state. The important gas laws and Avogadro's hypothesis were discovered by the middle of the Nineteenth Century and include Boyle's and Charles' laws, Dalton's law of partial pressures, Gay-Lussac's law, and Graham's law. Before developing a model to explain the behavior of gases, make certain the students know the meaning of the terms "force," "pressure," "momentum," "kinetic energy." Show the CHEM Study film "Gas Pressure and Molecular Collisions," which uses mechanical models to account for Brownian motion and the temperature-pressure-volume relationship of gases.

Develop the idea of force being related to the momentum of the particles.

A change in momentum is caused by a force. Develop the model of a gas as a collection of particles (molecules) which are colliding with each other and the sides of the container, causing pressure. Point out that the pressure (force per unit area) depends on (1) the frequency of collisions and (2) how much force each molecule exerts when it pushes against the sides of the container. The wall of the container pushes against the molecule, brings it to a stop, and then sets it in motion in another direction. The pressure exerted by the gas molecules is caused by the equal and opposite force (Newton's third law).

Impress upon your students that gas molecules do not all move at the same speed. Each time a molecule collides with another, energy is transferred, resulting in the two molecules rebounding at different speeds. Show them a Maxwell-Boltzmann distribution curve, contrasting it with the symmetrical Gaussian distribution curve (which holds for distribution of height in an adult population of the same sex). Point out that gas molecules have an average velocity, and since they are in motion, they possess kinetic energy. You can now introduce these postulates of the kinetic-molecular theory:

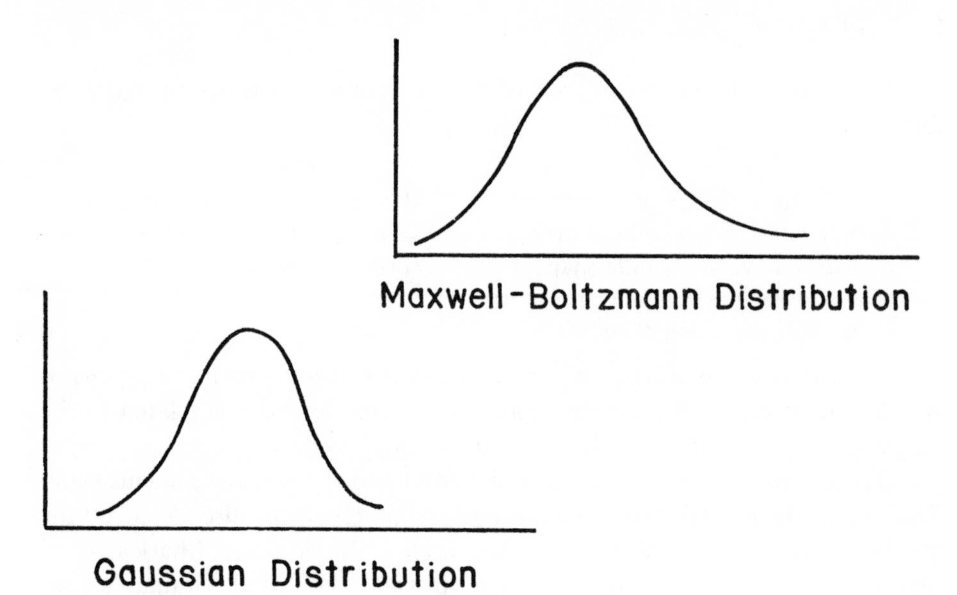

(1) Molecules are in a state of motion, and at a given temperature they have a certain average velocity and kinetic energy.

(2) Molecules undergo elastic collisions, transferring energy when they collide with each other.

As the temperature increases (keeping the volume constant), the pressure exerted by a gas increases. This means that the frequency of collisions has increased, the force exerted as a result of collisions has increased, or both. Interpret this observation in terms of the molecules moving faster. This leads to a higher frequency of collisions as well as greater momentum, resulting in greater force per collision. This leads to a third postulate of the kinetic-molecular theory:

(3) Molecular motion increases as the temperature increases.

Thomas Graham discovered a regularity in the behavior of different gases: their rate of diffusion varies inversely with the square root of their densities (molecular weights). Convince your students that this means that at a given temperature the average kinetic energy of all gas molecules is the same. Mathematically, Graham's law may be written:

$$\frac{v_1}{v_2} = \sqrt{\frac{M_2}{M_1}}$$

v_1 = molecular velocity of gas 1
v_2 = molecular velocity of gas 2
M_1 = molecular weight of gas 1
M_2 = molecular weight of gas 2

Squaring both sides and rearranging, we obtain:

$$M_1 v_1^2 = M_2 v_2^2$$

This equation contains the term mv^2, as does the formula for kinetic energy. The conclusion is that the average kinetic energy of different gases is the same at the same temperature. We can add this statement as a fourth postulate of the kinetic theory.

Demonstrations

(1) To show that HCl molecules move more slowly than NH_3 molecules, use a glass tube (about 1 cm inside diameter and about 1 meter in length) and clamp it in a horizontal position. Place a wad of cotton soaked in concentrated ammonia water in one end and a wad soaked with concentrated hydrochloric acid in the other end. Seal both ends with stoppers and wait a few minutes. A white ring of solid ammonium chloride will appear nearer the HCl end of the tube, showing that NH_3 molecules move faster than HCl molecules.

(2) To show the rapid diffusion of hydrogen gas, use a porous porcelain cup (the kind used for making electrochemical cells) and set up the apparatus as shown in the diagram. Fill the bottle with water, invert a beaker over the cup, and pour a bottle of hydrogen up into the beaker. Pressure builds up inside the cup, causing a stream of water to emerge from the tip. Direct the stream toward an unsuspecting victim. Removal of the beaker causes a drop in pressure. Use a diagram to show the rates of diffusion across the porous barrier, accounting for the pressure difference. Hydrogen molecules move faster than air molecules.

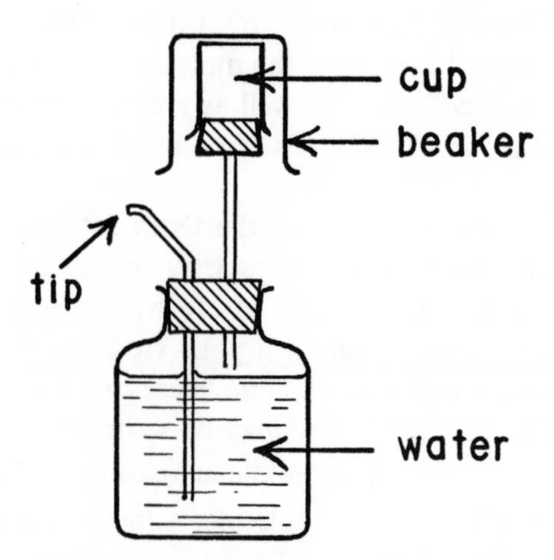

Gay-Lussac's law of combining volumes and Avogadro's hypothesis are well illustrated by the CHEM Study film "Gases and How They Combine." A simple way to illustrate the reasoning used and to show the application of these ideas is to assume that equal volumes of gases under the same temperature and pressure conditions contain the same number of molecules. Experimentally it is shown that one volume of hydrogen and one volume of chlorine combine to produce two volumes of hydrogen chloride (assume the formula HCl). For the sake of argument, use a tiny unit volume containing four gas molecules and diagram the reaction as follows:

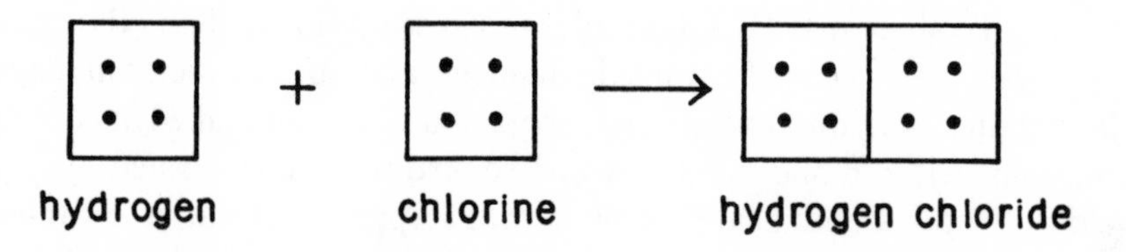

It follows that if we have eight molecules of HCl, we must have eight atoms of chlorine and eight atoms of hydrogen (atoms are indivisible; conservation of atoms). If eight atoms of chlorine are present in four molecules of chlorine, there must be two atoms per molecule. The same reasoning applies for hydrogen. More applications of these ideas will be presented later in this chapter, section 3.

Dalton did not buy Avogadro's hypothesis and did not put much stock in Gay-Lussac's findings. Dalton did not distinguish between atoms and molecules but spoke of simple atoms and compound atoms. He would not accept the idea of diatomic gases. He believed in the simplicity of nature.

Therefore, the compound atoms of water must be made up of one atom of hydrogen and one atom of oxygen (HO). His table of atomic weights assigned values of 1 for hydrogen and 8 for oxygen, as well as numerous other values which were much different from the presently-accepted ones. There were essentially two schools of thought in chemistry during the first half of the nineteenth century: followers of Dalton and those who accepted Avogadro's hypotheses (which, as shown in section 3, described water to be H_2O). Confusion reigned, since there was disagreement about a set of atomic weights as well as some formulas for compounds such as water. In 1860, the situation was so confused that an international meeting of chemists was held at Karlsruhe, Germany, at which Cannizzaro resurrected Avogadro's argument. Since most of Avogadro's critics and opponents were dead or retired and there was no other satisfactory method known to account for Gay-Lussac's findings, chemists were finally convinced that Avogadro was right.

Explain the gas laws in terms of the assumptions of the kinetic-molecular theory and Avogadro's hypothesis, treating them all together. Boyle's law is virtually self-evident, considering that reducing the volume increases the concentration of gas molecules, resulting in more frequent collisions. In accounting for Charles' law, raising the temperature makes the molecules move faster, resulting in more frequent collisions as well as greater force per collision. This leads to greater pressure. To maintain the pressure constant we must make the volume larger. Returning to Graham's law and using the idea of a mole being made up of Avogadro's number of things, we can express the molecular weights of gases 1 and 2 as Nm_1 and Nm_2 (N is the number of gas molecules per mole, m_1 and m_2 are the masses of individual molecules). Since the average kinetic energy of all gas molecules is the same at the same temperature, $m_1v_1^2 = m_2v_2^2$. Multiplying both sides by N, we obtain $Nm_1v_1^2 = Nm_2v_2^2$. Since $Nm_1 = M_1$ (molecular weight of gas 1) and $Nm_2 = M_2$ (molecular weight of gas 2), then $M_1v_1^2 = M_1v_2^2$. Rearranging we obtain Graham's law:

$$\frac{v_1}{v_2} = \sqrt{\frac{M_2}{M_1}}$$

2. DEVELOPING THE CONCEPT OF TEMPERATURE

Any student who has used a bicycle pump knows from experience that a gas becomes hot when it is compressed. You can interpret this in two ways. Since you are doing work on the gas when compressing it and since energy cannot be created or destroyed, the gas must acquire the energy from the work performed on it. This energy is acquired in the form of heat: a greater concentration of heat is present, as evidenced by the higher temperature. A second explanation, using the model of gas molecules, can be used with the help of a diagram. As the piston moves forward, the rebounding gas molecules move faster, with a corresponding rise in their temperature. Conversely, an expanding gas becomes cooler, since the gas molecules move more slowly than before collision with the retreating piston (the gas is doing work at the expense of its internal energy). Such reasoning leads the student to believe that temperature is related to the kinetic energy of molecules.

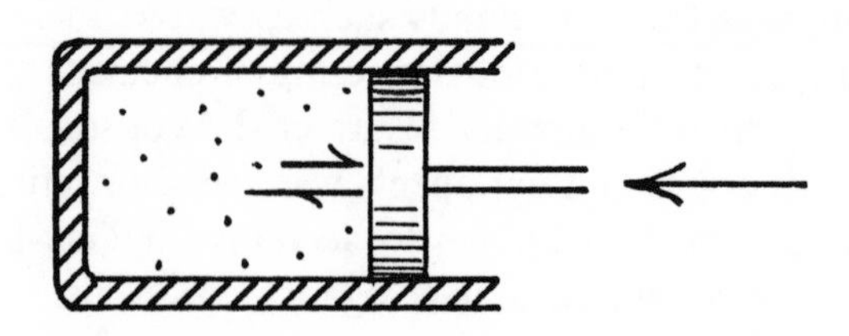

Perhaps the most useful way to develop the concept of absolute temperature is to use experimental data, such as in the CHEM Study film "Gas Pressure and Molecular Collisions." A gas sample is sealed in a container (constant volume) attached to a pressure gauge. Immerse the container in (1) boiling water, (2) ice water, (3) dry ice and alcohol mixture, (4) liquid nitrogen to obtain the pressure at 100°C, 0°C, – 78°C, – 196°C. Plot the pressure times volume versus temperature (this is justified, since V is constant). The points are connected by a straight line, which is extended (extrapolated) until it intersects the horizontal axis of the graph. Point out the physical significance of the value $PV = 0$. Since temperature is a measure of the kinetic energy of molecules and since there is apparently no kinetic energy at this point (pressure must be zero, indicating no translational motion of molecules), the temperature at this point must be the lowest possible temperature: absolute zero. The linear equation for this relationship is $PV = kT$ (k is the slope).

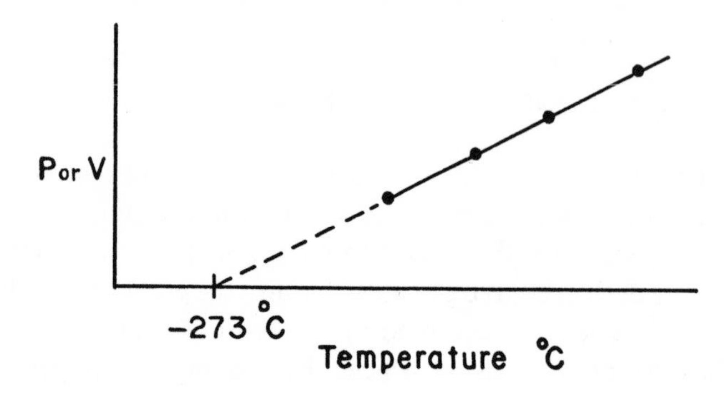

Impress upon your students that the absolute temperature scale (Kelvin scale) must be used when dealing with energy of molecules (this includes pressure and volume variation with temperature). Trap your more complacent students by asking them the volume of a gas at 200°C, if the sample originally occupied one liter at 100°C. If they say two liters, ask them for the volume at zero degrees C and minus 100°C. Give them enough simple Boyle's and Charles' law problems so that they appreciate the meaning of these laws and so that they get into the habit of using absolute temperature.

Sell your students on the use of common sense for solving volume conversion problems. Many teachers of high school chemistry use the old chestnut $P_1V_1/T_1 = P_2V_2/T_2$ and teach the students to plug in the necessary values. This involves transposing and rearranging the equation to solve for the unknown P, V, or T, leaving some room for human error. Instead of doing this, set up the following example in this fashion:

Calculate the volume of a gas sample at STP if 1.21 liters was measured at 32°C and 745 mm pressure. Since the pressure increases from 745 mm to 760 mm, the volume must decrease. Place the larger pressure on the bottom:

$$(1.21)\frac{(745)}{(760)}$$

The temperature is decreased from 305°K to 273°K, making the volume smaller. Therefore place the larger temperature on the bottom:

$$(1.21)\frac{(745)\,(273)}{(760)\,(305)}$$

The result is the same as substituting in $V_2 = \frac{V_1P_1T_2}{P_2T_1}$.

3. APPLYING AVOGADRO'S HYPOTHESIS

Although your students may be able to recite Gay-Lussac's law and Avogadro's hypothesis, they may not really understand the meaning of these ideas. Using the technique described in section 2.1 for showing that chlorine and hydrogen molecules are diatomic, convince your students that the formula for water must be H_2O and that oxygen is diatomic. Experimentally, two volumes of hydrogen plus one volume of oxygen produce two volumes of water vapor, measured under the same temperature and pressure conditions. Use four (or any other convenient number) of molecules per unit volume:

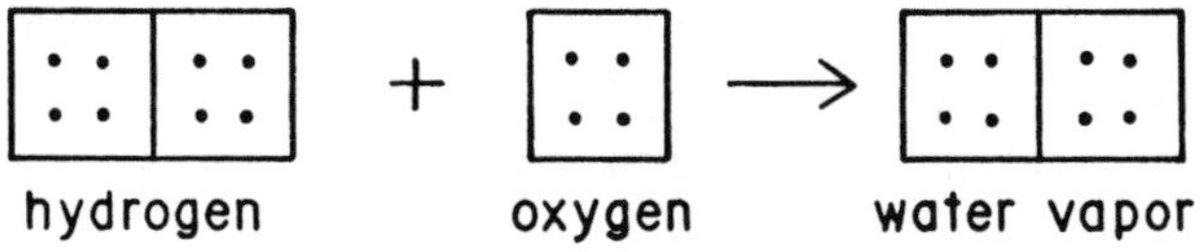

hydrogen + oxygen → water vapor

Having shown that hydrogen is diatomic (synthesis of HCl), we have a total of 16 hydrogen atoms in the eight molecules shown. The eight water molecules must contain a total of 16 hydrogen atoms and at least 8 oxygen atoms, giving each water molecule two hydrogen atoms and one oxygen atom. Since we must have 8 oxygen atoms, these must be divided between 4 oxygen molecules, making oxygen diatomic.

As you develop the application of Avogadro's hypothesis, stress the idea of a mole being a large number of particles. This "magic number" is called Avogadro's number, N. Referring to the example above, the ratio of numbers of molecules of hydrogen to oxygen in water is 8:4:8, or 2:1:2. We could take a much larger volume of gases and say we have $2N$ molecules of hydrogen, N molecules of oxygen, and $2N$ molecules of water, or 2 *moles* of hydrogen, 1 *mole* of oxygen, and 2 *moles* of water. The conclusion is: *the volume ratio of gases in a chemical reaction is the same as the mole ratio.* Give your students examples such as the following:

1) One liter of a certain gaseous hydrocarbon was burned in oxygen, yielding 2 liters of carbon dioxide and 2 liters of water vapor. Calculate the molecular formula for the hydrocarbon and the volume of oxygen needed.
   Applying the idea above, one mole of hydrocarbon yields 2 moles of CO_2 and 2 moles of H_2O. There must be 2 moles of carbon atoms and 4 moles of hydrogen atoms in 1 mole of hydrocarbon, and so the formula is C_2H_4. We can now write: $C_2H_4 + xO_2 = 2\ CO_2 + 2\ H_2O$
   Solving for x we obtain 3 moles of O_2, or 3 liters required.
2) One hundred milliliters of phosphorus vapor reacts with 600 ml hydrogen gas to produce 400 ml phosphine gas (PH_3). Calculate the molecular formula for phosphorus vapor. [P_4]
3) Calculate the volume of oxygen gas needed to burn 100 ml propane gas (C_3H_8), producing CO_2 and H_2O. [500 ml]

4. DERIVING THE GENERAL GAS EQUATION

Chemists seldom bother to convert gas volumes to STP. They are more interested in the number of moles of gas involved, which can be found simply by using the so-called "ideal gas equation," $PV = nRT$. Sell your students on its utility for solving problems involving the determination of molecular weights of gases, etc. Before they can use it, however, the students should have some idea of what this equation means and the significance of the constant R.

With the help of the CHEM Study film "Gas Pressure and Molecular Collisions," you can develop the relationship $PV = kT$ for a given sample of gas. The constant k applies only for a given sample. Since equal volumes of gases measured under the same temperature and pressure conditions contain the same number of molecules, this relationship holds for any gas sample containing the same number of molecules. If we wish to change the size of the sample, we must change the value for k. We can have our cake and eat it, too, if we choose a universal gas constant and adjust its value according to the size of the gas sample as follows: Let R be the constant for one mole of any gas and n be the number of moles of gas in the sample. Then $nR = k$, and we're in business. We now have $PV = nRT$.

Derive the values for R most frequently used by beginners as follows:

We know that one mole of a gas at 0°C and 1 atmosphere (760 mm) occupies 22.4 liters. Solve for R in $PV = nRT$ by substituting the appropriate values:

$\underline{n} = 1$ mole
$\underline{T} = 273$ deg
$\underline{P} = 1$ atm
$\underline{V} = 22.4$ l

$$R = \frac{PV}{nT} = \frac{(1 \text{ atm})(22.4 \text{ l})}{(1 \text{ mole})(273 \text{ deg})} = 0.0821 \text{ l atm deg}^{-1} \text{ mole}^{-1}$$

If pressure is in millimeters of mercury (torrs) instead of atmospheres, multiply the above value by 760mm atm^{-1} and obtain the value $R = 62.4$ l mm deg^{-1} mole^{-1}.

There are several other values for R which chemists use, but these are not encountered in elementary chemistry. Applications of the general gas equation are discussed in section 5.6.

5. DISTINGUISHING BETWEEN REAL AND IDEAL GASES

Impress upon your students that there is no such animal as an ideal gas which obeys the general gas law over all ranges of temperature and pressure. In the so-called "ideal gas" the molecules are point particles and have no volume. The straight line plot of PV versus T would follow a straight line, and PV would be zero at 0°K. An ideal gas wouldn't condense at absolute zero, since there are no intermolecular forces of attraction. Normally when gas molecules come close together, the attractive (Vander Waals) forces become larger, and if the molecules do not possess sufficient energy, the molecules will come together and condense into a liquid.

Under relatively low pressure and at temperatures which are well above its boiling point, the gas behaves pretty much like an ideal gas. When the pressure is great, however, the gas molecules move closer together, permitting attractive forces to become apparent. The result is that the product PV becomes less than expected. This is more true in the case of CO_2 than in the case of oxygen or hydrogen (see graph). As the pressure increases more and the molecules are being jammed together more closely, they begin to get in each other's way and refuse to be squeezed together any more, since they occupy space. The result is that at high pressure the volume does not decrease as fast as predicted by Boyle's law, and the product *PV* increases.

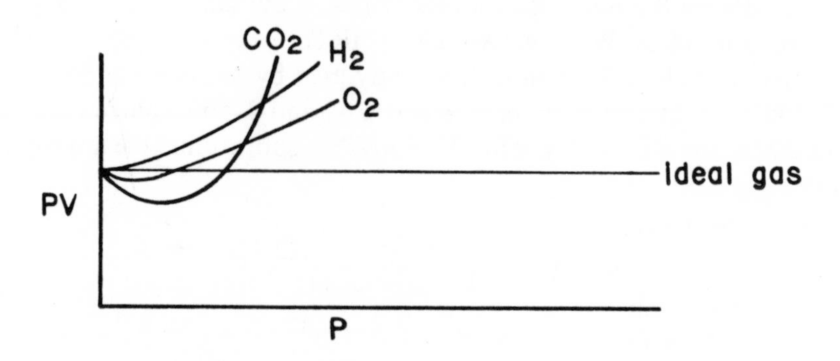

The Dutch scientist J. D. Vander Waals gave us an equation which bears his name and corrects for the deviation from ideal gas behavior:

$$\left(P + \frac{a}{V^2}\right)(V - b) = RT \qquad \text{(for one mole)}$$

The terms *a* and *b* are different for every gas. The term *a* represents attractive forces (when *V* is large they do not amount to much, as shown in the first part of the equation), and *b* represents molecular volume (this does not amount to much when *V* is large). By using this equation and the appropriate *a* and *b* terms the *PV* versus *P* plot for a gas approaches a straight line with slope zero, as does the ideal gas, for which *a* and *b* are zero.

We can now add another postulate to the kinetic-molecular theory: attractive forces exist between molecules, and these forces diminish rapidly as the distance between molecules increases. This postulate is used to account for the liquid and solid states.

6. ACCOUNTING FOR THE PHYSICAL PROPERTIES OF LIQUIDS AND SOLIDS AND CHANGES IN STATE

Since liquids and solids are much denser than gases and are virtually noncompressible, the molecules must be relatively close together in the condensed states. A good place to begin when discussing these states is to consider the properties of solids, which represent a high order of organization (low entropy).

X-ray diffraction is a technique by which scientists can determine the arrangement of atoms in a crystalline solid. In principle, waves are diffracted (scattered) by an object whose diameter is comparable to the length of the wave being diffracted. Experiments with ripple tanks demonstrate this phenomenon quite nicely, and the CHEM Study film "Crystals and Their Structures" demonstrates the principle of wave diffraction and the use of X-rays in determining crystal structure. Since atoms in a crystal are in the order of one Angstrom apart, X-rays of this wave length are readily diffracted by solids.

In discussing the structure of solids, compare a solid to a formation of soldiers on parade; they have structure. Although they are free to move (vibrate) in their respective positions, the overall shape of the body is maintained. When the formation is dismissed, the shape is destroyed, and the soldiers flow freely. The CHEM Study film "Molecular Motions" demonstrates the phenomenon of melting and vaporizing very lucidly using a model made up of glass beads, which are activated by a vibrator. The differences in energy between solid, liquid and gas are clearly revealed using this model.

Emphasize that liquids are fluid. Returning to the soldiers on parade, dismissal leads to a lowering of organization and the loss of shape. The soldiers may not be moving any faster upon dismissal, but they have a certain freedom which was not there before. In the solid state the attractive forces are quite large (see section 4.5), and energy (heat of fusion) must be added to overcome some of these forces. Emphasize that at the melting point solid and liquid phases coexist in equilibrium. Since they are at the same temperature, the molecules in the solid and liquid phases possess the same amount of kinetic energy. The liquid possesses more potential energy than the solid, however. In melting, the long range forces which hold the solid together have been partially disrupted, and the liquid consists of aggregates which are free to move around, giving this phase fluidity. The decrease in order going from solid to liquid is accompanied by an increase in entropy.

Compare the structure of a liquid to people in a crowded room. There is a small amount of empty space between some of the liquid molecules, as evidenced by the fact that liquids are compressible to the extent of about 1 to 2 per cent of their volume. If there were no space between the people in the room, they would be unable to move and flow. The same holds for liquids; if it were not for some pockets of empty space between aggregates, the viscosity of the liquid would be very high, approaching that of a solid.

In order to convert a liquid to a gas, the molecules must be separated and must be given sufficient energy to overcome attractive forces. At the boiling point of a substance, the molecules of the liquid and gas have about the same amount of kinetic energy, since the temperature is the same. The gas molecules must possess more potential energy, however, represented by the heat of vaporization. The change from liquid to gas is accompanied by an increase in entropy (order to disorder). An effective way to represent the volume change in going from liquid to gas is to show the students about 20 ml (approximately 1 mole) of liquid water and to point to a 5 gallon carboy, telling them that the molecules in 1 mole of water in the gaseous state would effectively occupy that volume. Gases consist mostly of empty space.

Summarize the changes in state as fololws:

$$\text{SOLID} \underset{\text{heat of fusion}}{\rightleftharpoons} \text{LIQUID} \underset{\text{heat of vaporization}}{\rightleftharpoons} \text{GAS}$$

$\longrightarrow$ increase in entropy

high order — intermediate order — no order

7. EXPLAINING VAPOR PRESSURE AND VAPOR PRESSURE DIAGRAMS

In order to understand the meaning of changes in state, your students should know something about vapor pressure and phase diagrams. Use the kinetic-molecular theory and the idea of dynamic equilibrium to explain vapor pressure. Consider the molecules at the surface of the liquid in the following diagram. They are being jostled around and are constantly colliding with each other. Some molecules acquire sufficient energy to overcome attractive forces and escape into the gaseous state. Since the concentration of liquid molecules is constant, the rate of escape depends only on the temperature of the liquid. As gas molecules accumulate above the liquid, some begin to condense as they collide with the liquid, and the rate of condensation varies directly with the concentration of gas molecules. A state of equilibrium is eventually reached. The pressure of the vapor in equilibrium with the liquid is called the vapor pressure. As the temperature increases, the rate of evaporation increases, and consequently more gas molecules must be present in order to achieve equilibrium. The result is that the vapor pressure increases with temperature.

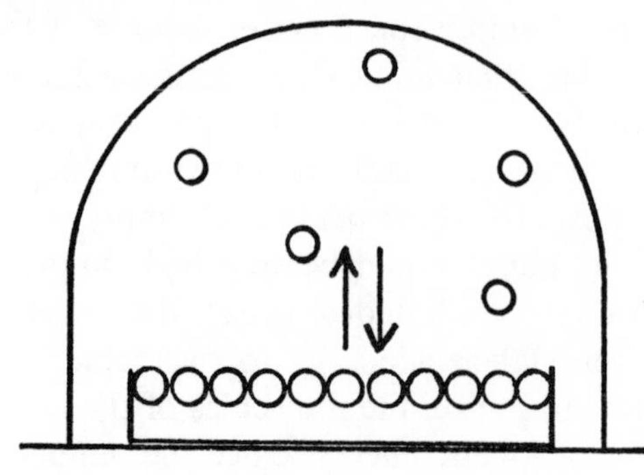

Evaporation only occurs at the surface (interface), and its rate is limited by the surface area. If the vapor pressure of the liquid exceeds the atmospheric pressure, bubbles of vapor begin to form below the surface of the liquid, increasing the area of the interface. This results in a much more rapid change from liquid to vapor, a phenomenon called *ebullition.* If the students can appreciate the above argument, they will have a better understanding of the definition of boiling point: the temperature at which the vapor pressure of a substance is equal to the atmospheric pressure. At the boiling point, therefore, the liquid and gas phases are in equilibrium.

The melting point of a substance can be presented as a dynamic equilibrium between solid and liquid. As the temperature of a solid increases, the molecules become more agitated, and eventually the highly-ordered structure of the solid begins to collapse. Aggregates of molecules become detached from the solid and enter the liquid phase, with the absorption of energy. At the melting point the liquid can be changed back to solid, with the evolution of energy. The melting point is the temperature at which a solid and liquid can exist in equilibrium.

Having considered the nature of the phase changes from the viewpoint of equilibrium, the students should be in a position to consider phase diagrams. Let us consider the diagram for water. The vertical axis is used to plot pressure, and the horizontal axis is for temperature. The three regions, labeled S, L, and G, represent the three phases, which are divided by solid-liquid, liquid-vapor, and solid-vapor phase boundaries. The curve ABC represents the vapor pressure curve for water, and the line BD represents the equilibrium between solid and liquid, or melting point curve. When the pressure is 1 atmosphere, the melting point (x) is 0°C and the boiling point (y) is 100°C. At 0° and 1 atmosphere the solid and liquid phases can exist in equilibrium. Between 0° and 100° and 1 atmosphere the only stable phase is liquid. Above 100° and 1 atmosphere the only stable phase is gas.

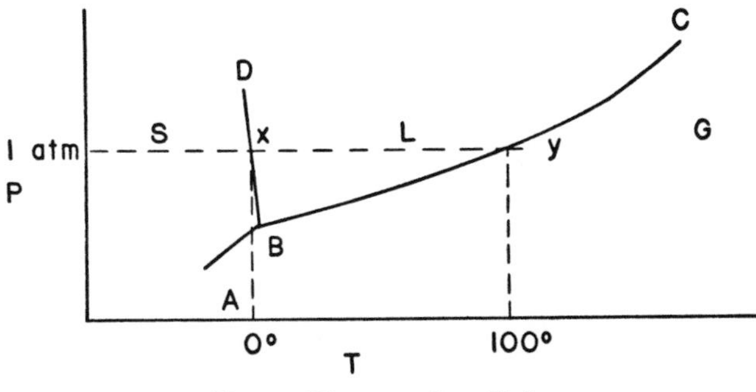

Phase Diagram for Water

Explain the slope of the melting point curve in terms of Le Chatelier's principle. Since ice is less dense than liquid water, an increase in pressure should favor the formation of the denser phase (which occupies a smaller volume). This is what happens when a skate runner rests on ice. The runner has a very small surface area in contact with the ice, resulting in a very high pressure. This high pressure causes the ice to melt, providing lubrication. For a substance whose solid phase is denser than its liquid phase, the solid-liquid boundary slopes toward the right instead of toward the left.

You can demonstrate the boiling of water at reduced temperature by using a filter flask and a water aspirator. Place some warm water and a couple of boiling chips in the filter flask, fitted with a one-hole stopper and thermometer. The water should boil under reduced pressure, causing a decrease in temperature. You can actually freeze water in a vacuum and then sublime the resulting ice, using an oil vacuum pump and dry ice trap.

Sublimation can be discussed using a phase diagram. At 0° water exerts a vapor pressure, given by curve AB. If the pressure is lower than that corresponding to point B (triple point, at which all three phases can coexist in equilibrium), the only stable phases are solid and gas. Ice exerts a vapor pressure, evidenced by the fact that ice and snow evaporate without melting. Reference to the phase diagram for carbon dioxide illustrates sublimation. The triple point corresponds to a temperature of –57°C and 5.2 atmospheres. The only stable phases at atmospheric pressure are solid and gas, and in order to have liquid CO_2 the pressure must be higher than 5.2 atmospheres. It's little wonder that dry ice sublimes at –78° at a pressure of 1 atomosphere.

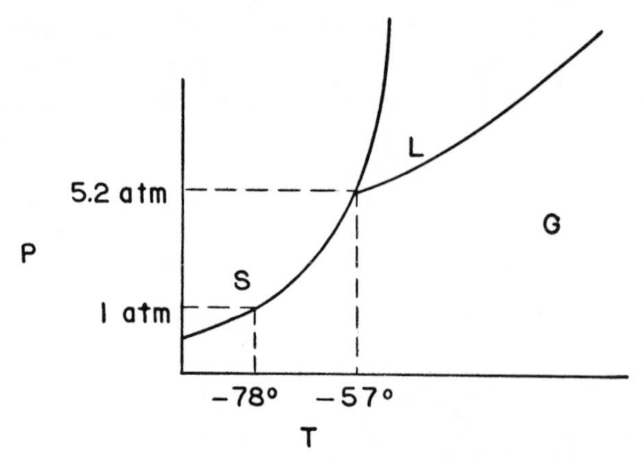

Phase Diagram for Carbon Dioxide

Demonstrate the effect of pressure on the phase change in iodine by sealing some iodine in two tubes: the first is sealed at nearly atmospheric pressure, and the second is sealed under vacuum. When heated, the iodine at the higher pressure actually melts, but the iodine in the low pressure tube sublimes. Such tubes can be purchased from the Welch Scientific Company. The crystals of subliming iodine can be seen jumping around, a phenomenon caused by the rapidly-moving molecules of iodine vapor leaving the solid.

Point out the utility of phase diagrams in reference to steam engines and steam turbines. Water boils at a temperture much higher than 100° under high pressure. Much heat is available to do work in high pressure steam. Organic chemists often purify compounds by distillation. Complex molecules quite frequently boil at a temperature higher than the temperature at which they begin to decompose. The boiling point often can be reduced below the decomposition temperature if the pressure is reduced. Vacuum distillation is a valuable process for purifying compounds that would otherwise decompose.

Point C on the phase diagram for water represents the critical point, at which it is impossible to distinguish between the liquid and gas phases. Point C corresponds to a temperture of 374°C and a pressure of 218 atomspheres. Above the critical temperature the molecules have so much energy that they overcome attractive forces. As the temperature increases, the density of a liquid decreases (it expands), and as the pressure on a gas increases, the density increases (it contracts). When the density of the gas and the liquid are the same, they have the same refractive index, and it is impossible to see a distinction between them. This happens at the critical point.

3

Explaining Atomic Structure and the Periodic Law

1. DEVELOPING THE CONCEPT OF ATOMIC WEIGHT

Dalton's assumptions that atoms of elements differ in mass and properties and that atoms are indivisible (only whole atoms unite to form compounds) led to the idea of an atomic weight scale. Dalton attempted to account for the law of definite composition by postulating the existence of atoms, which were the elementary particles making up all compounds.

Spend a few minutes discussing the possible make-up of matter: continuous and discontinuous structure. Some of the Greek philosophers speculated that if a piece of matter were subdivided, using a hypothetical knife, there would be no limit to the number of times matter could be subdivided: matter is infinitely divisible (continuous). Others, notably Democritus, speculated that one would reach a limit to the sub-divisions which could be made: eventually indivisible pieces of matter would be reached. These tiny units were called *atoms,* meaning indivisible. An atom, in a sense, is a quantum of matter. The ideas of Democritus were forgotten for centuries and were finally resurrected by Dalton.

For the sake of argument, assume that water is H_2O and the analysis is $88^+\%$ oxygen and $11^+\%$ hydrogen by weight. The ratio of the weight of two atoms of hydrogen to one atom of oxygen is 1:8, making the ratio of the weight of one atom of hydrogen to one atom of oxygen 1:16. Dalton erroneously assumed water to be HO (see section 2.1), making the ratio of the weight of one atom of hydrogen to one atom of oxygen 1:8. The idea of an atomic weight scale is a ratio of weights of atoms. During the first half of the nineteenth century, a number of atomic weight scales evolved, leading to confusion which was finally resolved in 1860 (see section 2.1).

The atomic weight scale which was used for many years was a ratio of weights of atoms, taking the weight of oxygen atoms as exactly 16.0000. Tell your students that oxygen was selected as the basis for the atomic weight scale because of the convenience involved; oxygen combined with most of the elements, and so it was relatively easy to compare the weights of other atoms to that of oxygen. Emphasize that naturally-occurring oxygen is really a mixture of isotopes mass 16, 17, 18 and that the weighted average of these isotopes was assigned the value 16.0000 on the chemists' atomic weight scale. Physicists, however, were interested in single isotopes and assigned oxygen 16 the atomic weight 16.0000. This led to a slight discrepancy between the chemists' and physicists' atomic weight scales. A compromise was reached in 1961, assigning the mass 12.0000 to carbon 12.

Remind your students that very often chemists take poetic license and use the words *mass* and *weight* interchangeably, although they are aware of the fundamental difference between these terms. Since atoms are so very small, the atomic mass scale is used. Tie in the idea of moles with the atomic mass scale. One mole of carbon 12 has a mass of 12.0000 grams and contains Avogadro's number of atoms. In terms of grams, therefore, one amu is the reciprocal of Avogadro's number of grams, or $1/6.02 \times 10^{23}$ grams per atomic mass unit.

2. USING EXPERIMENTAL RESULTS TO DEVELOP A MODEL OF THE ATOM

The fact that compounds have definite composition by weight was a good beginning for the development of the atomic theory. Further evidence for the existence of atoms was the successful prediction of the law of multiple proportions. The development of an atomic weight scale from chemical analysis and the use of atomic weights in chemical calculations strengthens our belief in atoms. The discovery of isotopes in 1913 by chemical analysis and mass spectroscopy, preceded by the discovery of radioactivity and the electron, provides more evidence for the existence of atoms which have a more complex nature than that postulated by Dalton. Acquaint your students with the use of chemical analysis in the determination of atomic weights (see section 5.3).

In 1913, Frederick Soddy determined that the atomic weight of lead from samples found in thorium and uranium ores was different (lead 208 is prod-duced by the nuclear decomposition of thorium and lead 206 by the nuclear decomposition of uranium). Since these values were well outside of experimental error, he concluded that atoms of different masses existed. The same year J. J. Thompson used a mass spectrograph and discovered that neon atoms have different masses.

Explain the principle of the mass spectrograph to your students. A molecule or atom is ionized, and the ion is accelerated through a magnetic field. The lighter the ion, the more it is bent by a magnetic field, enabling isotopes to be separated and identified. Since a very small sample of material is needed and the mass of a particle can be accurately determined using this technique, the mass spectrograph is a useful tool for determining atomic weights.

The method by which Thompson discovered the electron as an elementary particle common to all atoms is worth discussing with your students. In principle, Thompson used a crude type of TV picture tube, as shown in the diagram.

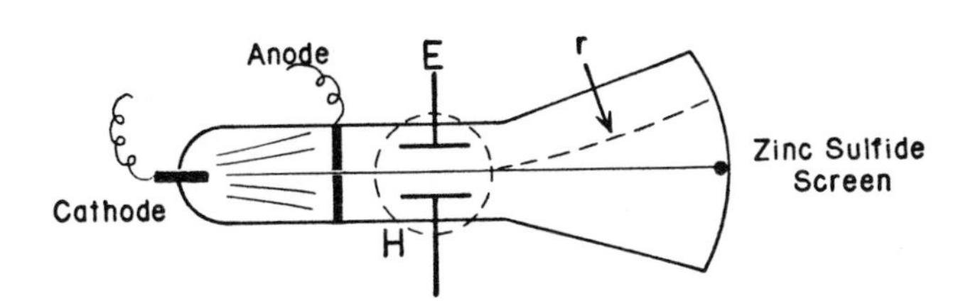

The cathode emits electrons, which are accelerated toward the anode. Some of these particles pass through the hole in the anode and proceed toward the screen, producing a bright spot when they strike the zinc sulfide. An electrical field, produced by charged plates, moves the beam parallel to the field. A magnetic field deflects the beam perpendicular to itself. If the magnetic field and electric field are perpendicular to each other, they both deflect the beam in the same plane but in opposite directions.

The experiment consists of two parts. An electron having mass m and charge q moving with velocity v passes through the magnetic field H and is bent with radius of curvature r (determined by the displacement of the spot on the screen). The force causing the deflection is given by the equation $f = Hqv$. This force is equal to the centripetal force (which changes the direction of the electron), given by the equation $f = mv^2/r$ (from centripetal acceleration, $a = v^2/r$, and $f = ma$). Therefore $Hqv = mv^2/r$. Rearranging we obtain $q/m = v/Hr$. Since *H* and *r* are already known, all we need to determine in order to calculate the charge to mass ratio for the electron is *v*. The second part of the experiment provides this value. The electrical field strength, *E*, is adjusted until it just balances the magnetic field strength, *H*, restoring the spot to its original position on the screen. The force of the electrical field is given by the equation $f = Eq$. Since the forces of the electric and magnetic fields are equal when the beam is not deflected, $Eq = Hqv$. Rearranging we obtain $v = E/H$.

Substituting in the earlier equation we now obtain the expression for the charge to mass ratio: $q/m = E/H^2r$. Thompson was convinced that this particle was common to all atoms, since he obtained similar results using electrodes made of different metals and tubes containing different residual gases after evacuation.

You can demonstrate the deflection of cathode rays by a magnet using a cathode ray tube available from Welch Scientific Company. It contains a slit and plate coated with zinc sulfide. Connect the electrodes to an induction coil and generate cathode rays, visible as a green line on the screen. Slowly bring a bar magnet toward the screen, causing the line to curve up or down, depending on the polarity of the magnet. This demonstrates that cathode rays are deflected perpendicular to a magnetic field. Reversing the polarity of the magnet causes the rays to be deflected the other way.

Robert Millikan determined the charge of the electron by means of his famous oil-drop experiment, which is performed in the PSSC Physics course. In this experiment, charged drops of oil having mass *m* and charge *q*, produced by an atomizer, are allowed to fall by gravity. The gravitational force is balanced by the force produced by an electrical field, *E*, and thus the charge of the drop is determined:

$$E_q = mg \text{ (g is the acceleration of gravity)}$$

Having made a number of determinations of charges on many oil drops, Millikan obtained data similar to these:

Drop	*Charge, coulombs* $\times 10^{-19}$
1	3.20
2	1.60
3	5.40
4	4.80
5	2.40

These values are all multiples of 1.60, indicating that the quantum of charge is 1.60×10^{-19} coulombs.

3. APPROACHING THE DEVELOPMENT OF ATOMIC STRUCTURE HISTORICALLY

In order to show that scientific ideas are constantly changing in response to new evidence, develop the model of an atom from a historical perspective. Dalton imagined that all atoms of a given element were alike in mass, size, and properties. They were like hard little spheres and were indivisible. During the 1830's Michael Faraday performed numerous experiments which consisted of passing an electric current through solutions, culminating in his discovery of the laws of electrolysis and the concept of electrolytes, non-electrolytes, and ions. The existence of positive and negative ions was the beginning of the end for Dalton's indivisible atom: ions must be formed from atoms by losing or gaining electric charge. The photoelectric effect and Becquerel's discovery of radioactivity revealed that atoms were, indeed, divisible.

J. J. Thompson's model of the atom was like a raisin bun. A neutral atom consisted of negative charges (his recently-discovered electrons) imbedded in the body of the atom, which contained an equal amount of positive charge. This model accounted for the formation of ions, since an atom could gain or lose electrons.

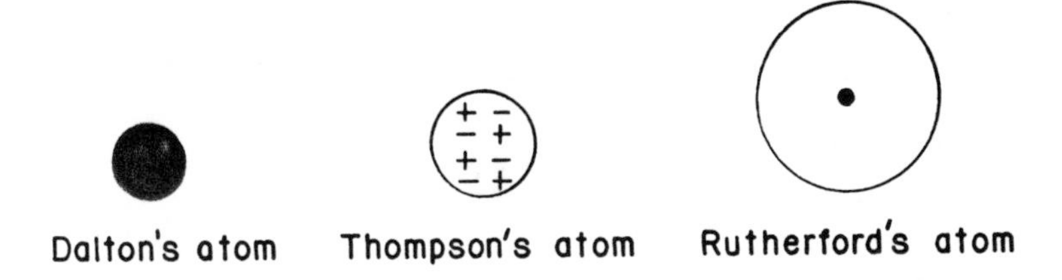

Before discussing Rutherford's experiment, spend a little time on radioactivity and the nature of α, β and γ rays. These are discussed in section 12.1.

Rutherford and Geiger tested Thompson's raisin bun model in 1911. They used polonium as a source of α-particles, which were directed toward a thin sheet of gold foil. If the atoms in the metal were made of uniformly-distributed charges as postulated by Thompson, the α-particles should plow right through the metal without being noticeably deflected, as a rifle bullet passing through a magazine. Rutherford discovered that a few α-particles were scattered through varying angles and, much to his amazement, a small percentage seemed to rebound from the sheet of metal. Analysis of the result convinced Rutherford that the atom consisted of a dense nucleus containing all the positive charge of the atom and that the electrons must reside somewhere outside the nucleus. The diameter of the nucleus was approximately

10^{-13} cm, compared to the diameter of an atom (about 10^{-8} cm). This is in the order of comparing the size of a pencil point to that of your classroom. The PSSC movie "The Rutherford Atom" gives an excellent (although long) presentation of this experiment.

The concept of the atom changed dramatically during the hundred years from Dalton to Rutherford. It is, indeed, divisible, and the discovery of isotopes put an end to the idea that atoms of the same element have the same mass. In section 5 we shall explore the development of the quantum atom.

4. ACCOUNTING FOR RADIOACTIVITY, ISOTOPES, AND OTHER PHENOMENA

Even if you decide to omit the topic of nuclear chemistry, you should give your students examples of radioactive decomposition, fission, and fusion. Most of this material is discussed in Chapter 12. A brief discussion of the photoelectric effect ties in well with the idea of quantum theory and ionization energy.

Radioactive isotopes are unstable atoms which emit particles and energy in order to stabilize themselves, resulting in a transmutation. Show your students the changes in nuclear composition and the nuclear equations for examples of α-decay and β-decay. An example of α-decay is radium emitting an α-particle, producing radon plus energy in the form of γ-rays.

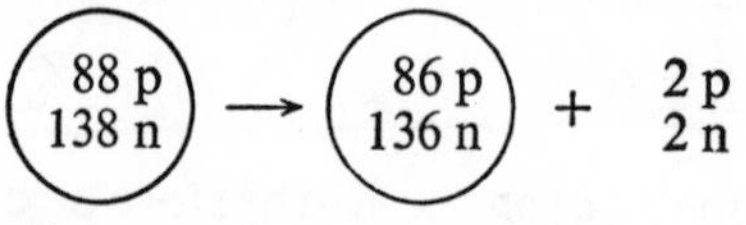

(88 p, 138 n) → (86 p, 136 n) + 2 p, 2 n

$$_{88}Ra^{226} \longrightarrow {}_{86}Rn^{222} + {}_{2}He^{4} + \gamma$$

An example of β-decay is lead 214 emitting a β-particle, producing bismuth 214 and energy.

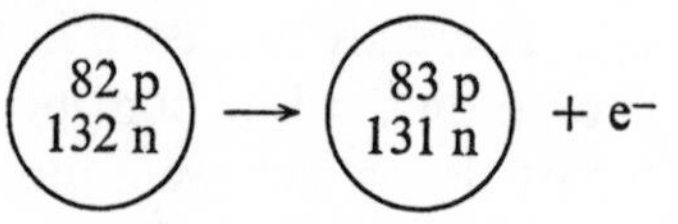

(82 p, 132 n) → (83 p, 131 n) + e^-

$$_{82}Pb^{214} \longrightarrow {}_{83}Bi^{214} + {}_{-1}e^{0} + \gamma$$

The lighter elements can undergo fusion reactions, and the heavier elements tend to undergo fission reactions (see Chapter 12). An example of fission is the decomposition of uranium 235 after it has captured a slow neutron.

$$_{92}U^{235} + {}_{0}n^{1} \longrightarrow {}_{56}Ba^{143} + {}_{36}Kr^{90} + 3\,{}_{0}n^{1} + \text{energy}$$

The emission of more neutrons leads to further neutron capture and a chain reaction. In general, fission reactions lead to the formation of new nuclei having about half the mass of the original nucleus.

In the case of fusion reactions, light nuclei must come very close together in order to fuse. This means that a great deal of energy must be supplied to overcome the repulsive forces when the positively-charged nuclei approach each other. An example of fusion is the overall production of helium from hydrogen in stars at a temperature of millions of degrees.

$$4\,{}_{1}H^{1} \longrightarrow {}_{2}He^{4} + 2\,{}_{+1}e^{0} + \text{energy}$$

Before discussing isotopes with your students, you should acquaint them with protons and neutrons, which are the chief constituents of atomic nuclei. Rutherford discovered the proton several years after the discovery of the nuclear atom. It was not until 1932 that the neutron was discovered by James Chadwick, although its existence had been postulated by Rutherford. The atomic number or nuclear charge, Z (see section 8), is equal to the number of protons in the nucleus, and the mass number is equal to the sum of protons and neutrons.

Pure isotopes have mass numbers that are integers, but naturally-occurring elements frequently have atomic weights which are not whole numbers. This is because the atomic weight is actually the weighted average of the mixture of isotopes found in the naturally-occurring element. Chlorine, for example, is a mixture of about 3 parts chlorine 35 and one part chlorine 37, which averages out to about 35.5. Early in the nineteenth century an English physician by the name of William Prout had postulated that all elements are made up of hydrogen atoms. Since there were numerous elements whose atomic weights were not whole numbers, however, this hypothesis was discarded, only to be resurrected in the twentieth century.

The photoelectric effect not only provides evidence that atoms are divisible but also helps us understand the nature of light. When light strikes a metal, electrons are emitted. The light must have sufficiently high frequency to do this, however, which means that there is a certain minimum energy needed to remove electrons from the atoms of the metal. This phenomenon is the principle on which the photoelectric cell operates. The more active the metal used in the cell (the lower the ionization energy), the lower the frequency of the light needed to produce electrons. (See section 7).

Another interesting phenomenon associated with atoms and electrons is the thermoionic effect. When a metal wire is heated to a sufficiently high temperature, enough energy is available to cause the metal atoms to emit electrons. Thermoionic tubes operate on this principle. A good illustration of the photoelectric and thermoionic effects is given in the CHEM Study film "Ionization Energy."

5. DEVELOPING THE IDEAS OF QUANTUM MECHANICS AND THE QUANTUM ATOM

The next step taken after Rutherford's nuclear atom in developing the modern view of atomic structure was taken by Niels Bohr in 1913. He successfully accounted for the spectral lines of hydrogen, assuming the electron of hydrogen traveled around the nucleus in a circular orbit. According to classical physics, a charge undergoing acceleration (change in direction) should radiate energy, which would result in the electron coming closer and closer to the nucleus, resulting in the atom collapsing. Since this does not occur, Bohr assumed that the macroscopic laws of physics do not apply on the atomic scale. He made the further assumption that there are certain permitted orbits which the electron may occupy (quantum condition). When an electron in a lower energy level (orbit nearer the nucleus) absorbs the right amount of energy, it is excited to a higher energy level (further from the nucleus). When going from a higher to a lower energy level, it emits energy in the form of electromagnetic waves. His theory worked well in the case of hydrogen, since it agreed with experiment, but it failed when he tried to apply it to more complicated atoms.

Before discussing the Bohr atom with your students, they should be introduced to the ideas of quanta and the nature of light waves and photons. Show them the electromagnetic spectrum, pointing out the relationship between energy, wave length, and frequency. Make certain that your students understand the relationship between wave length, frequency and velocity. Diagram a wave and label the wave length and amplitude.

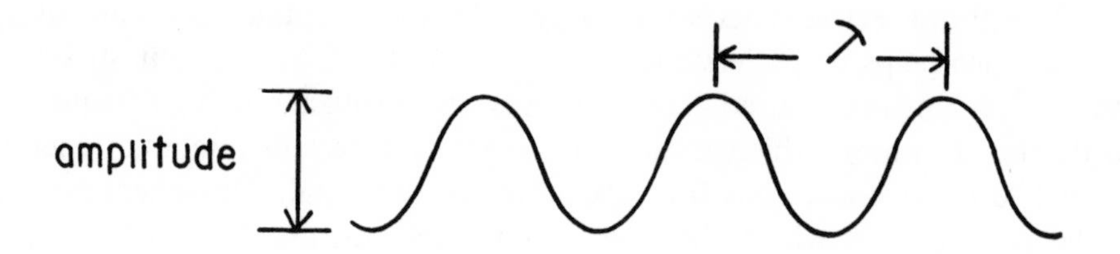

The train analogy is an effective way to demonstrate the relationship between wave length (λ), frequency (υ), and velocity (c). Suppose a freight train is moving past an observer standing by the side of the tracks. If each car is 50 feet long, the observer can count the number of cars that pass him per unit of time. If ten cars pass in one minute, the distance traveled by one car is 500 feet in one minute, or the velocity of the train is 500 ft/min. In the case of waves, the velocity is euqal to the wave length times the frequency, or $c = \lambda \nu$.

Point out the parts of the electromagnetic spectrum which are of interest to chemists:

(1) microwave region, associated with molecular rotation
(2) infrared region, associated with vibrations of molecules (bonding)
(3) visible region, associated with excitation of electrons in atoms
(4) ultraviolet region, associated with resonance in molecules
(5) X-ray region, associated with the excitation of inner electrons in atoms

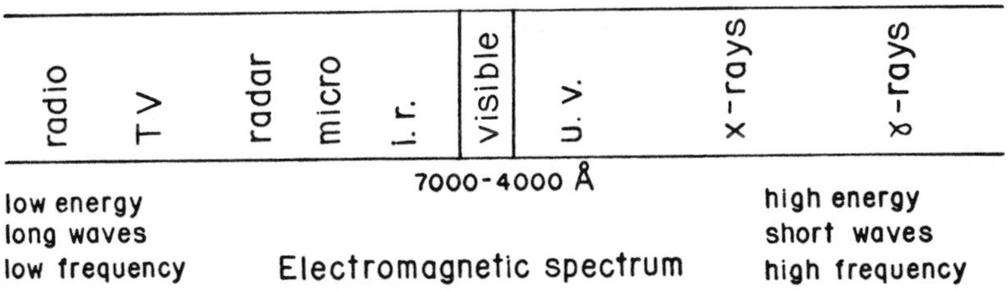

radio	T V	radar	micro	I. r.	visible	u. v.	x-rays	γ-rays

7000-4000 Å

low energy
long waves
low frequency

Electromagnetic spectrum

high energy
short waves
high frequency

Make sure your students appreciate the meaning of *quantum,* which involves the idea of paticles or "bundles" of something. In a sense, an atom is a quantum of matter, and an electron is a quantum of electric charge. In dealing with a quantum of energy, the staircase analogy is useful. If a ball rests on the fourth stair, it has more potential energy than when resting on the third, second, or first stair. If it falls down one stair, it loses a discrete amount of potential energy, and if it falls down two stairs, it loses twice as much potential energy. In this example, a quantum of energy is that which the ball loses (or gains) when going down (or up) one stair. In order to account for the continuous spectrum of incandescent solids (energy radiated by the quivering atoms in the solid), Max Planck assumed that radiant energy was emitted in bits, or quanta, and that the energy was proportional to the frequency of the radiation: $E = h\nu$.

In order to account for the photoelectric effect, Einstein expanded Planck's idea of light quanta. He assumed that radiant energy travels through space in small bits, or particles, which he called *photons.* This idea was a rejection of Maxwell's theory of elctromagnetic waves, just as Newton's corpuscular theory of light was incompatible with Huygens' wave theory. These ideas are compatible, however. Einstein considered the wave nature of light suitable for explaining large-scale phenomena, but used the idea of photons to account for those phenomena involving the interaction of atoms and light.

In 1924, Louis de Broglie offered an explanation for the dual nature of electromagnetic radiation. He proposed that every moving body has the property of waves, i.e., wave length. The relationship between momentum (mv) and wave length (λ) of a particle is given by the equation $\lambda = h/mv$, in which h is Planck's constant. Point out that for particles having a very small mass λ becomes appreciable.

We can now return to Bohr's model of the atom and make some changes. In the case of the hydrogen atom, an electron can occupy certain permitted stable orbits and nothing in between, just as a ball may rest on a stair but not be suspended in midair between two stairs. By absorbing a photon or by being excited by electron bombardment in a gas discharge tube, the electron can be promoted to a higher energy level. On returning to a lower energy level, the electron will emit a discrete amount of energy having a definite wave length and frequency. Diagram some changes in energy for your students.

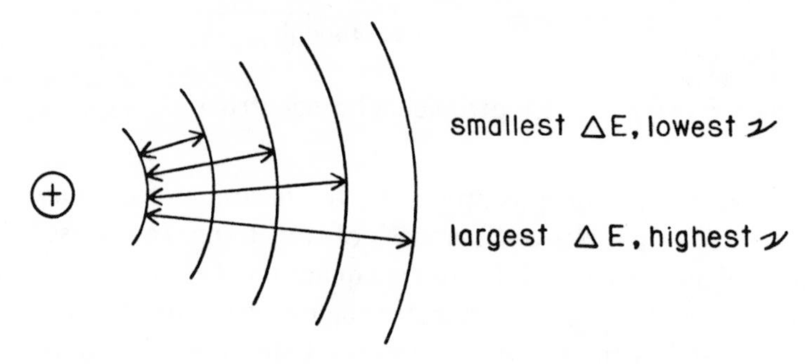

These "quantum jumps" account for line spectra.

Bohr's assumption that the elctron is a particle which revolves around the nucleus in a circular orbit does not agree with experimental evidence that electrons have wave properties, as postulated by de Broglie and verified by electron diffraction. If an electron having wave length λ is moving around a nucleus, the wave length must divide into the circumference of the orbit a whole number of times. If it did not, the wave would destructively interfere with itself. This idea may be expressed mathematically: $n\lambda = 2\,\Pi\, r$, in which n is an integer and r is the radius of the orbit. This is the quantum condition.

In 1927, Heisenberg showed that one could not know precisely the position and momentum of an electron. In plain English, you can't pinpoint an electron. Bohr's idea that an electron revolves around the nucleus like a planet around the sun is not valid. We can only speak of a region of space where we can most likely find an electron. Such a probability distribution is called an *orbital.*

Wave mechanics, developed largely by Erwin Shrödinger, develops a mathematical model for the atom using the equations for standing waves (vibrating strings) and the quantum idea. The result of this treatment is a set of solutions describing the probability distributions of electrons around the nucleus. These ideas are presented rather well in the CHEM Study film "The Hydrogen Atom as Viewed by Quantum Mechanics (Advanced Version)."

An effective way to convey the idea of an electron effectively occupying a region of space around the nucleus is to compare the electron to a propeller. When not in motion, the location of the propeller is plainly evident, but when it is moving, we cannot see the propeller. Don't stick your hand into the region of space occupied by the propeller, however.

6. DEVELOPING THE ELECTRONIC DISTRIBUTION IN ATOMS, SHAPES AND ORIENTATIONS OF ORBITALS

Having established the idea that electrons do not follow circular paths but occupy certain regions of space around the nucleus, you are almost ready to proceed with the distribution of electrons around the nucleus. Before doing this, however, spend a little time developing the magnetic and spin properties of electrons.

When a line spectrum is generated in a magnetic field, the principal lines are split into several (Zeeman effect), indicating that orbitals are oriented in different directions around the nucleus. In 1921, Stern and Gerlach vaporized neutral silver atoms and passed a beam of this vapor through a magnetic field. Half of the atoms were deflected in one direction, and the other half in in the opposite direction. This experiment provided evidence for the idea that electrons spin in either a clockwise or counterclockwise direction as they go around the nucleus. Since a spinning electrical charge generates a magnetic field, oppositely-spinning electrons would generate magnetic fields oriented in opposite directions, which accounts for the deflection of the silver atoms in opposite directions. Electron spin is useful in accounting for paramagnetism.

In describing the quantum atom, four quantum numbers are used: (1) the principal quantum number, n, which designates the main energy level; (2) the orbital quantum number, 1, which is associated with the shape of the orbital; (3) the magnetic quantum number, m_l, which designates the orientation of the orbital; (4) the spin quantum number, m_s, which designates the direction of spin of the electron in question. For the purpose of a high school chemistry course, it is not really necessary to go into the details of how these quantum numbers are used. Merely point out that the electronic configuration of atoms is described by the use of quantum numbers.

Pauli's exclusion principle, Hund's rule, and the aufbau principle should be understood by your students. These can be made meaningful if you utilize the idea of spining electrons. Pauli's principle states that no two electrons in an atom may be described by the same set of quantum numbers. In plain English, this means a given orbital can hold no more than two electrons, provided they have opposite spins. Since electrons have the same charge, they repel each other; but if the electrons have opposite spins, their magnetic fields will attract each other and overcome some of the repulsion. A third electron will meet too much opposition if it tries to enter an orbital already occupied by two oppositely-spinning electrons, so it must enter a different orbital (three's a crowd). Hund's rule states that electrons having parallel spins will populate unoccupied orbitals of the same energy level before pairing up, which is reasonable, considering the fact that like charges repel each other. The aufbau principle states that orbitals of the lowest energy will be occupied first, just as water fills a bathtub from the bottom up. Once your students buy the ideas mentioned above, they should be ready to tackle electronic configuration.

Give your students the order of energy of the different orbitals in the main energy levels, pointing out that the digit preceding the orbital letter (*s, p, d, f*) refers to the main energy level and the superscript following the orbital letter indicates the number of electrons in that level. There are one *s*, three *p*, five *d*, and seven *f* orbitals. The order of filling can be systematized as shown in the following diagram:

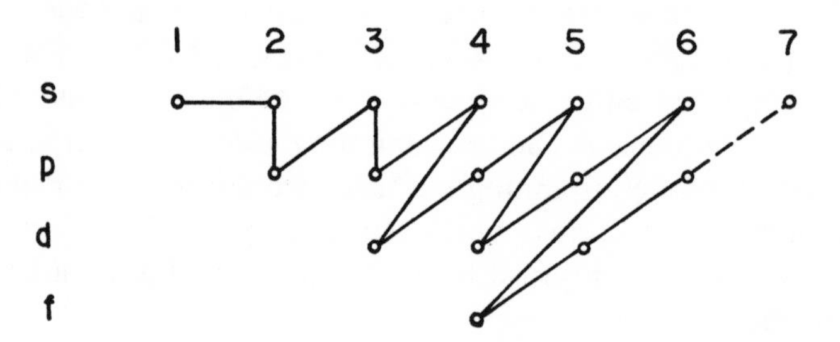

Show your students how the electronic configurations of the first 36 elements are predicted, following the aufbau principle, the exclusion principle, and Hund's rule. Helium completes the first period (two electrons having opposite spins in the 1*s* orbital). For lithium the third electron must enter the next available energy level (2*s*). In boron, carbon and nitrogen, electrons successively enter each of the 2*p* orbitals, and in oxygen, fluorine and neon, the next three electrons pair up. Going from sodium to argon, the 3*s* and 3*p* levels fill up in a similar fashion. Potassium and calcium take care of the 4*s* level, and then the fun begins. According to the energy level diagram, the next available orbitals are the 3*d*, which fill up going from scandium to zinc. At this level the exceptions (chromium and copper) are not worth laboring; but if an inquisitive student should ask about these, point out that an especially stable electronic configuration is achieved when a sub-level is either half filled or completely filled. This explanation accounts for the configuration of chromium ($1s^2\ 2s^2\ 2p^6\ 3s^2\ 3p^6\ 4s^1\ 3d^5$) and copper ($1s^2\ 2s^2\ 2p^6\ 3s^2\ 3p^6\ 4s^1\ 3d^{10}$).

The order of the elements in the periodic table is correlated to atomic structure. Point out that the transition elements in the fourth, fifth and sixth periods each comprise ten elements, characterized by filling *d* orbitals. The lanthanide and actinide series each consist of fourteeen elements, characterized by the filling of the 3*f* and 5*f* levels.

The shapes and orientations of orbitals is important when dealing with molecular geometry, and so your students should know something about *s* and *p* orbitals (*d* orbitals are generally beyond the scope of a high school course). Show your students models of orbitals (you can make these from styrofoam spheres and eggs), pointing out that these merely represent regions in space in which electrons are most likely to be found. Use Cartesian coordinates to show the orientation of the *p* orbitals. A kit consisting of plastic straws and metal jacks (available from Prentice-Hall, Inc.) is very useful for showing orientations of orbitals and hybrids (see section 4.4).

7. RELATING COULOMB'S LAW TO IONIZATION ENERGY, ELECTRON AFFINITY, ATOMIC RADIUS, NUCLEAR CHARGE, SHIELDING EFFECT AND PERIODIC PROPERTIES

In the previous section atomic structure was correlated to the periodic table. Since the chemical properties of elements are largely dependent upon ionization energy and electron affinity, your students should have some idea of what causes the periodic variation of these properties. The basis for their interpretation is Coulomb's law.

Before starting out, make sure your students know the differences between electron affinity, electronegativity, and ionization energy. Electron affinity refers to the energy released when an isolated neutral atom gains an electron. Electronegativity, on the other hand, refers to the tendency of an atom to attract a pair of electrons in a bonding situation. Ionization energy is the energy needed to remove an electron completly from an isolated atom. The CHEM Study film "Ionization Energy" gives the students insight into how this property is determined experimentally. The other two, however, are more difficult to treat in detail in a high school course. As a rule of thumb, the three properties parallel each other; low ionization energy is an indication of low electron affinity and electronegativity.

Your students should readily appreciate the relation of atomic radius (distance between valence electron and nucleus) and nuclear charge to Coulomb's law. Shielding effect, however, warrants some explanation. A good way is to discuss the principle of thermoionic tubes. Diagram a simple diode, pointing out that when the filament is heated, sufficient energy is provided to cause the emission of electrons, which migrate toward the positive plate. Such a device can be used to rectify alternating current. If a grid is inserted between the plate and the filament, we convert the tube into a triode, which can be used to amplify signals. In principle, when the grid is charged positively, many electrons are caught by the grid and never reach the plate. When negatively charged, many electrons are deflected (repulsion) and don't reach the plate.

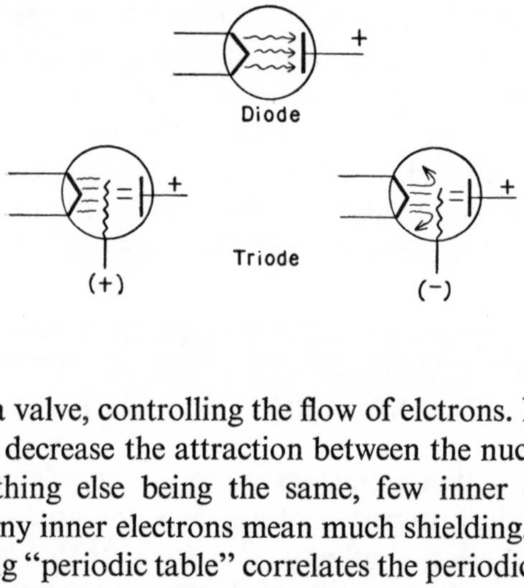

Diode

Triode

The grid acts as a valve, controlling the flow of elctrons. In an atom the inner electrons tend to decrease the attraction between the nucleus and the valence electrons. Everything else being the same, few inner electrons mean low shielding and many inner electrons mean much shielding.

The following "periodic table" correlates the periodic trends of ionization energy, electron affinity, metallic and mon-metallic properties with atomic radius, nuclear charge, and shielding effect. In addition to providing your students with such a diagram, a chart of sizes of atoms and ions is very useful. Point out that metallic behavior and activity are characterized by low ionization energy and that non-metallic behavior and activity is characterized by high electron affinity.

Remind your students that the general trends shown on this chart are somewhat simplified, especially the shielding effect. On the high school level you shouldn't get into the differences contributed by *s, p, d,* and *f* orbitals. Impress upon your students that if they know the meanings of the terms used on the chart and really understand their relationships and periodic trends,

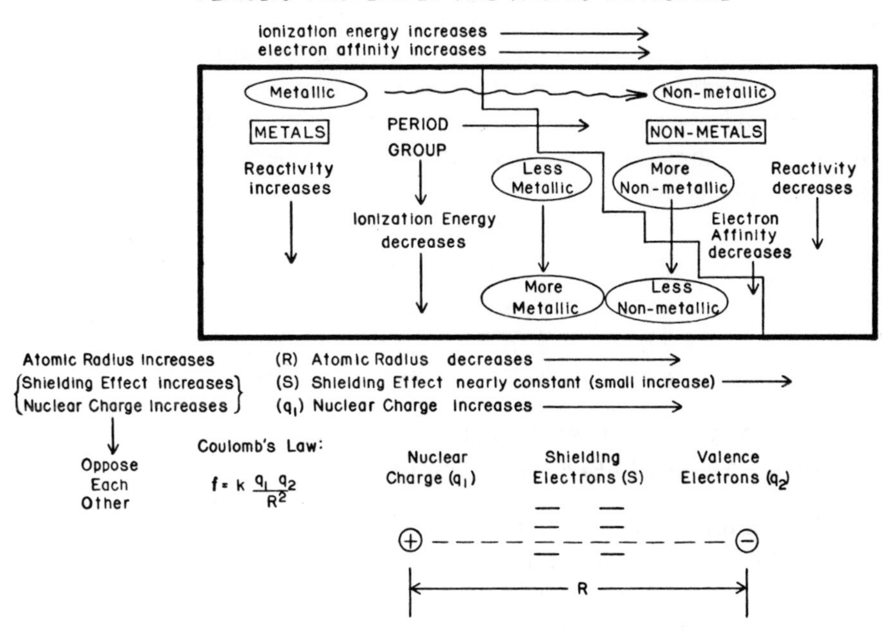

they will have a much better understanding and appreciation of the science of chemistry and have a real framework on which to build.

Discuss the trend in ionization energy going from lithium to neon, diagramming the change as follows:

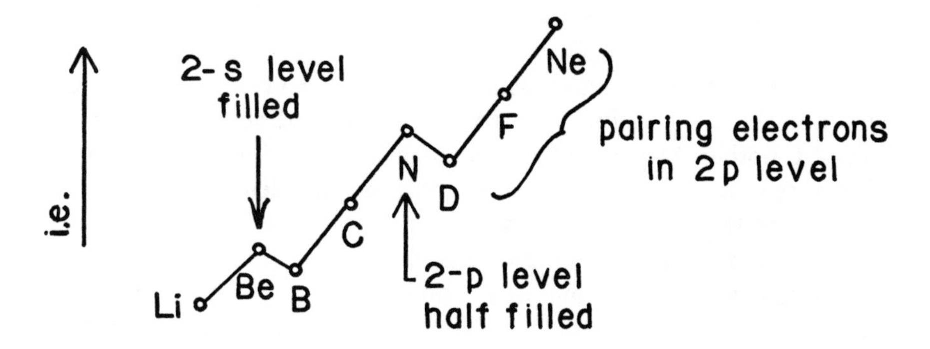

The increase going from lithium to beryllium is due primarily to increasing nuclear charge (shielding does not change). The slight decrease going from beryllium to boron is due to the next electron entering the $2p$ level, which is farther from the nucleus (also slight increase in shielding due to 2*s* electrons making a partial contribution). The slight decrease going from nitrogen to oxygen is due to the pairing up of elctrons in the 2*p* level (some repulsion).

Emphasize that large increases in ionization energy when removing successive electrons is due to removing electrons from a lower energy level, which provides a clue to the number of valence electrons. For example, use the successive ionization energies of the first three elements in the third period, measured in electron volts:

	Ionization Energy				*Valence*
Element	*1st*	*2nd*	*3nd*	*4th*	*Electrons*
Na	5.1	47.3	71.7	98.9	1
Mg	7.6	15.0	80.1	109.3	2
Al	6.0	18.8	28.4	120.0	3

8. DEVELOPMENT OF PERIODIC LAW FROM MENDELEEFF TO MOSELEY

One of the earliest attempts to classify elements was made by the German chemist Dobereiner, who noticed that a number of elements having similar properties occurred in sets of three ("triads"). Around 1829 he discovered that the atomic weight of the middle element in each of these triads was the mean of the atomic weights of the first and third member.

first	Li	7	Ca	40	S	32	Cl	35
third	K	39	Ba	137	Te	128	1	127
average		23		89		80		81
middle	Na	23	Sr	88	Se	79	Br	80

About 1864 an Englishman by the name of Newlands arranged elements in groups of seven, with the eighth element repeating the behavior of the first, just as the notes on a musical scale comprise an octave. His law of "octaves" was not taken seriously by his colleagues. Several years later, the German chemist Lothar Meyer and the Russian Dmitri Mendeleeff independently discovered that the properties of the (known) elements were a periodic function of their atomic weights.

Meyer plotted the atomic volume (volume occupied by one mole of the solid element) against atomic weight and obtained a repetitive pattern (periodicity). Point out to your students that attempts to correlate data is a technique used by scientists in order to discover regularities in nature.

Mendeleeff arranged the known elements in horizontal rows in order of increasing atomic weight, placing elements having similar properties under each other. He left a number of blank spaces in his table, presuming that there were undiscovered elements which would eventually fit into these spaces.

In several cases inversions had to be made, notably argon and potassium as well as tellurium and iodine. His table enabled scientists to predict the properties of undiscovered elements and to correlate the properties of the elements by arranging them in family groups. Point out that Mendeleeff's periodic table was the result of experimental observation and correlation of data (empirical) and not based on the electronic configuration of atoms (which was not known at the time). The discovery of the noble gases near the end of the nineteenth century added another column to the periodic table.

The CHEM Study film "Chemical Families" is worth showing to your students, because it illustrates how scientists discover similarities by experiment and arrange their findings in an orderly fashion. Classification of data is one of the techniques by which scientists discover regularities in nature. Demonstrate the similarity in behavior between lithium, sodium, and potassium. Cut a small piece of each metal, pointing out the increasing softness going from lithium to potassium and the similarity in activity (tarnishing). Ask the students why lithium floats on oil (low density, a sign of a large atom). Drop each metal into covered beakers containing water and ask them which reacts least vigorously and which reacts most vigorously. Add a few drops of phenolphthalein to each beaker after the metals have dissolved. This demonstration should convince your students that the reactivity of metals in a family increases with atomic weight. Conversely, the reactivity of nonmetals in a family decreases with atomic weight.

In 1913, Henry Moseley determined the X-ray spectra of a number of elements. In the process he discovered that the elements having a higher atomic weight produced X-rays having a higher frequency. He obtained a straight line plot of the square root of the frequency against integers, which he concluded to be the nuclear charge of the atoms, or the atomic number. When the elements were arranged in order of increasing atomic number, the two exceptions to Mendeleeff's periodic law (and the positions of cobalt and nickel) were accounted for and rectified. When atomic structure was finally worked out a few years later, it agreed with the arrangement of atoms as a

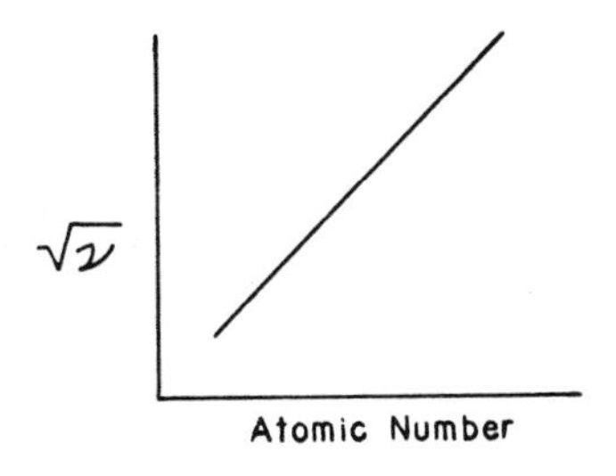

periodic function of atomic number. This represents one of the many triumphs of chemical science.

An explanation of the source of X-ray spectra is worth giving in order to reinforce the discussion of atomic spectra previously given. X-rays are radiations having high energy (short wave length, high frequency), and they are produced by electrons occupying inner energy levels being excited by high energy electrons bombarding them and then falling back to their former energy levels. As the nuclear charge increases, the attractive force between nucleus and inner electrons increases. This means that more energy is associated with quantum jumps of inner electrons, resulting in a higher frequency X-ray.

Diagram an X-ray tube, pointing out that the frequency of the X-ray is dependent upon the energy of the electrons striking the target as well as the nuclear charge of the atoms in the target. The higher the accelerating voltage used to produce the bombarding electrons, the higher their energy, and the more penetrating the X-ray will be.

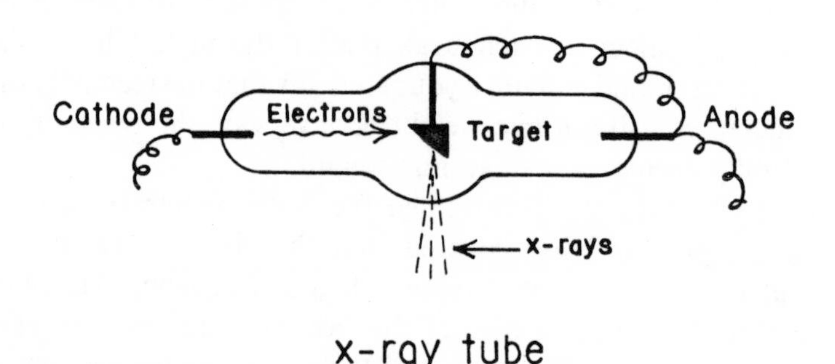

x-ray tube

9. CORRELATING PERIODIC PROPERTIES OF METALS AND NON-METALS WITH ATOMIC STRUCTURE

Ionization energy and electron affinity variations with atomic radius, nuclear charge and shielding effect were discussed in section 7. Develop the notion of metallic and non-metallic properties throughout the course. A summary of some properties is summarized in the following table:

Metals	*Non-Metals*
electrical conductors	non-conductors
ductile and malleable	brittle (as solids)
basic oxides	acidic oxides
basic hydrides	acidic hydrides

produce cations	produce anions
good reducing agents	good oxidizing agents
low ionization energy	high ionization energy
low electronegativity	high electronegativity
low electron affinity	high electron affinity

The acid-base properties of elements will be treated in Chapter 7, and the oxidation-reduction properties will be covered in Chapter 10. As you develop the concepts of chemistry, refer to atomic structure and the notion of periodicity whenever the opportunity presents itself. You will find some examples of using descriptive chemistry to illustrate periodicity in Chapter 13. A number of periodic properties depend upon electronegativity and the nature of bonding involved. Chapter 4 will cover some aspects of these.

4

Correlating Chemical Bonding and Properties of Compounds

1. DEVELOPING THE CONCEPT OF VALENCE

Historically, valence referred to combining capacity and was defined as the number of hydrogen atoms with which one atom of an element combined or replaced when forming a compound. Developing this idea is well worth the time if you plan to include the concept of equivalents in your course. In terms of more current ideas of chemical bonding, the valence of an element (or radical) is the number of electrons gained, lost, or shared in the formation of a compound. In the case of simple ions, the valence is merely the charge of the ion. Make certain that your students avoid confusing valence with oxidation number (see section 3). The use of valences is essential in writing formulas, as was discussed briefly in section 1.6.

If you develop the concept of valence in terms of the number of hydrogen atoms, let the students develop their own table of valences as follows. Give them a few formulas of binary compounds of hydrogen, such as HCl, H_2O, NH_3, H_2SO_4, HNO_3, etc. Applying the definition of valence, the students should deduce that chlorine has a valence of 1 (one atom of chlorine combines with 1 atom of hydrogen), oxygen 2, nitrogen 3, sulfate radical 2, nitrate radical 1. Follow this with the following formulas: $NaCl$, K_2O, $CuSO_4$, NH_4NO_3, $AlCl_3$. With little guidance (stress chemical equivalence in terms of combining capacity), the students should determine the valence of sodium is 1, potassium 1, etc. An effective technique is to tell them that hydrogen is worth one dollar, and then ask them to tell you how much the other atoms (or radicals) are worth in terms of an equivalent amount. Ask the students to use their table of valences to write the formulas for sodium sulfate, copper nitrate, aluminum oxide, ammonium chloride, etc. Such an approach to valence and formula writing (although somewhat archaic) gives students a feel for chemical equivalence.

The more commonly-used approach to formula writing involves the use of positive and negative valences. Stress the idea that a compound is electrically neutral. Therefore, the sum of the positive and negative valences must be zero. Referring to a table of valences, ask the students to write some formulas, such as that for aluminum sulfate. Aluminum is +3 and sulfate is –2. The least common denominator is six. Two aluminums add up to + 6, and three sulfates add up to –6, making the sum of aluminum and sulfate zero. Students who can't understand this bit of arithmetic will have much trouble with chemistry. These unfortunate souls might learn to write formulas if you ask them to "cross" the valence numbers as follows:

$$\overset{+3}{\text{Al}}\_\;\; \times \;\; \overset{-2}{\text{SO}_4}\_ \qquad \text{gives} \qquad Al_2(SO_4)_3$$

As your students begin to understand chemical bonding, the concept of valence will become more meaningful.

Your students should know how to write and interpret Lewis electron-dot formulas. The symbol stands for the nucleus plus the inner electrons and is called the "kernel." The valence electrons are represented by dots and are arranged around the kernel in a manner indicating the electron configuration in the valence shell. Paired electrons in an orbital are shown by a pair of dots, and unpaired electrons are represented by single dots. The following examples can be used to illustrate the proper way to write electron-dot formulas. In each example, the kernel consists of the nucleus and the $1s^2$ electrons, and the valence electrons consist of the $2s$ and $2p$ electrons.

Li	($1s^2\ 2s^1$)	Li·	
Be	($1s^2\ 2s^2$)	Be:	
B	($1s^2\ 2s^2\ 2p^1$)	$\dot{\text{B}}$:	(when hybridized, ·$\dot{\text{B}}$·)
C	($1s^2\ 2s^2\ 2p^2$)	·C: (with dot below)	(when hybridized, ·$\dot{\text{C}}$· with dot below)
N	($1s^2\ 2s^2\ 2p^3$)	·$\dot{\text{N}}$: (with dot below)	
O	($1s^2\ 2s^2\ 2p^4$)	·$\dot{\text{O}}$: (with pair below)	
F	($1s^2\ 2s^2\ 2p^5$)	:F: (with pairs above and below)	

2. EXPLAINING COVALENT, COORDINATE-COVALENT, AND IONIC BONDING

Before your students begin to explore chemical bonding, they should be familiar with ionization energy, electron affinity, electronegativity, and Coulomb's law. If your students are weak, begin with the formation of sodium chloride from an atom of sodium and an atom of chlorine. If they are well-prepared and able, develop ionic bonding in a more sophisticated fashion, using the Born-Haber cycle.

A simple example of the formation of the ionic bond involves a sodium atom donating an electron to a chlorine atom. Don't make the mistake of giving the students the impression that a sodium atom "wants to give away" an electron. Energy is needed to remove an electron from a sodium atom (ionization energy). The chlorine atom releases some energy when it accepts an electron (electron affinity). Much energy is released when a sodium ion and a chloride ion attract each other and come together to form the ionic lattice characteristic of a sodium chloride crystal (lattice energy). Tell your students that chlorine is an electron hog (highly electronegative) and snatches an electron from sodium, as a bully takes a lollipop from a baby. Since sodium has a low electronegativity, it offers little resistance to chlorine's piracy.

Explain why a positive ion is smaller than a neutral atom. In the case of sodium, for example, the valence electron is lost, leaving a positive ion. The remaining electrons, which are closer to the nucleus, are drawn in even closer by the net positive charge remaining, making the ion smaller. The higher the positive charge, the smaller the ion. Point out this trend on a chart which shows relative sizes of ions and atoms.

Conversely, a negative ion is larger than a neutral atom. When a neutral atom gains an electron, the valence shell acquires an additional electron. Since electrons repel each other and a net negative charge has been produced, the valence shell swells, resulting in a larger ion than the neutral atom. The higher the negative charge, the larger the ion.

Why doesn't an "inert" element, such as neon, form positive or negative ions by reacting with other elements? The electronic configuration of neon is like that of a fluoride ion, which is quite stable. Neon has a greater nuclear charge and is smaller than a fluoride ion, and so more energy is required to remove an electron from a neon atom than a fluoride ion (refer to Coulomb's law). No element is capable of doing this, and so neon does not form a positive ion. Its ionization energy is too high. The neon atom has the same electronic configuration but has a smaller nuclear charge and greater diameter than the sodium ion. Neon's nucleus doesn't have a large enough charge to attract an additional electron and hold it in the next available shell. Therefore, it does not form a negative ion. The same type of argument applies to the other noble gases.

Your more capable students should be able to understand the energetics involved in the reaction between one mole of sodium and a half mole of chlorine molecules, using the Born-Haber cycle. The following diagram can be used to illustrate the steps involved in the reaction, which produces considerable energy (exothermic). Energy must be supplied to start the reaction, but more energy is released in the formation of solid NaCl than is consumed in producing the gaseous ions.

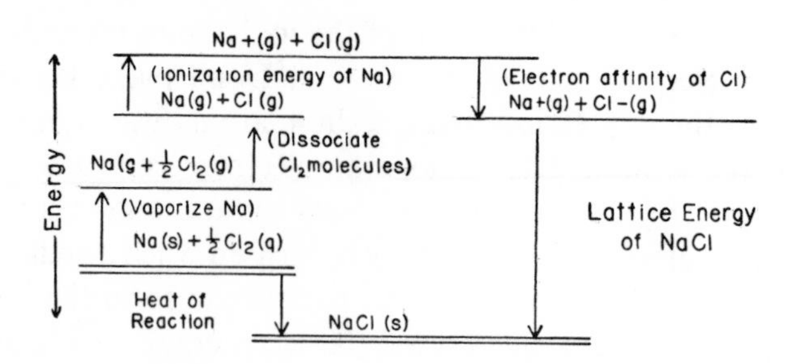

Explain the steps involved and the idea that the driving force of the reaction is the large amount of energy released when the gaseous ions come together to form the crystals (lattice energy). Chapter 9 treats these energy changes in greater detail.

An ionic compound (salt) is generally produced when a metal combines with a non-metal. Non-metals usually combine to form a covalent compound. Prediction of bond type depends upon the difference in electronegativity between the elements involved, and this subject will be treated in section 3.

A simple covalent compound is produced when neither element involved tends to produce a positive ion (the ionization energy is too high). As two atoms approach each other, their nuclei attract electrons of the approaching atom. As the atoms come closer together, energy is released. When the two nuclei come closer together, they begin to repel each other. Energy is required to bring them closer together, which means that they resist approaching each other beyond a given distance. The energy released when this bond is formed is called the bond energy, and the distance separating the nuclei at the minimum energy of the system is the bond length. Show your students the following diagram, which illustrates these ideas.

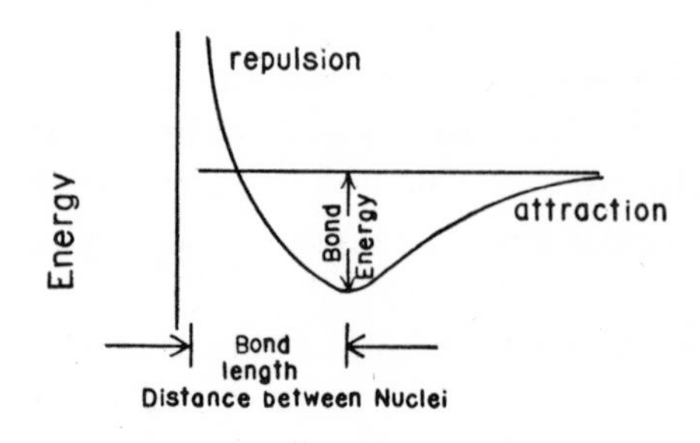

Discuss the formation of a hydrogen chloride molecule in the following manner. Hydrogen, consisting of one proton and one electron, may react in one of two ways: it can give up an electron to produce a simple positive hydrogen ion (a bare proton), or it can gain an electron and produce a hydride ion (isoelectric with helium). Ask your students which of these ions they think is more stable. The bare proton is exceedingly small and has a tremendously high charge density, but the hydride ion is much larger and has a much lower charge density than the proton. The hydride ion should be much more stable. Bare protons can exist only in a very high energy environment, such as the interior of stars or in a gas discharge tube. The only simple ion that hydrogen can form in a chemical reaction is the hydride ion.

Compare the elements to people who are striving to get ahead, but beware of the dangers of anthropomorphism. The "noble" gases have it made; they are very satisfied with their complete outer shells. A metal, such as sodium, doesn't have to pay a very high price to be like a noble gas. By giving up an electron, sodium can become like neon. A non-metal, such as chlorine, will work hard to gain an electron and become a socially-acceptable atom like argon. Which way will hydrogen behave? By giving up an electron, he will be a proton, but by gaining an electron, he will be like helium, who is socially acceptable. Since hydrogen cannot take an electron from chlorine (who won't relinquish an electron) and since chlorine can't take an electron from hydrogen (who doesn't want to become a nonentity), the only way these two elements can improve their lot is to form a partnership and share a pair of electrons. Such a sharing situation leads to the formation of a covalent bond, and a hydrogen chloride molecule. The formation of an HCl molecule from an H atom and a Cl atom can be represented using electron-dot formulas:

$$\mathrm{H}\cdot + \cdot\underset{\cdot\cdot}{\overset{\cdot\cdot}{\mathrm{Cl}}}: \longrightarrow \mathrm{H}:\underset{\cdot\cdot}{\overset{\cdot\cdot}{\mathrm{Cl}}}:$$

When two atoms form a covalent bond, each contributes an electron to form a shared pair, enabling each atom to simulate a noble gas in electronic configuration. Double and triple bonds are produced by the sharing of two or three pairs of electrons.

The only difference between a covalent and a coordinate-covalent bond is the manner in which it is formed. When one atom contributes both electrons in the shared pair and the other atoms goes along for a free ride, the bond is sometimes called a coordinate-covalent or dative bond. An example is the formation of the ammonium ion from a molecule of ammonia accepting a proton:

$$\mathrm{H^+} + \begin{array}{c} \mathrm{H} \\ :\underset{\cdot\cdot}{\overset{\cdot\cdot}{\mathrm{N}}}:\mathrm{H} \\ \mathrm{H} \end{array} \longrightarrow \left(\begin{array}{c} \mathrm{H} \\ \mathrm{H}:\underset{\cdot\cdot}{\overset{\cdot\cdot}{\mathrm{H}}}:\mathrm{N} \\ \mathrm{H} \end{array} \right)^+$$

Once the bond has been formed, there is no difference between it and the other N-H bonds: these four bonds are equivalent. When an ammonium ion loses a proton, any one of the hydrogen atoms may leave a pair of electrons, producing ammonia. Another example is the classic reaction between ammonia and boron trifluoride:

```
                   ..            ..
     H            :F:          H:F:
     ..            ..  ..      .. ..     ..
   H:N:    +       B:  F:  =  H:N:B  :  F:
     ..            ..  ..      .. ..     ..
     H            :F:          H:F:
                   ..            ..
```

The formation of coordinate-covalent bonds will be discussed in more detail in Chapter 7, which deals with acid-base concepts.

The formation of covalent bonds can be interpreted in two ways: the valence bond theory and the molecular orbital theory. The valence bond theory is simpler (although less correct) and easier for high school students to grasp. This theory describes a covalent bond as an overlap of atomic orbitals, resulting in a pair of electrons occupying the overlapped orbitals. Show your students examples of this idea by drawing the overlapping of the half-filled *s* orbitals of two hydrogen atoms in a hydrogen molecule and the overlapping of the half-filled *p* orbitals of a sulfur atom with the half-filled *s* orbitals of two hydrogen atoms to form an H_2S molecule.

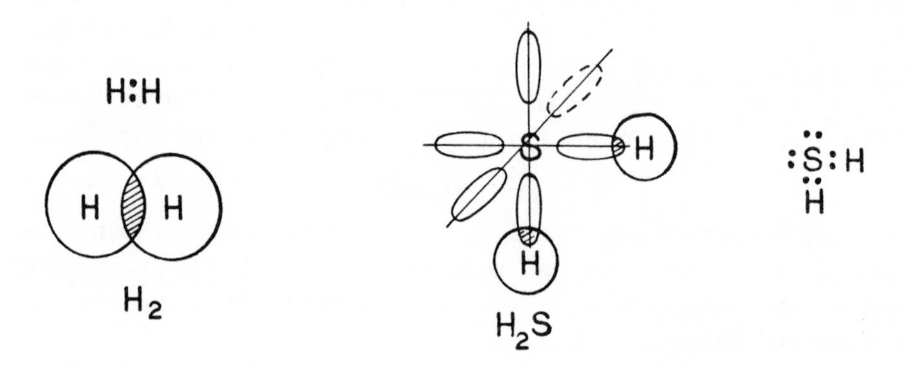

The molecular orbital theory considers the electrons as belonging to the entire molecule and places them in energy levels which belong to the molecule as a whole. The average high school chemistry student generally buys the idea that the shared electrons can occupy the space around the two nuclei forming the bond, spending most of their time somewhere between the two nuclei. Since the electrons now have more space in which to roam, the bonding arrangement represents a more stable system than isolated atoms.

3. USING ELECTRONEGATIVITY SCALE TO PREDICT TYPES OF BONDING AND OXIDATION NUMBERS

Just as things are neither all black nor all white, chemical bonds are neither completely ionic nor covalent. There are many shades of gray between the two extremes. Linus Pauling developed an electronegativity scale (based on bond energies, ionization energies, etc.) to predict the "shades of gray" in bonding situations. In general, electronegativity parallels ionization energy and electron affinity. The most electronegative element (fluorine) is located in the upper right hand portion of the periodic table, and the least electronegative (cesium or francium) is located in the lower left hand portion. Electronegativity refers to the relative attraction an atom has for a pair of electrons in a bonding situation.

Discuss the bonding in a chlorine molecule. Both chlorine atoms have the same attraction for the pair of shared electrons, and so they each own 50 per cent of the pair. The shared electrons spend half of their time with one chlorine and the other half of their time with the other, making the bond

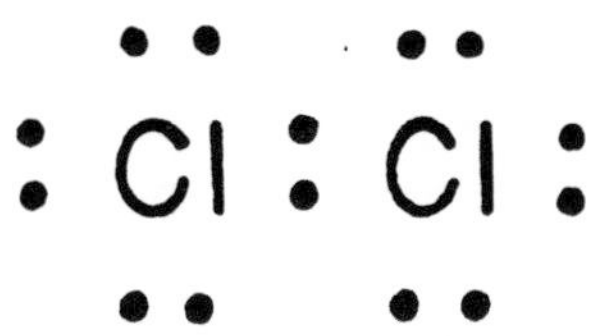

:Cl:Cl:

non-polar covalent bond

completely covalent. Whenever two like atoms share electrons, the bond is 100 per cent covalent (electronegativity difference is zero) and is called a non-polar covalent bond. Chlorine molecules are non-polar.

Discuss the case of hydrogen chloride. Chlorine shares a pair of electrons with hydrogen, but since chlorine is more electronegative than hydrogen, the electron pair spends more time around the chlorine than around the hydrogen. In other words, the electron pair is closer to the chlorine than to the hydrogen, making the chlorine end of the molecule slightly negative and the hydrogen end slightly positive. Such a lop-sided situation gives the bond some ionic character, and it is called a polar-covalent bond. Hydrogen chloride molecules are polar. Polar-covalent bonds result when two different kinds of atoms having different electronegativities share electrons.

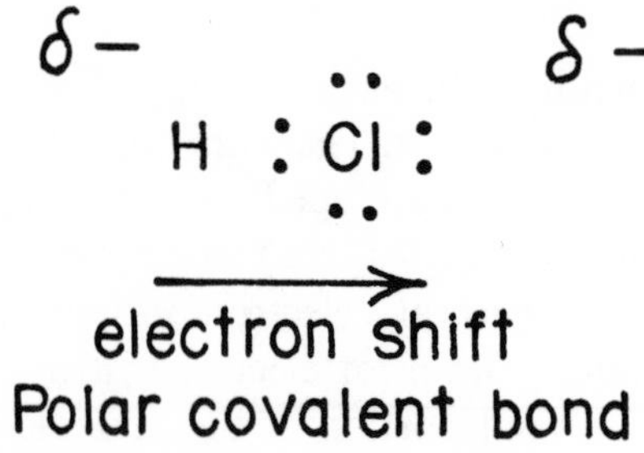

$\delta -$ $\delta -$

H : Cl :

electron shift

Polar covalent bond

In the case of sodium chloride, the bond is considered ionic, since the difference in electronegativity of sodium and chlorine is relatively large. We know from experiment that liquid hydrogen chloride does not conduct electricity and is therefore not ionic, whereas molten sodium chloride is a good conductor of electricity, showing the presence of ions. Using the difference in electronegativity, we can set up a scale for predicting per cent ionic or covalent character in a bond. The greater the difference in electronegativity of the bonded atoms, the greater the ionic character of the bond.

Electronegativity can also be used to assign oxidation numbers, which is really a bookkeeping device used to keep track of which atom controls the electrons. The oxidation number of simple ions is the charge of the ion. In the case of complex ions and molecules, however, we must use electronegativity and examine the electronic distribution to determine which atoms have gained and lost control of electrons.

Consider the chlorine molecule. Since there is no difference in electronegativity between the chlorine atoms, each atom has a 50 per cent share in the pair of electrons, and we split them down the middle. A neutral chlorine atom has seven valence electrons, and each chlorine atom has seven electrons after having assigned the electrons in the pair to the majority stock holder. Since the chlorines have neither gained nor lost electrons, they have an oxidation number of zero.

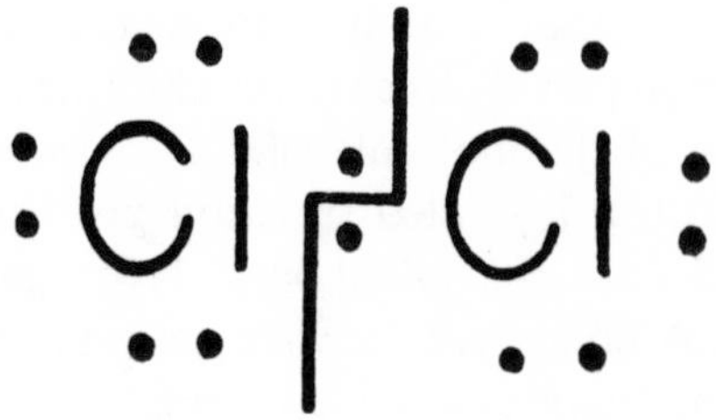

: Cl : Cl :

Return to the case of hydrogen chloride. Since chlorine has a higher electronegativity than hydrogen, the two electrons in the pair are assigned to chlorine, which is the majority stock holder. Hydrogen has, in effect, lost control of one electron, making its oxidation number +1. Chlorine, having gained control of one electron, has an oxidation number of −1.

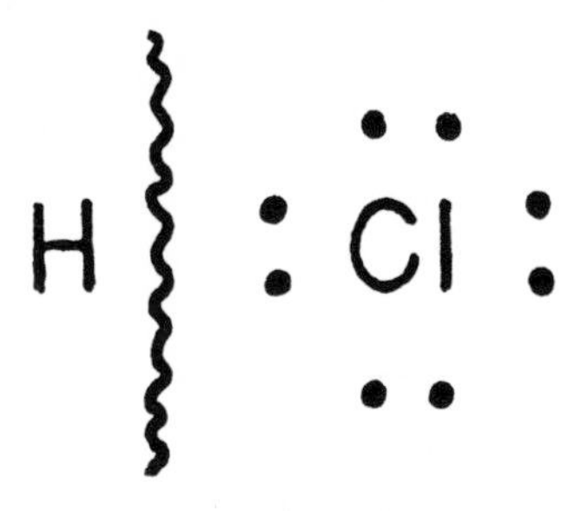

To show your students that valence and oxidation number do not mean the same thing, analyze the case of formaldehyde. Draw the electron dot formula for the molecule and assign the shared electrons to the more electronegative element. Hydrogen (2.1) is the least, carbon (2.5) is intermediate, and oxygen (3.5) is the most electronegative element in the compound. Each hydrogen has lost one electron, resulting in an oxidation number of +1.

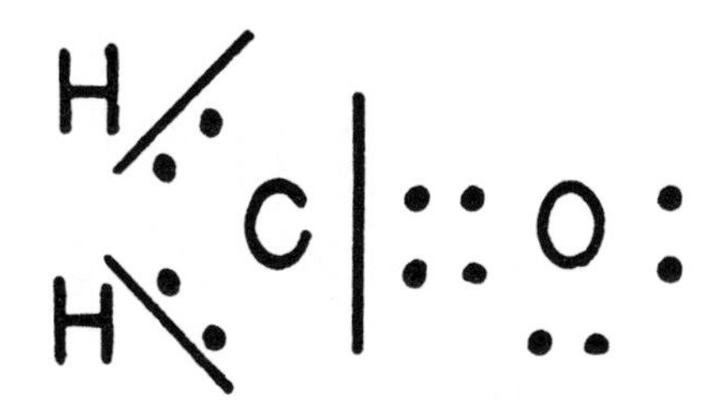

Carbon has lost two and gained two electrons, which gives it the same number of electrons with which it started. The oxidation number of carbon is zero, but its valence is four. Since oxygen has two more electrons than it had as a neutral atom, it has an oxidation number of −2. The sum of the oxidation numbers in the compound is zero. Chapter 10 discusses oxidation numbers in greater detail.

4. PREDICTING PROPERTIES FROM MOLECULAR GEOMETRY AND TYPE OF BONDING, INCLUDING HYBRIDIZATION OF ORBITALS

Molecular geometry and the polarity of bonds determines many properties of molecular compounds. The concept of hybrid orbitals is of great value in accounting for molecular geometry, bond angles, and the nature of single, double, and triple bonds. The case of methane illustrates the need for the hybrid orbital concept.

Consider carbon in its ground state: $1s^2\ 2s^2\ 2p^2$. There are two half-filled *p* orbitals, with which two hydrogen atoms could bond, resulting in the compound CH_2. The H-C-H bond angle would be 90°. This is not the case, however, since methane is CH_4, in which all the bonds are equivalent. If we uncoupled the electron pair in the 2*s* orbital and promoted one electron to the empty 2*p* orbital, we would have four half-filled orbitals which could be used for bonding purposes. The result would be a molecule in which three

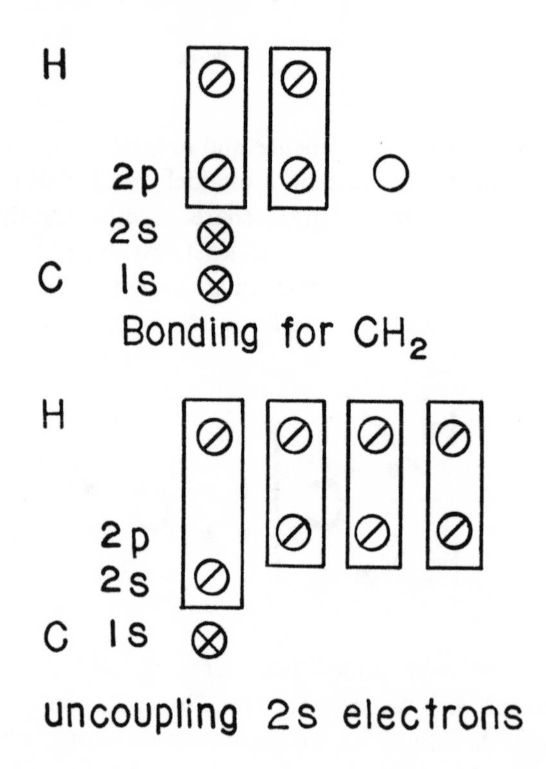

C-H bonds would have a 90° bond angle and a fourth bond having an indefinite angle (the *s* orbital is spherical). Since the *p* orbitals extend farther out than the *s* orbital and are of higher energy, the *p* orbitals would overlap with the *s* orbitals of hydrogen to a greater extent than the *s* orbital of carbon, resulting in one bond being weaker than the other three. We know from experiment that the four bonds are of equal strength and have bond angles of 109° 28′. Therefore, a different description of the bonding in methane must be used. Show your students a ball and stick model of methane.

If the 2*s* orbital and three 2*p* orbitals of carbon combined to produce four new hybrid orbitals (sp^3) of equal energy and extending in three dimensions to give maximum separation, four equivalent bonds would be produced. Geometrically, the carbon nucleus would be in the center of a tetrahedron, and the bonds would extend toward the vertices, making the bond angles 109° 28′. This description agrees with experimental observations. It also results when the wave functions of the *s* and three *p* orbitals are added. Our picture of methane then becomes:

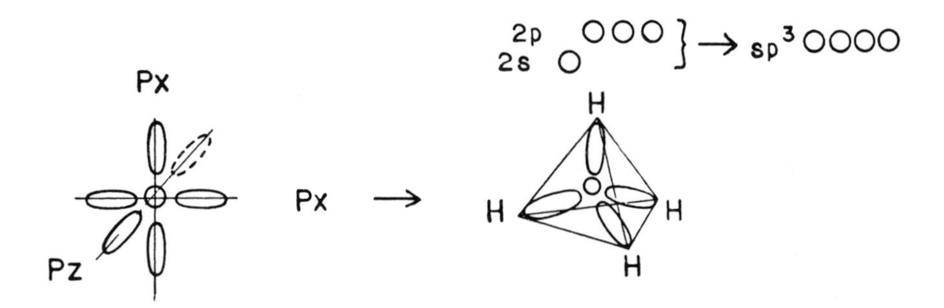

Experimental measurements reveal that water has a bond angle of 105°. One possible explanation is that the two half-filled *p* orbitals of oxygen ($1s^2$ $2s^2$ $2p^4$) overlap with hydrogen, which would produce a bond angle of 90° (p^2 bonding). The bond angle is extended to 105° by the mutual repulsion of the partially-positive hydrogen atoms. A 15° stretch in bond angle is difficult to accept, however. A more satisfactory explanation is sp^3 hybridization for oxygen, placing pairs of electrons in two hybrid orbitals and a single electron in the other two. The lone electron pairs would repel each other, causing the H-O-H bond angle to narrow down from 109° 28′ to 105° (difference of less than 5°).

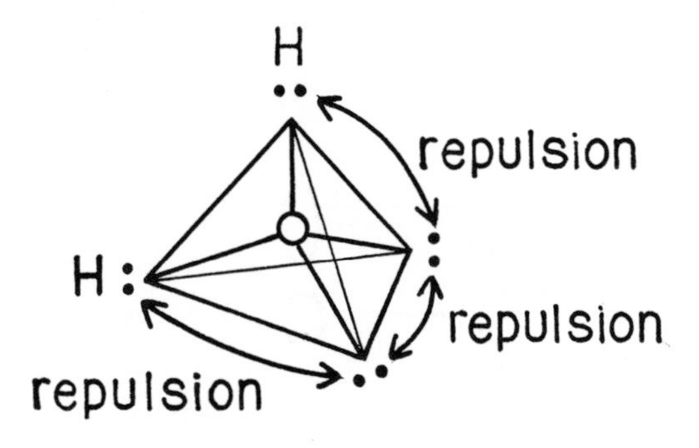

The situation in ammonia is much the same as in water. The bond angle in NH_3 is about 107°, which is close to the tetrahedral angle. Nitrogen most probably forms sp^3 hybrid orbitals containing one electron pair in one orbital and three single electrons in the other three, which bond with three hydrogen atoms.

The bond angle in hydrogen sulfide is 92°. The valence shell of sulfur ($3s^2\ 3p^4$) is similar to that of oxygen. A satisfactory explanation for this bond angle is to assume that the two half-filled $3p$ orbitals of sulfur overlap with hydrogen to produce an H_2S molecule (p^2 bonding).

The planar geometry and 120° bond angle in ethylene can be attributed to the double bond and sp^2 bonding. An electron is promoted from the $2s$ orbital to a $2p$ orbital of carbon, and two $2p$ orbitals and the $2s$ orbital combine to produce three hybrid sp^2 orbitals. Since the two p orbitals are in the same plane, the resulting sp^2 hybrids are in one plane. The bond angle of 120° is consistent with the geometry of three electrons remaining as far from each other as possible on the surface of a sphere. The unhybridized p orbital is perpendicular to the plane of the hybrids.

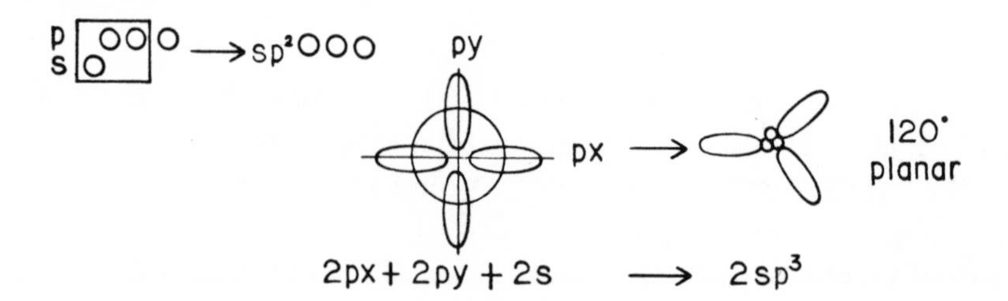

In forming ethylene, one hybrid from each carbon overlap with each other to produce the C-C bond (sigma bond, symmetrical about the line joining the carbon nuclei) and the other two overlap with hydrogen to form the C-H bonds (sigma bonds). The double bond consists of the sigma bond and the overlap of the unhybridized p orbitals above and below the plane of the molecule, forming a pi bond. Since the p orbitals in the pi bond must be parallel to each other for maximum overlap and lowest energy, there is restricted rotation about the double bond, and the molecule tends to remain

H H
C—C
H H
pi
bond

planar. You can show the planar nature and restricted rotation of the ethylene molecule using a ball and stick model with two springs representing the double bond. A straw and jack model can be used to indicate the direction of the orbitals and the pi bond.

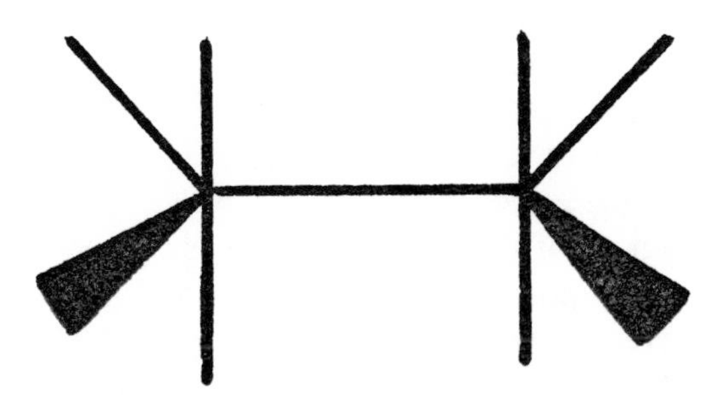

Acetylene, which contains a triple bond, is a linear molecule. This geometry and bonding can be explained by the formation of *sp* hybrid orbitals. One 2*s* electron of the carbon atom is promoted to a 2*p* orbital, and the *s* and one of the *p* orbitals combine to produce two *sp* hybrids, directed away from each other (180° bond angle). An *sp* hybrid from each carbon overlap with each other, and the other *sp* hybrids overlap with hydrogen, forming sigma bonds. The two unhybridized *p* orbitals are perpendicular to the line joining the H-C-C-H atoms and to each other, overlapping to produce two pi bonds. Show your students a ball and stick model, using three springs for the triple bond, to illustrate the geometry and bonding in the acetylene molecule. A straw and jack model can be used to show the directions of the orbitals.

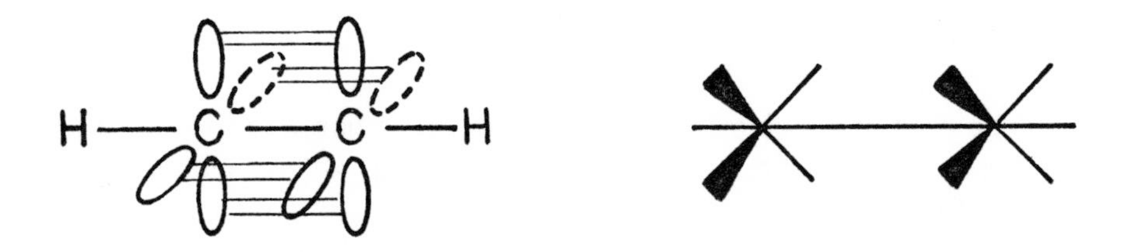

Summarize the types of bonding as shown in the following table. Other types of bonding (dsp^2, dsp^3, $d^2 sp^3$) may be included for the more able students.

Bonding	*Shape and Angle*	*Examples*
p^2	bent, 90°	H_2S
sp^3	tetrahedral, 109° 28′	CH_4, H_2O, NH_3, NH_4^+ ion
sp^2	trigonal planar, 120°	BF_3, $H_2C{=}CH_2$, NO_3^- ion
sp	linear, 180°	$HC{\equiv}CH$, $Ag(NH_3)_2^+$ ion
dsp^2	square planar, 90°	$Cu(NH_3)_4^{+2}$ ion
d_2sp^3	octahedral, 90°	SF_6, $Fe(CN)_6^{-3}$ ion

More examples of types of bonding can be developed when discussing descriptive chemistry of the elements (Chapter 13).

The polarity of molecules is determined by molecular geometry. Show your students a diagram of the water molecule as well as a model. Point out that the H-O bonds are polar, giving the H a partial positive charge and the O a partial negative charge. The center of negative charge in the water molecule is somewhere in the oxygen atom, and the center of positive charge is between the hydrogen atoms. Since there is a separation of charge centers, the molecule is a dipole.

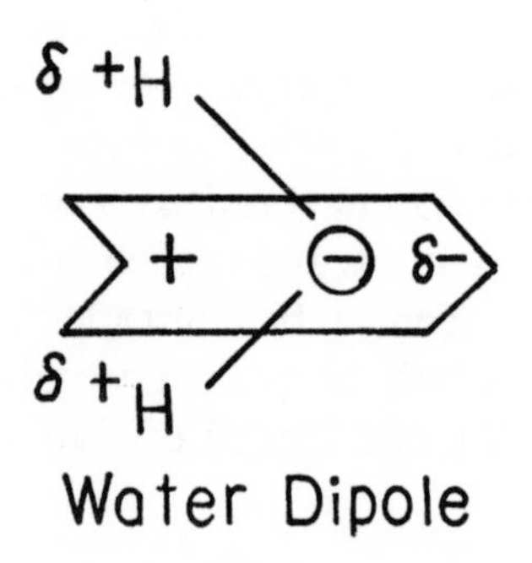

Water Dipole

The carbon dioxide molecule, on the other hand, is linear. The C=O bonds are polar, but the centers of negative and positive charge are in the middle of the carbon atoms. Since there is no separation of charge centers, the molecule is non-polar. The CHEM Study film "Shapes and Polarities of Molecules" does an excellent job of predicting polarity and properties associated with polar and non-polar molecules. Extend these ideas to account for the solubility of ammonia in water and other phenomena. Since dipoles attract each other (see next section), ammonia molecules are attracted by water molecules and therefore dissolve extensively.

5. USING TYPES OF ATTRACTIVE FORCES TO EXPLAIN PROPERTIES OF SUBSTANCES

Physical properties of compounds depend upon the types of attractive forces between molecules and/or ions. These, in turn, can be correlated using Coulomb's law. Discuss the properties of several compounds with your students, relating these to the attractive forces between the particles.

Non-polar molecules, such as methane, hydrogen, carbon dioxide, etc., generally have low melting and boiling points. Crystals of these substances are soft. This suggests that the forces of attraction between such molecules are quite small. Since isolated molecules of these substances do not have charged portions which can lead to mutual attraction, something must happen when such molecules approach each other. Consider the melting and boiling points and heats of vaporization of the halogens.

Substance	*Melting Point °C*	*Boiling Point °C*	*Heat of Vaporization Kcal/mole*
F_2	–223	–187	1.64
Cl_2	–102	–34.6	4.42
Br_2	–7.3	58.8	7.42
I_2	114	183	10.4

Attractive forces must increase with the complexity of the molecules, paralleling the increase in the total number of electrons in the molecules. When two molecules approach each other, the nuclei begin to repel each other and attract electrons in the other molecule, which results in a distortion of the electronic distribution in each molecule. This results in temporary (induced) dipoles. The attraction between induced dipoles is called Vander Waals forces, which are the weakest attractive forces between molecules.

The attraction between polar molecules (permanent dipoles) is intermediate between those of non-polar molecules and ions. The ends of polar molecules are only partially charged, as opposed to the full charges carried by ions. The melting and boiling points of polar compounds are intermediate between those of ionic and non-polar compounds. Show your students some data to illustrate this generality, as summarized in the following table.

Compound	*Type*	*Melting Point °C*	*Boiling Point °C*
CH_4	non-polar	–184	–161
HCl	polar	–115	–85
NaCl	ionic	801	1413

Crystals of non-polar compounds are generally soft, but those of ionic compounds are hard and brittle. Polar compounds form crystals which are harder than those of non-polar compounds. Show your students a model of a sodium chloride crystal, pointing out that the ions of opposite charge attract each other while ions having the same kind of charge repel each other. Oppositely-charged ions are nearest neighbors in space, while like-charged ions tend to remain as far apart as the structure will allow. The net result produces a rigid structure of considerable hardness. When the crystal is distorted, ions having the same charge line up next to each other, and the repulsive forces cause the crystal to cleave along a layer of ions. Illustrate these effects by means of diagrams.

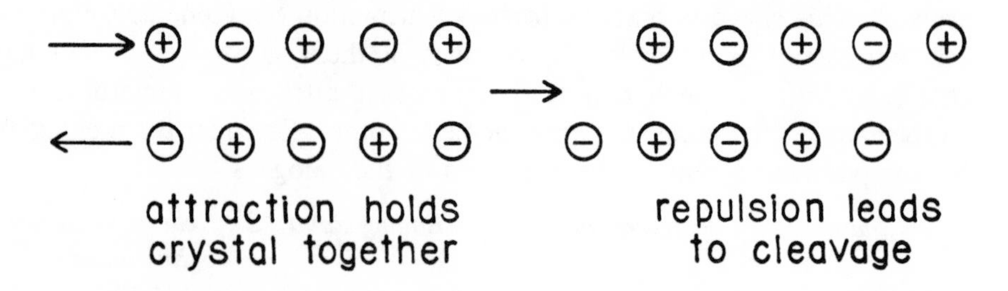

Discuss the properties of metals as a consequence of the structure of metallic crystals. Metal atoms hold electrons rather loosely, and the few valence electrons are free to move between the positive centers. The forces that hold the metal atoms together are the attractions between the electrons and the metal ions; the metal crystal is, in a sense, a group of positive ions held together by an electron "glue," as shown in the diagram. Such crystals

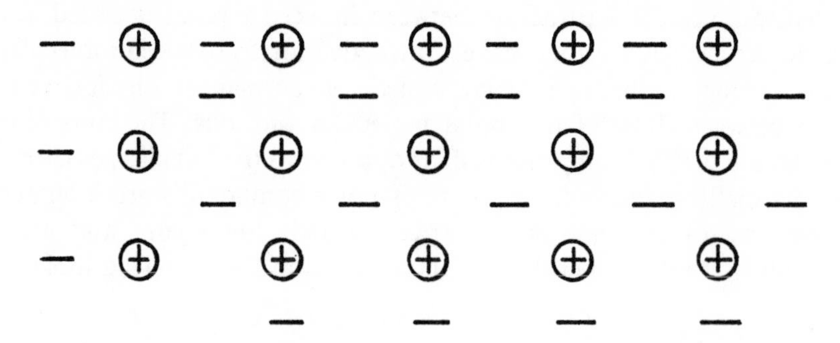

can be distorted without cleavage, since the electrons continue to hold the ions together. Conductivity can be explained by the movement of electrons through the crystal. As the temperature increases, conductivity decreases. This can be explained by the increased vibrations of the atoms, which tend to interfere with the free movement of electrons in the crystal. Metallic lustre is due to the absorption and immediate radiation of most of the frequencies in the visible spectrum.

If you have some exceptional students, point out the variation of hardness in metals going from group one (soft, low melting point), from the left to middle of the transition elements (hard, high melting point), to the end of the transition series (soft, low melting point). Metals in the left half of the transition series have partially-filled *d* orbitals which can form covalent bonds, resulting in greater hardness and higher melting points.

Covalent (atomic) crystals, such as diamond, quartz, silicon carbide, etc., are hard and have high melting points. Each crystal is, in effect, a giant molecule held together by covalent bonds. Some examples will be discussed in Chapter 13.

The common types of attractions in order of increasing strength are: Vander Waals forces (non-polar molecules), dipole-dipole, ion-dipole, ion-ion. Correlate these using Coulomb's law. Some of these attractions are developed to a greater extent in sections 4.6 and 6.2. The CHEM Study film "Crystals and Their Structure" illustrates some properties of crystals and how their structures are determined by X-ray diffraction.

6. USING RESONANCE CONCEPT AND CHARGE DENSITY TO INTERPRET PROPERTIES

The concept of resonance is useful for explaining the stability of certain compounds and ions. Ask your students to write an electron dot formula for ozone. Some will write (if correct)

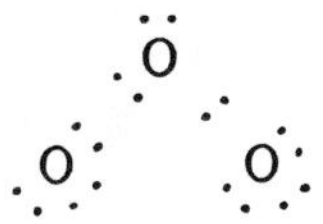

O

O O and others O

O O

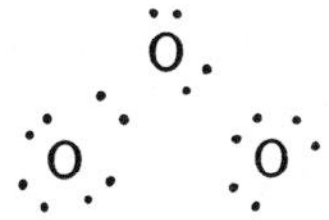

Neither structure represents the actual electronic distribution, however. The real structure is a hybrid of both, as a mule is a hybrid of a horse and jackass. The electrons seem to have shifted from one part of the molecule to another:

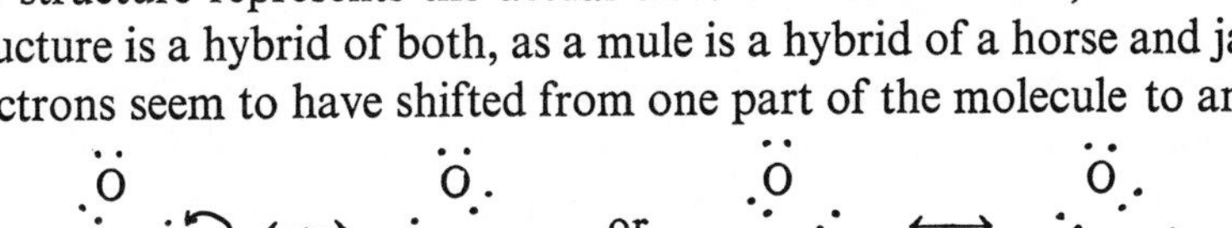

O O O O

O O ⟷ O O or O O ⟷ O O

The electrons are "delocalized" and occupy a larger space than shown in either electron-dot formula. This, in effect, helps stabilize the molecule. Delocalization of electrons increases stability, since the electrons roam over the entrire molecule. When one can write more than one electronic structure for a specie, we have a phenomenon called resonance. No single electron-dot formula describes the structure of the substance. Its true structure is the average of all the electronic structures that can be written.

Another example of resonance is found in the carbonate ion:

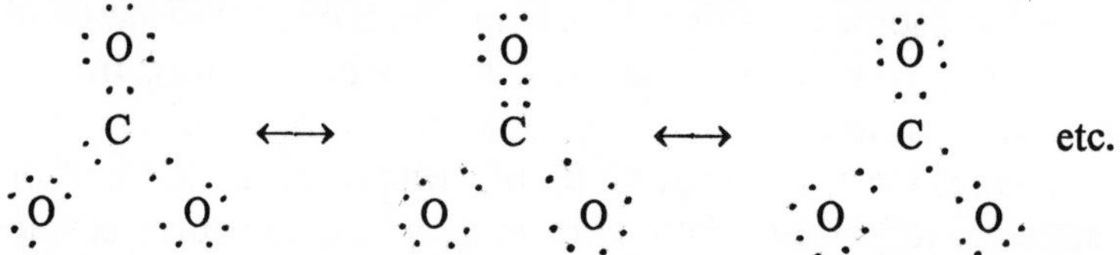

This substance is more stable than either electron-dot structure due to the electrons spreading themselves over the entire ion. The carbonate ion is trigonal planar, indicating sp^2 bonding. This suggests that the three bonds are of equal strength and length, which is not shown in the individual electron-dot formulas. The true structure is a hybrid of these structures. More examples of resonance, including the classic case of benzene, will be discussed in Chapter 11.

Show your students the following list of melting points of various ionic compounds:

Compound	*Charge of ions*	*Melting Point, °C*
NaF	+1, −1	990
NaCl	+1, −1	801
KCl	+1, −1	776
CaF_2	+2, −1	1362
CaO	+2, −2	2580
Al_2O_3	+3, −2	2050

Point out that the higher the melting point, the higher the lattice energy. Use the concept of charge density to account for the differences in lattice energy. The fluoride ion is smaller than the chloride ion: the charge density of F^- is higher than that of Cl^-, which means that there is greater attraction between Na^+ and F^- than between Na^+ and Cl^- ions, accounting for the higher melting point of NaF. Since the potassium ion is larger than the sodium ion (lower charge density), there is less attraction between K^+ and Cl^- than between Na^+ and Cl^- ions, which accounts for NaCl having a higher melting point than KCl. Likewise, the charge density of Ca^{+2} is considerably higher than that of Na^+, which explains why CaF_2 has a considerably higher melting point than NaF.

The same idea can be applied to explain the melting points of the other substances on the table, except for Al_2O_3. We would expect Al_2O_3 to have a higher melting point than CaO, but when considering the differences in electronegativity between Al (1.5) and Ca (1.0), we realize that CaO has more ionic character than Al_2O_3. This accounts for Al_2O_3 having a lower melting point than CaO.

In general, the higher the charge density of ions (a function of size and charge of the ion), the greater the lattice energy, and the higher the melting (and boiling) point. Ask your students to apply this generalization to predict the approximate melting points of compounds such as $NaNO_3$ (307), MgO (2800), CsI (621), $Sr(NO_3)_2$ (570). When predicting lattice energy we must consider differences in electronegativity and (in the case of ionic compounds) charge density.

7. CORRELATING IONIC RADIUS AND CHARGE WITH LATTICE ENERGY AND HYDRATION ENERGY, HYDROGEN BONDING

The application of charge density (a function of ionic radius and charge) to lattice energy was discussed in the previous section. The effect of charge density on the ease of solvation of ions is discussed in section 6.2, and the energy relationship will be treated quantitively in Chapter 9. The qualitative treatment of hydration energy can be explained in terms of charge density.

Ask your students which compound they think would give off more energy when dissolved in water: LiCl or NaCl. Suggest that they consider the charge density of Li^+ as opposed to Na^+ ions. The attractions involved are ion-dipole. Since Li^+ is smaller than Na^+, the attractive force between Li^+ and H_2O dipoles should be greater than between Na^+ and H_2O. More energy is released when LiCl is dissolved in water.

Ask your students to explain why calcium chloride (anhydrous) is used as a drying agent or to keep down the dust on dirt roads and tennis courts. The high charge density on the Ca^{+2} ions (small size, multiple charge) means a high attractive force between these ions and water, and so $CaCl_2$ is hygroscopic.

Ask your students to explain why calcium carbonate is not very soluble but calcium bicarbonate dissolves appreciably in water. Again, the explanation can be made in terms of charge density. The multiply-charged calcium and carbonate ions mean that there is a high lattice energy which must be overcome to dissolve the compound. Since the bicarbonate ion has a single negative charge, its charge density is a good deal lower than that of the carbonate ion. Calcium bicarbonate has a lower lattice energy than calcium carbonate, and the ions are more easily separated.

You can use charge density very profitably in explaining numerous chemical and physical phenomena, including hydrogen bonding. Consider the following graph of boiling points: The hydride of the first element of groups V, VI and VII have significantly higher boiling points than the next members of each series, but methane has the lowest boiling point in the group IV series. Consider the electronic formulas for the compounds which

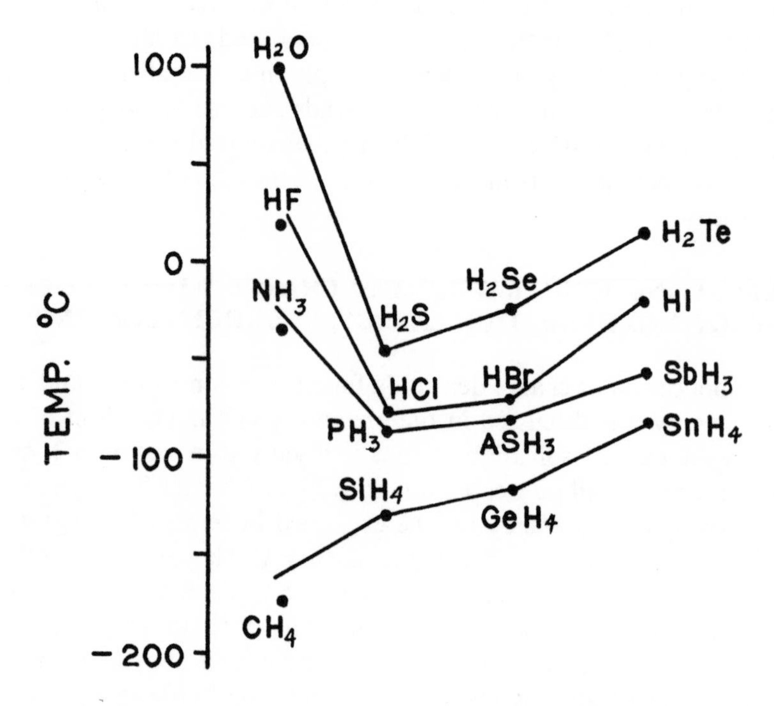

exhibit anomalous behavior and contrast their common feature with the structure of methane: the presence or absence of an unshared pair of electrons. Obviously a greater attractive force exists between H_2O, NH_3, and HF molecules than betweeen the others. These molecules associate via the hydrogen bond. The boiling points of the other members in each series rise rather regularly because of increased Vander Waals forces as the molecular weights increase.

The features common to HF, H_2O, and NH_3 include at least one hydrogen atom and an unshared pair of electrons on a small, highly-electronegative atom. Oxygen, fluorine, and nitrogen atoms are highly electronegative, which means that they attract electrons and acquire high electron density. Hydrogen assumes a partially positive charge in each case and is attracted by the oxygen, fluorine or nitrogen of a neighboring molecule. A weak bond is formed via the unshared pair of electrons, and hydrogen acts like the filling in a peanut butter sandwich, holding the two slices of bread together. The two small, highly-electronegative atoms and hydrogen are in a straight line, as shown in the diagram.

Hydrogen bonding is responsible for water expanding when it freezes. The water molecules arrange themselves in a three-dimensional open hexagonal lattice. Many textbooks have pictures of the model for the structure of ice. When energy is added, the structure begins to vibrate sufficiently to break some of the hydrogen bonds, and the structure begins to collapse, resulting in a smaller volume. As the temperature increases, more hydrogen bonds break, and the structure collapses even more. The temperature of maximum density for water is 4 °C. As more heat is applied, the molecules vibrate more and begin to push each other apart, accounting for the expansion of the water when the temperature increases.

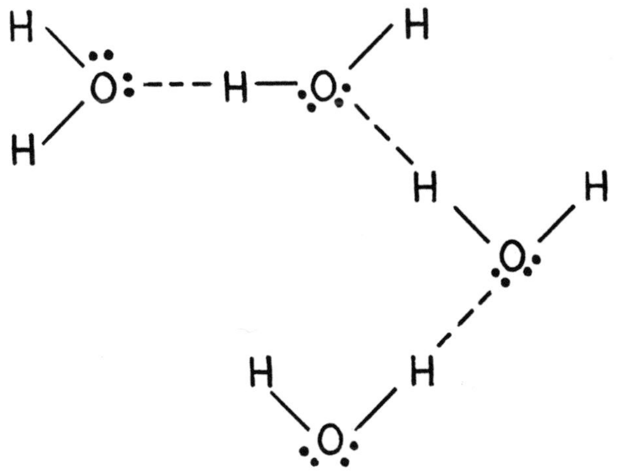

The structures of numerous substances of biological interest (including DNA) are held together by hydrogen bonds. Organic molecules which contain –OH or $-NH_2$ groups dissolve in water because of hydrogen bonding. Substances containing several carbon atoms are generally insoluble in water because of their non-polar nature (see Chapter 6), but sucrose, which contains 12 carbon atoms and a number of –OH groups (hydrophilic, or water-loving groups) dissolves readily in water because of extensive hydrogen bonding.

5

Teaching Chemical Calculations Using the Mole Concept

1. DEVELOPING THE MOLE CONCEPT

The mole concept is a logical, powerful, and elegant tool for solving many types of problems. Sell your students the idea that they will seldom encounter simple, garden-variety problems in life, whether they be lawyers, mechanics, or scientists. Problem solving involves thought, no memorization of a method followed by plugging numbers into a formula. Memorizers can be easily tripped up by giving them very simple problems and then twisting them around slightly. If they can't think, they can't solve them. You will be doing your students a greater service by teaching them the mole concept instead of solving "weight-weight," "weight-volume," and "volume-volume" types of problems by setting up proportions (the rote method). Forget the classic titration problems using $N_1V_1 = N_2V_2$. Chemists are more interested in determining how much material is in an unknown sample rather than the concentration of an unknown solution. Only a small portion of analytical chemistry involves aicd-base titrations, so give your students examples of other types of titrations (precipitation of silver chloride, etc.) lest they be left with a host of misconceptions. If your students can learn to use the mole concept, they will be able to solve all kinds of problems by using their brains and not throw up their hands in despair when they encounter something they have never seen before.

The use of Avogadro's hypothesis in determining molecular formulas for gases and mention of moles was made in section 2.3, and the general gas equation, PV = nRT, was developed in section 2.4. Begin the systematic development of the mole concept by stating that the mole is to the chemist what the dozen is to the grocer: a package containing a certain number of units. Suppose you have one dozen friends coming for breakfast and you want to serve each two fried eggs. The ratio of eggs to friends is 2:1 .You would need two dozen eggs to feed one dozen friends, or a 2:1 ratio of packages. The same mental process is used by chemists when they use moles. The plot is the same, but the characters are different. In order to make one mole of water (H_2O), you need two moles of hydrogen atoms to one mole of oxygen atoms. Once the students understand that one mole contains Avogadro's number of units and understand the reasoning used in the illustrations above, they can begin to use moles in the solution of problems.

Give your students a summary of what kinds of units a chemist places in the package he calls the mole:

> 1 mole contains 6.02×10^{23} "things," atoms, ions, molecules, electrons, or 1 gram atomic weight (gram atom), 1 gram molecular weight, 1 gram formula weight, 22.4 liters of a gas at STP, or 9.65×10^{4} colulombs (1 mole of electrons)

Give your students some simple problems such as calculating the number of moles in the following:

(1) 12 g magnesium [0.5]
(2) 11.0 g CO_2 [0.25]
(3) 6.60 g $(NH_4)_2\ SO_4$ [0.05]
(4) 3×10^{22} molecules of aspirin [0.05]
(5) 1.12 liters of helium gas at STP [0.05]
(6) 128 g oxygen gas at 27°C, 750 mm (irrelevant data) [4]
(7) 1 liter of liquid water at STP [55.5]
(8) gram atoms of H in 1.40 g $C_2\ H_4$ [0.2]

The following outline summarizes the steps involved in solving the problems which are discussed in this chapter.

Mole Type Problems

1. Write a balanced equation. The coefficients give the mole ratios.
2. Calculate the number of moles of material given.
3. Using the mole ratios from (1) and number of moles from (2), calculate the number of moles (*n*) of material sought.
4. Translate the number of moles of material sought (*n*) into *mass* or *volume* (of gas or solution):
   a) Mass = (*n*) (grams per mole) = grams
   b) Volume of *gas:*
      (1) at STP: (*n*) (22.4 liters/mole) = liters

(2) *not* at STP: Use $PV = nRT$

$$V = \frac{nRT}{P} = \text{liters}$$

c) Volume of *solution:*

$$\text{Molarity (M)} = \frac{\text{moles}}{\text{liters}} \qquad \frac{n}{\text{Molarity}} = \text{liters}$$

$$\text{Normality (N)} = \frac{\text{equivalents}}{\text{liters}} \qquad \text{(N) (liters)} = \text{eq}$$

equivalents/mole = total positive valence
equivalents = (n) (total positive valence)

d) Electrochemistry:

(1) 1 mole of electrons = 9.65×10^4 coulombs = 1 eq
coulombs = (amperes) (seconds)

(2) Calculate moles of material from moles of electrons, using mole ratios, or equivalents of material equal to moles of electrons

Although the value for Avogadro's number (N) does not have to be known to use the idea of moles, your students might be interested in how it may be determined. Over fifteen experimental methods have been used to determine N, but the easiest to understand is counting electrons:

One mole of electrons (9.65×10^4 coulombs) is required to deposit one mole of silver metal (108 grams) from a solution containing silver ions, as shown in the equation

$$Ag^+ + e^- = Ag$$

The charge of one electron is 1.60×10^{-19} coulombs. Electrons per mole is Avogadro's number:

$$\frac{9.65 \times 10^4 \text{ coul mole}^{-1}}{1.60 \times 10^{-19} \text{ coul electron}^{-1}} = 6.02 \times 10^{23} \text{ el mole}^{-1}$$

This number should convince your students that a chemist must deal with huge numbers of atoms and molecules in his work. This requires him to use packages containing many units: the mole.

2. EXPLAINING THE CONCEPT OF EQUIVALENTS

Many college teachers are in favor of omitting the use of equivalents in introductory courses, especially at the high school level. This concept can be taught quickly when a student takes a course in analytical chemistry. If you teach equivalents, relate the historical meaning of valence (combining capacity) to the idea of equivalents. One equivalent (equivalent weight or combining weight) of a substance is the weight of substance that contains one gram (one mole) of replaceable hydrogen or is chemically equivalent to one gram of hydrogen, or the weight of an element that combines with 8.0000 grams of oxygen (half a mole of oxygen atoms). A corollary to this definition of equivalents is based on electrons: one equivalent is chemically equivalent to one mole of electrons. This definition is useful for solving problems in electrochemistry and redox. The utility of the concept of equivalents is based on the law of equivalents: equivalents react with equivalents to produce equivalents. This concept is convenient to use, but any problem involving equivalents can be solved using moles. The students should have a working knowledge of the mole concept before tackling equivalents.

Correlate the idea of replacing hydrogen and the number of electrons involved, using simple examples.

Example 1 $Zn + H_2SO_4 = H_2 + ZnSO_4$

One mole of zinc has replaced two moles of hydrogen atoms (2 grams). Therefore 0.5 mole of zinc is one equivalent (replaces 1 g H). The half-reaction for the change in oxidation number of zinc is $Zn = Zn^{+2} + 2\,e^-$.
One mole of zinc loses two moles of electrons, therefore 0.5 mole of zinc is equivalent to 1 mole of electrons (1 eq). Since one mole of H_2SO_4 contains 2 g replaceable hydrogen, 0.5 mole of H_2SO_4 is one equivalent. One mole of H_2 gas was produced by two moles of H^+ reacting with 2 moles of electrons (2eq). Therefore, one equivalent of H_2 is 0.5 mole. $ZnSO_4$ was produced from one mole of H_2SO_4, and so one equivalent of $ZnSO_4$ is 0.5 mole. The total positive valence in $ZnSO_4$ is +2, and so there are two equivalents per mole.

Example 2 Analyze the reaction of 9 g Al (1/3 mole) with H_2SO_4.

$2\,Al$	+	$3\,H_2SO_4$	= $3\,H_2$	+	$Al_2(SO_4)_3$
1/3 mole		1/2 mole	1/2 mole		1/6 mole
1 eq		1 eq	1 eq		1 eq

The balanced equation gives the mole ratios. Calculate the number of moles of H_2SO_4, H_2, and $Al_2(SO_4)_3$:

$$\left(\frac{1\text{ mole Al}}{3}\right)\left(\frac{3\,H_2SO_4}{2\,Al}\right) = \frac{1}{2}\text{ mole } H_2SO_4$$

$$\left(\frac{1\text{ mole Al}}{3}\right)\left(\frac{3\,H_2}{2\,Al}\right) = \frac{1}{2}\text{ mole } H_2$$

$$\left(\frac{1\text{ mole Al}}{3}\right)\left(\frac{1\,Al_2(SO_4)_3}{2\,Al}\right) = \frac{1}{6}\text{ mole } Al_2(SO_4)_3$$

Calculate the number of equivalents in each substance: Since one mole Al loses 3 moles electrons, there is 3 eq/mole of Al. One mole H_2SO_4 contains 2 g replaceable H, so there is 2 eq/mole of H_2SO_4. One mole of H_2 gas was produced by replacing 2 g H, so there is 2 eq/mole of H_2. Since the total positive valence in $Al_2(SO_4)_3$ is + 6, there is 6 eq/mole of $Al_2(SO_4)_3$.

Point out to your students that the law of equivalents is illustrated in this example. Use as many examples as you need to familiarize your students with the concept of equivalents. Practice is the best teacher, once they have been shown the rudiments and know the basic definitions.

The corollary of equivalent weight is combining weight. One mole (32 g) of sulfur combines with one mole of oxygen (32 g) to produce one mole of SO_2. Since we have 8 g/eq of O, there are 4 eq in 32 g O_2. There must be 4 eq S in 32 g. Therefore, the equivalent weight of sulfur is 8 g/eq, which is consistent with dividing 32 by the change in oxidation number (from 0 to +4). Give your students examples such as the following:

An oxide was produced by reacting 31.0 g phosphorus with 4.00 g oxygen. Calculate:

(a) the equivalent weight of phosphorus in the compound.

$$\frac{3.10}{4.00} = \frac{x}{8.00} \qquad x = 6.20 \text{ g/eq}$$

(b) the valence of P in the compound.

$$\text{valence} = \frac{\text{atomic wt.}}{\text{eq. wt.}} = \frac{31.0}{6.20} = 5$$

(c) the formula for the compound: P_2O_5

3. USING EXPERIMENTAL DATA TO DETERMINE ATOMIC AND MOLECULAR WEIGHTS

Atomic weights can be determined by either chemical means (analysis and Cannizzaro's principle, and Dulong and Petit's law applied to metals) or physical means (mass spectroscopy). Since there are many topics to be covered in a chemistry course and since chemists no longer make a practice of determining atomic weights, don't spend much time on the subject. Dulong and Petit's law is no longer taught in many courses, but some of your more advanced students might benefit from exposure to it.

Atomic weights of metals can be determined approximately by using an empirical relationship discovered early in the nineteenth century by Dulong and Petit: atomic weight of metal times its specific heat equals approximately 6.3. An examination of the units used leads to an interesting conclusion.

$$(\text{grams mole}^{-1})\ (\text{calories gram}^{-1}\ \text{degee}^{-1}) = \text{cal mole}^{-1}\ \text{deg}^{-1}$$

The molar heat capacity of metals is approximately 6.3 cal mole^{-1} deg^{-1}.

Knowing the specific heat of any metal, we can calculate its approximate atomic weight. If we know the equivalent weight of the metal, we can determine its valence (whole number). Then we can multiply the combining weight by the valence to determine the atomic weight accurately.

Example The specific heat of aluminum is 0.22 cal $g^{-1}deg^{-1}$. A 2.25 g sample of aluminum was found to combine with 2.00 g oxygen. Calculate the atomic weight of aluminum.

Step 1: determine approximate atomic weight (x):

$$(0.22)(x) = 6.3 \qquad x = 28.6 \text{ g mole}^{-1}$$

Step 2: determine combining weight (y):

$$\frac{2.25}{2.00} = \frac{y}{8.00} \qquad y = 9.00 \text{ g eq}^{-1}$$

Step 3: determine valence and exact atomic weight:

$$\frac{28.6}{9.00} = 3 \text{ (whole number)}$$

$$(3)(9.00) = 27.0 \text{ g mole}^{-1} \text{ (atomic weight)}$$

Cannizzaro's principle states that the lowest weight of an element that can occur in one molecule of a compound is the weight of one atom of the element (atoms are indivisible). If we know the per cent by weight of an element in each of a series of compounds, we can determine the weight of the element in one mole of each compound. The lowest common denominator is the weight of one mole of atoms of the element.

Example The analysis of a series of chlorine compounds is:

Compound	*mol. wt.*	*% Cl*	*wt. Cl*	*atoms/molecule*
chlorine	71.0	100	71.0	2
CCl_4	154	92.2	142	4
HCl	36.5	97.4	35.5	1
$CHCl_3$	120	89.0	106.5	3

The approximate atomic weight of chlorine (molecular weights can be determined only approximately from vapor density or freezing point depression data) is about 35.5. The exact atomic weight can then be determined from the combining weight of Cl.

Molecular weights can be determined approximately using gas data (Dumas method, Victor Meyer method, etc.) or from freezing point depression data. Elemental analysis of the compound leads to the empirical formula, from which the molecular formula may be determined. Then the exact molecular weight can be determined from the atomic weights of the constituent elements. The general gas equation is discussed in section 6.

Example 1 A 0.490 g sample of carbon dioxide was found to occupy a volume of 250 ml at STP. Calculate the molecular wight of CO_2.

Step 1: Calculate the vapor density of CO_2 at STP:

$$\frac{0.490 \text{ g}}{0.250 \text{ l}} = 1.96 \text{ g liter}^{-1}$$

Step 2: Calculate the molecular weight of the gas:

$$(1.96 \text{ g liter}^{-1})(22.4 \text{ liter mole}^{-1}) = 44 \text{ g mole}^{-1}$$

Example 2 A 2.50 g sample of propane gas occupied a volume of 1.41 liters at 27°C (300°K) and 756 mm pressure. Calculate the molecular weight of propane.

Use the general gas equation and substitute g/M for n (grams of sample $= g$, molecular weight $= M$). Solve for M. Since the pressure is in mm Hg, use the value R = 62.4 1 mm deg^{-1} mole^{1}.

$$PV = \frac{gRT}{M} \text{ solved for } M\text{: } M = \frac{gRT}{PV}$$

$$M = \frac{(2.50\text{ g})(62.4\text{ l mm deg}^{-1}\text{ mole}^{-1})(300\text{ deg})}{(756\text{ mm})(1.41\text{ l})} = 44\text{ g mole}^{-1}$$

Example 3 A 0.500 g sample of urea was dissolved in 25 g water, and the resulting solution was found to freeze at –0.62°C. Calculate the molecular weight of urea. From Raoult's law we know that 1 mole of a non-electrolyte dissolved in 1000 g solvent depresses the freezing point of the solution by an amount called the freezing point constant, K_f. The value of K_f for water is 1.86°

Step 1: Calculate the molality of the solution:

$$\text{freezing point depression} = 0.00° - (-0.62°) = 0.62°$$

$$\text{Molality} = \frac{\text{freezing pt. depr.}}{K_f} = \frac{0.62}{1.86}$$

$$= 0.333 \text{ moles solute/1000 g solvent}$$

Step 2: Calculate the weight of solute per 1000 g solvent:

$$\frac{0.500\text{ g urea}}{25\text{ g water}} = \frac{x}{1000\text{ g water}}$$

$$x = 20\text{ g urea}$$

Step 3: Calculate the molecular weight from molality and weight of solute per 1000 g solvent:

$$\frac{20\text{ g urea}}{0.333\text{ moles}} = 60\text{ g mole}^{-1} \text{ (molecular weight of urea)}$$

Example 4 Solvents other than water may be used to determine molecular weight by freezing point depression. A solution of 1.48 g p-dichlorobenzene dissolved in 20.0 g benzene had a freezing point of 3.11°. The freezing point of pure benzene is 5.53° and K_f for benzene is 5.12°. Calculate the molecular weight of p-dichlorobenzene.

$$\text{freezing pt. depression} = 5.53° - 3.11° = 2.42°$$

$$\frac{2.42}{5.12} = 0.473 \text{ moles solute/1000 g solvent}$$

$$\frac{1.48\text{ g compound}}{20.0\text{ g benzene}} = \frac{x}{1000\text{ g benzene}}$$

$$x = 74.0\text{ g}$$

$$\frac{74.0\text{ g}}{0.473\text{ mole}} = 157\text{ mole}^{-1}$$

4. APPLYING THE MOLE CONCEPT TO PER CENT COMPOSITION, DETERMINATION OF EMPIRICAL FORMULAS, PROBLEMS IN STOICHIOMETRY

Since chemists use a huge number of "things" in their work, a formula generally represents a mole of material and not a single molecule, atom, or ion. A formula such as $(NH_4)_2SO_4$ tells us that there are four moles of nitrogen atoms, eight moles of hydrogen atoms, one mole of sulfur atoms, and four moles of oxygen atoms in one mole of ammonium sulfate. The molecular weight in grams (for a covalent compound) or formula weight in grams (for a salt) contains one mole of what the formula advertises.

If we want to determine the per cent by weight of any element in a compound from its formula, we assume that we have one mole of compound. The weight of each element (number of moles of atoms times gram atomic weight) divided by the weight of one mole of compound times 100 is the per cent by weight of the element in the compound. Returning to the case of ammonium sulfate:

$$\begin{array}{lll}
\text{4 moles N atoms} = 4 \times 14 & = & \text{56 grams N} \\
\text{8 moles H atoms} = 8 \times 1 & = & \text{8 grams H} \\
\text{1 mole S atoms} = 1 \times 32 & = & \text{32 grams S} \\
\text{4 moles O atoms} = 4 \times 16 & = & \underline{\text{64 grams O}} \\
\text{1 mole } (NH_4)_2\,SO_4 \text{ contains} & & \text{160 grams}
\end{array}$$

$$\text{Per cent nitrogen: } \frac{56}{160} \times 100 = 35.0\%$$

$$\text{hydrogen: } \frac{8}{160} \times 100 = 5.0\%$$

$$\text{sulfur: } \frac{32}{160} \times 100 = 20.0\%$$

$$\text{oxygen: } \frac{64}{160} \times 100 = 40.0\%$$

If we are given the per cent composition of a compound, we can determine the empirical (simplest) formula for the compound. This formula tells us the ratio of the number of atoms which have combined to produce the compound. For example, the percentage composition of enthylene glycol is found to be 38.7% carbon, 9.7% hydrogen, 51.6% oxygen by weight. Assume that we have 100 g of compound and calculate the weight of each element, which gives us the number of moles of each element in 100 g of compound. We now have the ratio of moles of the elements and the empirical formula.

$$\frac{38.7 \text{ g C atoms}}{12 \text{ g mole}^{-1}} = 3.23 \text{ moles C atoms}$$

$$\frac{9.7 \text{ g H atoms}}{1 \text{ g mole}^{-1}} = 9.7 \text{ moles H atoms}$$

$$\frac{51.6 \text{ g O atoms}}{16 \text{ g mole}^{-1}} = 3.23 \text{ mole O atoms}$$

The empirical formula is $C_{3.23}H_{9.7}O_{3.23}$. Whole numbers are simpler than fractional numbers. Therefore, we convert the subscripts to whole numbers as follows:

$$\frac{3.23 \text{ moles C atoms}}{3.23} = 1 \text{ mole C atoms}$$

$$\frac{9.7 \text{ moles H atoms}}{3.23} = 3 \text{ moles H atoms}$$

$$\frac{3.23 \text{ moles O atoms}}{3.23} = 1 \text{ mole O atoms}$$

The mole ratios are then used in the formula CH_3O.

In order to establish the molecular formula for a compound, we must know the empirical formula and the molecular weight. Divide the empirical formula weight, which is 31 for ethylene glycol, into the molecular weight, 62, and obtain a whole number, 2. Multiply each subscript by this whole number to obtain the molecular formula, $C_2H_6O_2$. Give your students enough problems of this type to enable them to develop an understanding of the meaning of empirical and molecular formulas, as well as the utility of the mole concept.

Empirical formulas may also be derived from masses of reactants and products involved in reactions.

Example 1 When 4.00 g iron oxide was reduced, 2.80 g iron was produced. Calculate the empirical formula for the oxide. The problem consists of finding the number of moles of iron and oxygen, then finding the ratio of moles of iron to oxygen.

4.00 g iron oxide
2.80 g iron
____
1.20 g oxygen

$$\frac{2.80 \text{ g iron}}{56 \text{ g mole}^{-1}} = 0.050 \text{ moles iron atoms}$$

$$\frac{1.20 \text{ g oxygen}}{16 \text{ g mole}^{-1}} = 0.075 \text{ moles oxygen atoms}$$

$$\frac{0.050}{0.075} = \frac{2}{3} \text{ ratio of iron to oxygen atoms}$$

The empirical formula for the oxide is Fe_2O_3.

An alternate method for solving this problem is to use the concept of equivalents (combining weight).

$$\frac{2.80 \text{ g Fe}}{1.20 \text{ g O}} = \frac{\text{eq. wt. Fe}}{8.00 \text{ g O}}$$

$$\text{eq. wt. Fe} = 18.7 \text{ g eq}^{-1}$$

$$\text{Valence of iron} = \frac{\text{atomic wt.}}{\text{eq. wt.}} = \frac{56}{18.7} = 3$$

The formula is Fe_2O_3.

Example 2 When 1.86 g phosphorus was reacted with bromine, 16.26 g bromide was produced. Calculate the empirical formula. Just as above, the problem consists of finding the ratio of moles of P to moles of Br which have combined.

16.26 g phosphorus bromide
1.86 g phosphorus

14.40 g bromine

$$\frac{1.86 \text{ g P}}{31 \text{ g mole}^{-1}} = 0.060 \text{ mole P atoms}$$

$$\frac{14.40 \text{ g Br}}{80 \text{ g mole}^{-1}} = 0.18 \text{ moles Br atoms}$$

$$\frac{0.060}{0.18} = \frac{1}{3} \text{ ratio of P to Br atoms}$$

The empirical formula for the compound is PBr_3.

Problems involving stoichiometry consist of determining the number of moles of starting material, from which the number of moles of material sought can be obtained, using the mole ratios given by the balanced equation. The moles of material sought can then be converted to mass or volume. Give your students a variety of examples.

Example 1 Given the equation for the reaction between propane gas and oxygen producing carbon dioxide and water:

$$C_3H_8 + 5\ O_2 = 3\ CO_2 + 4\ H_2O$$

Starting with 11.0 g propane, calculate the volume of CO_2 gas produced at STP and the mass of water produced. Apply the steps outlined in section 1.

$$\text{moles propane} = \frac{11.0 \text{ g } C_3H_8}{44 \text{ g mole}^{-1}} = 0.25 \text{ moles } C_3H_8$$

$$\text{moles } CO_2 = (0.25 \text{ mole } C_3H_8)\left(\frac{3\ CO_2}{1\ C_3H_8}\right) = 0.75 \text{ moles } CO_2$$

$$\text{volume } CO_2 \text{ at STP} = (0.75 \text{ mole } CO_2)(22.4 \text{ liter mole}^{-1})$$
$$= 16.8 \text{ liters } CO_2$$

$$\text{moles } H_2O = (0.25 \text{ mole } C_3H_8)\left(\frac{4\ H_2O}{1\ C_3H_8}\right) = 1.00 \text{ mole } H_2O$$

$$\text{mass of } H_2O = (1.00 \text{ mole})(18 \text{ g mole}^{-1}) = 18 \text{ grams}$$

Example 2 Calculate the volume of hydrogen gas liberated at 29°C and 750 mm pressure when 4.50 g aluminum is reacted with sulfuric acid as shown in the equation

$$2\ Al + 3\ H_2SO_4 = 2\ Al_2(SO_4)_3 + 3\ H_2$$

$$\text{moles Al} = \frac{4.50 \text{ g Al}}{27 \text{ g mole}^{-1}} = 0.167 \text{ mole Al}$$

$$\text{moles } H_2 = (0.167 \text{ mole Al})\left(\frac{3 \; H_2}{2 \; Al}\right) = 0.25 \text{ mole } H_2$$

Solve for V using PV = nRT [see section 6]:

$$V = \frac{(0.25 \text{ mole})(62.4 \text{ lmm deg}^{-1} \text{ mole}^{-1})(300 \text{ deg})}{750\text{mm}}$$

$$= 6.24 \text{ liters } H_2$$

Example 3 Calculate the volume of 3 M H_2SO_4 consumed in the reaction of 4.50 g aluminum as shown in Example 2. [see section 5]

$$\text{moles } H_2SO_4 = (0.167 \text{ mole Al}) \frac{3 \; H_2SO_4}{2 \; Al} = 0.25 \text{ mole}$$

Calculate the volume of 3 M H_2SO_4 which contains 0.25 moles.

$$\text{Molarity} = \frac{\text{moles}}{\text{liters}} \qquad \text{rearranged: liters} = \frac{\text{moles}}{\text{moles liter}^{-1}}$$

$$\text{Liters } H_2SO_4 \text{ solution} = \frac{0.25 \text{ moles}}{3 \text{ moles liter}^{-1}} = 0.0833 \text{ l} = 83.3 \text{ ml } 3 \text{ M } H_2SO_4$$

Example 4 Calculate the volume of hydrogen gas liberated at STP when aqueous H_2SO_4 is electrolyzed using a current of 10 amperes for 1 hour.

The problem consists of calculating the number of coulombs of charge used, from which we can calculate the number of moles of electrons used (see section 8). The rest is routine. The equation gives the mole ratio:

$$2 H^+ + 2 e^- = H_2$$

$$(10 \text{ amps})(3600 \text{ sec}) = 3.6 \times 10^4 \text{ coulombs}$$

$$\frac{3.6 \times 10^4 \text{ coulombs}}{9.65 \times 10^4 \text{ coulombs mole}^{-1}} = 0.373 \text{ moles of electrons}$$

$$(0.373 \text{ mole } e^-)\left(\frac{1 \; H_2}{2 \; e^-}\right) = 0.187 \text{ mole } H_2$$

$$(0.187 \text{ mole } H_2)(22.4 \text{ l mole}^{-1}) = 4.19 \text{ liter } H_2$$

Example 5 Calculate the volume of 0.25 M $AgNO_3$ needed to precipitate all the chloride ion as AgCl from a solution containing 4.75 g $MgCl_2$ as shown in the equation

$$MgCl_2 + 2 \; AgNO_3 = 2 \; AgCl + Mg(NO_3)_2$$

First of all, establish the number of moles of $MgCl_2$ and determine the number of moles of $AgNO_3$ which are chemically equivalent to this number. The rest is routine.

$$\left(\frac{4.75 \text{ g } MgCl_2}{95 \text{ g mole}^{-1}}\right)\left(\frac{2 \; AgNO_3}{1 \; MgCl_2}\right) = 0.10 \text{ mole } AgNO_3$$

$$\frac{0.10 \text{ mole } AgNO_3}{0.25 \text{ mole liter}^{-1}} = 0.40 \text{ liter} = 400 \text{ ml}$$

Example 6 What weight of calcium carbonate is precipitated when all the CO_2 from the complete combustion of 2.90 g butane, C_4H_{10}, is bubbled into excess limewater? The equations are

$$C_4H_{10} + 6\tfrac{1}{2}\ O_2 = 4\ CO_2 + 5\ H_2O$$
$$CO_2 + Ca(OH)_2 = CaCO_3 + H_2O$$

Determine the moles of C_4H_{10} and the mole ratio of C_4H_{10} to $CaCO_3$. The rest is easy.

$$\left(\frac{5.90\ g\ C_4H_{10}}{58\ g\ mole^{-1}}\right)\left(\frac{4\ CO_2}{1\ C_4H_{10}}\right)\left(\frac{1\ CaCO_3}{1CO_2}\right) = 0.20\ mole\ CaCO_3$$

$$(0.20\ mole\ CaCO_3)\ (100\ g\ mole^{-1}) = 20\ g\ CaCO_3$$

Example 7 A sample of $Ca(ClO_3)_2$ was decomposed as shown in the equation $Ca(ClO_3)_2 = CaCl_2 + 3\ O_2$.

Calculate the volume of oxygen liberated at STP if 3.59 g AgCl was precipitated when the $CaCl_2$ produced was treated with excess $AgNO_3$ solution as shown in the equation

$$CaCl_2 + 2AgNO_3 = 2AgCl + Ca(NO_3)_2$$

Calculate the number of moles of AgCl produced and then the number of moles of oxygen, using the mole ratios. The volume of gas can then be calculated.

$$\frac{3.59\ g\ AgCl}{143.5\ g\ mole^{-1}} = 0.025\ mole\ AgCl$$

$$(0.025\ mole\ AgCl)\left(\frac{1\ CaCl_2}{2\ AgCl}\right)\left(\frac{3\ O_2}{1\ CaCl_2}\right) = 0.0375\ mole\ O_2$$

$$(0.0375\ mole\ O_2)\ (22.4\ l\ mole^{-1}) = 0.840\ l = 840\ ml\ O_2$$

Example 8 Calculate the number of molecules of oxygen needed to react with 2.20 g propane as shown in the equation

$$C_3H_8 + 5\ O_2 = 3\ CO_2 + 4\ H_2O$$

$$\left(\frac{2.20\ g\ C_3H_8}{44\ g\ mole^{-1}}\right)\left(\frac{5\ O_2}{1\ C_3H_8}\right) = 0.25\ mole\ O_2$$

$$(0.25\ mole)\ (6.02 \times 10^{23}\ molecules\ mole^{-1}) = 1.51 \times 10^{23}\ molecules$$

Give your students rather simple problems at the beginning of their training and gradually sneak in more sophisticated ones. When they begin to think in terms of moles, they will be able to attack most problems, provided they have the ability to think instead of memorizing set-ups for problem types.

5. USING MOLAR AND NORMAL SOLUTIONS

Most students have difficulty with molar and normal solutions until they understand them. After that, they usually find them easy. You should have more success teaching this topic using the mole concept, reminding your students that molarity is a concentration unit defined as moles of solute per liter of solution. Use dimensional analysis in setting up problems. A good way to begin is to have them fill in a table similar to the one below. Have your students solve problems similar to the examples following the table.

Substance	formula weight	grams solute / mole	M	moles solute / liter	grams solute / liter
NaOH					80
H_2SO_4			3		
$CaCl_2$				0.5	
$AgNO_3$			0.1		

Example 1 Calculate the number of moles and grams of NaOH in 250 ml 2 M solution.

$$(2 \text{ moles liter}^{-1})\ (0.250 \text{ liters}) = 0.5 \text{ mole} = 20 \text{ g NaOH}$$

Example 2 Calculate the volume of 0.50 M H_2SO_4 solution which contains 4.9 g H_2SO_4.

$$\frac{4.9 \text{ g } H_2SO_4}{98 \text{ g mole}^{-1}} = 0.05 \text{ mole } H_2SO_4$$

$$\frac{0.05 \text{ mole}}{0.50 \text{ mole l}^{-1}} = 0.1 \text{ liter} = 100 \text{ ml}$$

or: $$\frac{0.05 \text{ moles}}{x} = 0.50 \text{ mole liter}^{-1}$$

$$x = 0.1 \text{ liter}$$

Example 3 Calculate the molarity of a solution made by dissolving 1.12 liters HCI gas (at STP) in water and diluting the resulting solution to a volume of 200 ml.

$$\frac{1.12 \text{ l HCl}}{22.4 \text{ l mole}^{-1}} = 0.05 \text{ mole HCl}$$

$$\frac{0.05 \text{ mole}}{0.2 \text{ liter}} = 0.25\text{M}$$

Example 4 What volume of 2 M NaOH solution is needed to react completely with 500 ml 2 M H_2SO_4 as shown in the equation?

$$2\ NaOH + H_2SO_4 = Na_2SO_4 + 2\ H_2O$$

$$(2 \text{ mole l}^{-1}\ H_2SO_4)\ (0.5 \text{ l}) \left(\frac{2\ NaOH}{1\ H_2SO_4}\right) = 2 \text{ moles NaOH}$$

$$\frac{2 \text{ mole NaOH}}{2 \text{ mole liter}^{-1}} = 1 \text{ liter NaOH}$$

Some other examples of problems using molar solutions are given in the previous section. Give your students plenty of practice.

Before your students tackle normal solutions, they should have a working knowledge of the concept of equivalents. Have them fill in a table similar to the following:

Compound	*Formula Weight*	*Equivalents Per Mole*	*Equivalent Weight (g)*
NaOH			
H_2SO_4			
$CaCl_2$			
$AgNO_3$			
$Al_2(SO_4)_3$			
Na_2CO_3			

Normality is a concentration unit defined as the number of equivalents of solute per liter of solution. Have them solve problems similar to the following examples, using dimensional analysis.

Example 1 Calculate the weight of H_2SO_4 needed to make up 500 ml 0.5 N solution.

$$(0.5 \text{ eq } 1^{-1})\ (0.5\ 1)\left(\frac{1 \text{ mole}}{2 \text{ eq}}\right)(98 \text{ g mole}^{-1}) = 12.25 \text{ g}$$

Example 2 Calculate the volume of 0.25 N solution which contains 2.12 g Na_2CO_3.

$$\left(\frac{2.12 \text{ g}}{106 \text{ g mole}^{-1}}\right)\left(\frac{2 \text{ eq}}{1 \text{ mole}}\right)\left(\frac{1}{0.25 \text{ eq } 1^{-1}}\right) = 0.16 \text{ liter} = 160 \text{ ml}$$

Example 3 What volume of 0.5 N HCI is needed to react with 200 ml 0.25 N triethanolamine solution?

The students shouldn't be afraid of the funny name. As long as they can determine the number of equivalents of triethanolamine, they know that the same number of equivalents of HCI is needed for the reaction. Note that the form for the set-up is the familiar $N_1V_1 = N_2V_2$ found (but not explained) in many high school texts. $N_1V_1 = eq_1$ and $N_2V_2 = eq_2$. Since $eq_1 = eq_2$, $N_1V_1 = N_2V_2$.

$$(0.25 \text{ eq } 1^{-1})\ (0.200\ 1) = (0.5 \text{ eq } 1^{-1})\ (x)$$
$$x = 0.100 \text{ liter} = 100 \text{ ml HCl}$$

Example 4 A student titrated a 0.265 g sample of Na_2CO_3 with 40 ml HCI solution. Calculate the normality of the HCl. The equation for the reaction is

$$2\ HCl + Na_2CO_3 = 2\ NaCl + H_2O + CO_2$$

$$\frac{0.265 \text{ g}}{53 \text{ g eq}^{-1}} = 0.005 \text{ eq } Na_2\ CO_3 = 0.005 \text{ eq HCl}$$

$$\frac{0.005 \text{ eq}}{0.04 \text{ liter}} = 0.125 \text{ N}$$

As stated earlier, one may use molarity in place of normality for solving titration problems. Normality is a valuable tool, however, since its use is based on the law of equivalents.

6. USING THE GENERAL GAS EQUATION AND AVOGADRO'S HYPOTHESIS

The ideal gas equation, PV = nRT, and values for *R* were derived in section 2.4, and their use in calculations was illustrated in sections 3 and 4. A student should understand the significance of this equation before using it. He should also know which value of *R* to choose in solving problems and in which units to express his answer. The student must also remember that T is expressed in degrees Kelvin. Give your students plenty of examples.

Example 1 Calculate the volume occupied by 16 grams of oxygen gas at 30°C and 2.05 atmospheres pressure.

The first thing to do is tabulate the information.

$$P = 2 \text{ atm}$$
$$T = 30°\text{C} = 303°\text{K}$$
$$V = ?$$
$$n = \frac{16 \text{ g } O_2}{32 \text{ g mole}^{-1}} = 0.50 \text{ mole}$$
$$R = 0.082 \text{ 1 atm deg}^{-1} \text{ mole}^{-1} \text{ (because } P \text{ is in atm)}$$

Rearrange the equation PV = nRT and solve for V.

$$V = \frac{(0.50 \text{ mole})(0.082 \text{ 1 atm deg}^{-1} \text{ mole}^{-1})(303 \text{ deg})}{2.05 \text{ atm}}$$
$$= 6.06 \text{ liters}$$

Show the students how the units cancel, leaving liters. If the value $R = 62.4$ 1 mm deg^{-1} mole^{-1} is used, the mm and atm don't cancel. Carrying the units through in the solution of a problem serves as a good check on the method.

Example 2 Calculate the weight of carbon dioxide gas in a sample which occupies a volume of 250 ml at 25°C and 756 mm. Here we can say that n = g/M, where g is the weight of sample and M is the molecular weight of the gas. Substituting for n we obtain PV = gRT/M. Rearrangè and solve for g.

$$g = \frac{\text{MPV}}{\text{RT}} = \frac{(44 \text{ g mole}^{-1})(756 \text{ mm})(0.250 \text{ 1})}{(62.4 \text{ 1 mm deg}^{-1} \text{ mole}^{-1})(298 \text{ deg})} = 0.447 \text{ g}$$

Since the pressure is expressed in millimeters of mercury, we use $R =$ 62.41 mm deg^{-1} mole^{-1}. The volume was changed to liters, and the temperature was expressed in degrees Kelvin.

These problems and the ones in sections 3 and 4 could have been solved by finding the volume of gas at STP, etc., which is a longer method and not as elegant as the use of the ideal gas equation. The beauty of this equation is that the conversion to STP is embodied in the value for R, which saves calculating time as well as providing one with a more direct and less cumbersome method for solving gas problems.

Applications of Avogadro's hypothesis and Gay Lussac's law have already been explored in Chapter 2. Give your students problems similar to those in section 2. 3.

Another application of Avogadro's hypothesis, using Dalton's law of partial pressures, is finding the partial pressures of gases in a mixture.

Examine a mixture consisting of 12 molecules of gas A and 4 molecules of gas B in a container which is one unit of volume. The total pressure is 16 units of pressure. If the molecules were segregated, the volume occupied by gas A would be 3/4 of a unit of volume, and the volume occupied by gas B would be 1/4 of a volume unit. Each would exert a pressure of 16 units when occupying the small volumes. If each gas occupied the total volume of the mixture, the volume of A would be increased by 4/3, and its pressure would become 3/4 of 16, or 12 pressure units. If B occupied the total volume, its volume would be increased by a factor of 4, and its pressure would become 1/4 of 16, or 4 pressure units. The sum of the partial pressures of the gases is equal to the total pressure of the mixture, and the partial pressure of each gas is the total pressure times its mole fraction (moles of component divided by total moles in the mixture).

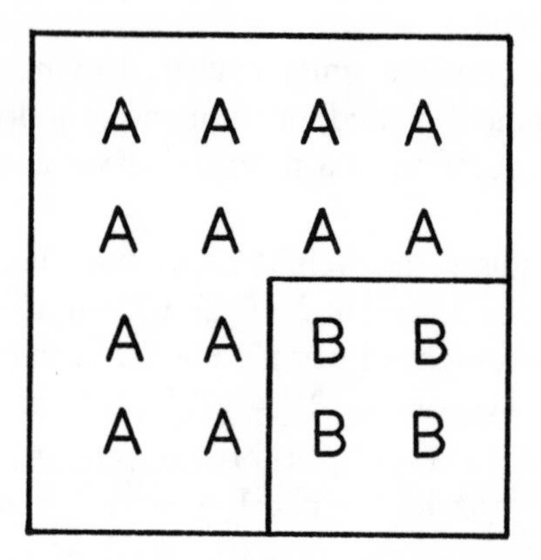

Example 1 Calculate the partial pressure of oxygen in the atmosphere at standard atmospheric pressure, if air is 20% oxygen by volume. Avogadro's hypothesis leads us to the conclusion that the mole fraction of oxygen in air is 0.20, and so the partial pressure of oxygen is (0.20) (1 atm) or 0.20 atmospheres.

Example 2 Calculate the partial pressure of carbon dioxide in a mixture of 11 g CO_2 and 16 g O_2 if the pressure of the mixture is 720 mm.

$$\frac{11 \text{ g } CO_2}{44 \text{ g mole}^{-1}} = 0.25 \text{ mole } CO_2$$

$$\frac{16 \text{ g } O_2}{32 \text{ g mole}^{-1}} = \underline{0.50 \text{ mole } O_2}$$

$$0.75 \text{ mole gas}$$

$$\text{Pressure of } CO_2 = \left(\frac{0.25}{0.75}\right) (720\text{mm}) = 240 \text{ mm}$$

7. CORRECTING PRESSURE FOR GASES COLLECTED OVER WATER

In many cases, gases are collected by displacement of a liquid, such as water. Before using the gas equation we must know the partial pressure of the gas in question (pressure of the dry gas). A good starting point might be to find the pressure of a gas collected over mercury, which illustrates the idea of the difference in level correction.

Diagram a bottle of gas inverted over mercury as shown in Diagram 1. Ask the students to predict whether the pressure of gas inside the bottle is higher or lower than the atmospheric pressure, and then proceed to calculate the pressure of gas in the bottle. Do the same for the second example shown in Diagram 2. Analyze the forces as follows: In the first example, the atmospheric pressure is balanced by the pressure of gas plus that exerted by the difference in mercury level: $P_{gas} + P_{Hg} = P_{atm}$. To find the pressure of the gas we must subtract the difference in mercury level (mm Hg) from the atmospheric pressure expressed in the same units (mm Hg). In the second example, the gas pressure is greater by a pressure equal to the difference in mercury level, so this value must be added to the atmospheric pressure.

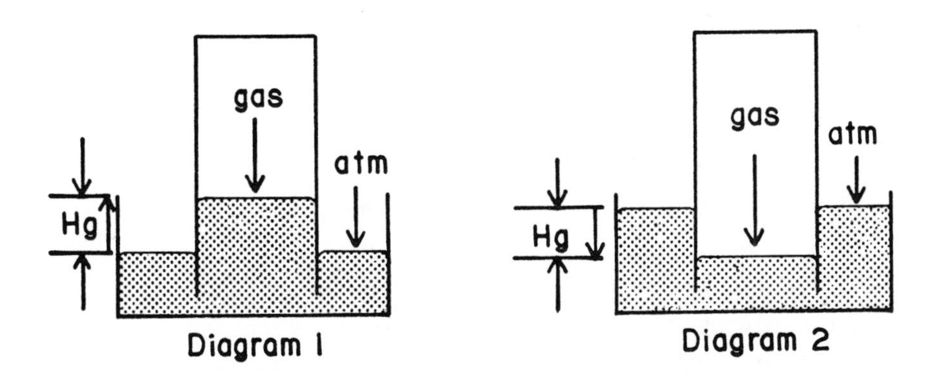

Diagram 1 Diagram 2

The problem of finding the pressure of dry gas collected over water is the same as far as the difference in level is concerned, except that the difference in water level must be converted to mm mercury. Since mercury is 13.6 times denser than water, the difference in water level (mm H_2O) is divided by 13.6 to convert to mm mercury. A second correction must be made, however. Water exerts a vapor pressure and therefore contributes to the total gas pressure in the bottle. According to Dalton's law of partial pressures, the total pressure of a mixture of gases is the sum of the partial pressures of the gases in the mixture. Therefore $P_{total} = P_{gas} + P_{H_2O\ vapor}$. In order to find the pressure of gas in a bottle standing over water, we must subtract the vapor pressure of water at the temperature of the mixture from the total gas pressure in the bottle.

Example A sample of hydrogen is collected over water at 30°C and a barometric pressure of 754 mm. The water in the bottle is 4.2 cm above the level of the water outside. Calculate the pressure of hydrogen. A diagram may help the beginner.

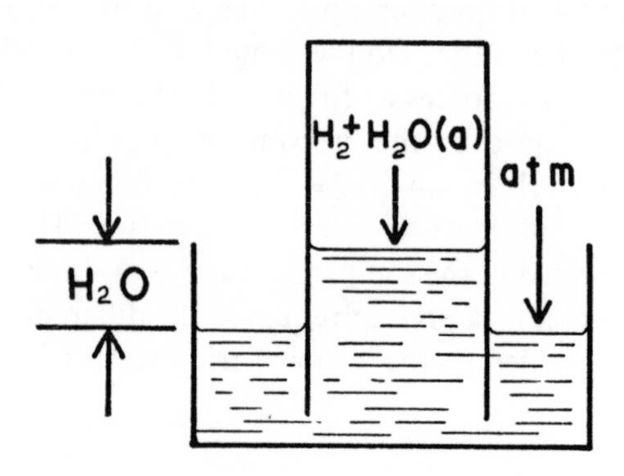

Convert all pressures to mm mercury.

$$P_{atm} = 754 \text{ mm Hg}$$
$$P_{H_2O} \text{ at } 20° = 18 \text{ mm Hg}$$
$$\text{Level difference} = \frac{42 \text{ mm } H_2O}{13.6} = 3 \text{ mm Hg}$$
$$P_{H_2} = P_{atm} - P_{\Delta\ level} - P_{H_2O\ vapor}$$
$$= 754 \text{ mm} - 3 \text{ mm} - 18 \text{ mm} = 733 \text{ mm}$$

Give your students similar examples until they get the idea. Quantitative experiments involving collecting gases over water to determine the equivalent weight of a metal from the volume of hydrogen displaced or the molecular weight of a gas provide the students with practical applications.

8. SOLVING PROBLEMS IN ELECTROCHEMISTRY, AND USING THE OXIDATION POTENTIAL CONCEPT

Faraday's first law of electrolysis states that the amount of a substance liberated during electrolysis is proportional to the time current passes through the system. His second law may be paraphrased as follows: one equivalent of material is produced by one mole of electrons (1 equivalent). Before solving problems in electrochemistry, a student should know something about redox (Chapter 10) and about amperes and coulombs. The mole concept can then be used to solve such problems.

Electric charge is measured in coulombs, defined in terms of the amount of silver deposited during the electrolysis of silver nitrate. The rate of flow of charge, or current, is measured in amperes. One ampere is a current of one coulomb per second. If we have an ammeter and a clock, we can calculate the amount of charge that has passed through a system: coulombs = (amperes) (seconds). One mole of electrons has a charge of 9.65×10^4 coulombs, which is called one Faraday. Electrode reactions (half-reactions) are discussed in Chapter 10.

Give your students examples similar to the following.

Example 1 Calculate the amount of copper deposited from a solution of copper sulfate by a current of 10 amperes passing through the solution for 2 hours. The half-reaction is

$$Cu^{+2} + 2e^- = Cu$$

Calculate the number of coulombs, which gives the moles of electrons used. From this we can obtain the moles of copper.

$$(10 \text{ amps})\ (2 \text{ hrs})\ (3600 \text{ sec hr}^{-1}) = 7.2 \times 10^4 \text{ coulombs}$$

$$\left(\frac{7.2 \times 10^4 \text{ coul}}{9.65 \times 10^4 \text{ coul mole}^{-1} \text{ el}^{-1}}\right)\left(\frac{1 \text{ Cu}}{2 \text{ el}}\right)\left(\frac{63.5 \text{ g}}{\text{mole}}\right) = 23.7 \text{ g Cu}$$

Example 2 Calculate the time needed to produce 400 ml chlorine gas (measured at STP) in the electrolysis of NaCl, using a current of 20 amperes. The half-reaction is

$$2\,Cl^- = Cl_2 + 2e^-$$

Calculate the moles of chlorine, from which we can get the moles of electrons and coulombs.

$$\left(\frac{0.400 \text{ liter } Cl_2}{22.4 \text{ liter mole}^{-1}}\right)\left(\frac{2 \text{ el}}{1\ Cl_2}\right) = 0.0357 \text{ moles electrons}$$

$$(0.0357 \text{ mole el})\left(9.65 \times 10^4 \frac{\text{coulomb}}{\text{mole el}}\right) = 3450 \text{ coulombs}$$

$$\frac{3450 \text{ coulomb}}{20 \text{ amperes}} = 173 \text{ sec} = 2 \text{ min } 53 \text{ sec}$$

Example 3 Calculate the current needed to produce 100 g calcium metal in 2 hours by electrolyzing molten $CaCl_2$.

$$Ca^{+2} + 2e^- = Ca$$

$$\left(\frac{100 \text{ g Ca}}{40 \text{ g mole}^{-1}}\right)\left(\frac{2 \text{ el}}{1 \text{ Ca}}\right) = 5.00 \text{ moles electrons}$$

$$\frac{(9.65 \times 10^4)\ (5.00) \text{ coulombs}}{(2)\ (3600) \text{ sec}} = 67 \text{ amperes}$$

The oxidation potentials of half-reactions can be used to calculate the voltage produced by an electrochemical cell. The sum of the half-reactions (properly balanced as shown in Chapter 10) and the $E°$ values gives the equation for the overall reaction and the approximate voltage of the cell. If the voltage is positive, the reaction proceeds spontaneously as shown, and if the voltage is negative, the spontaneous reaction is the reverse one.

Example 1 Calculate the $E°$ value for the reaction between aluminum and aqueous H_2SO_4. Is the reaction feasible? Write the half-reactions and balance the net equation for the reaction producing hydrogen and aluminum ions. Emphasize that the voltage is independent of the quantity of material but is dependent upon concentration. The $E°$ for the cell is the sum of the $E°$ values for the half-reactions.

$$2\,(Al = Al^{+3} + 3e^-) \qquad + 1.67 \text{ volts}$$
$$3\,(2\,H^+ + 2e^- = H_2) \qquad 0.00 \text{ volts}$$
$$\overline{2\,Al + 6\,H^+ = 2\,Al^{+3} + 3H_2 + 1.67 \text{ volts}}$$

The forward reaction proceeds spontaneously.

Example 2 Calculate the $E°$ value for silver metal reacting with copper ions to produce copper. Predict whether or not the reaction is feasible.

$$1\,(Cu^{+2} + 2\,e^- = Cu) \qquad + 0.34 \text{ volts}$$
$$2\,(Ag = Ag^+ + e^-) \qquad - 0.80 \text{ volts}$$
$$\overline{2\,Ag + Cu^{+2} = 2Ag^+ + Cu \quad - 0.46 \text{ volts}}$$

The reverse reaction proceeds but the forward reaction is not feasible.

Example 3 Predict whether or not chloride ion is oxidized to free chlorine in acid solution by permanganate ion.

$$2\,(5e^- + MnO_4^- + 8H^+ = Mn^{+2} + 4H_2O) + 1.51 \text{ v}$$
$$5\,(2\,Cl^- = Cl_2 + 2e^-) \qquad - 1.36 \text{ v}$$
$$\overline{2MnO_4^- + 10Cl^- + 16H^+ = 2Mn^{+2} + 5Cl_2 + 8H_2O}$$
$$\text{cell voltage} = + 0.15 \text{ volts}$$

Since the $E°$ for the reaction is positive, the reaction proceeds spontaneously.

9. CALCULATING pH AND SIMPLE PROBLEMS INVOLVING EQUILIBRIUM CONSTANTS

Your students must have an understanding of logarithms before they tackle pH. A working definition of pH (which refers to the power of the hydrogen ion concentration or potential of a concentration cell using hydrogen electrodes) is: $pH = -\log [H^+]$. The development of the concept of pH can be found in section 7.9.

Attempt equilibrium problems only with your more able students. Equilibrium constants are discussed in Chapter 8. Calculations involving equilibrium constants must satisfy two conditions: (1) the stoichiometry as shown in the equation and (2) the equilibrium constant. For our purposes we may use approximations (this avoids quadratic and other complicated equations). The only practical method for teaching calculations involving equilibrium is to discuss examples with your students and stress the two requirements mentioned above. The use of a mole table is very helpful. Discuss examples as illustrated below.

Example 1 Calculate the pH of a 0.05 M HCI solution, assuming complete ionization.

The equation for the reaction between water and HCl is

$$H_2O + HCl = H_3O^+ + Cl^-$$

We can simplify this and write $HCl = H^+ + Cl^-$.

From this equation we can deduce that in one liter of solution 0.05 moles HCl produces 0.05 moles H^+. Therefore $[H^+] = 0.05$, or

$[H^+] = 5 \times 10^{-2}$

$\log [H^+] = \log 5 + \log 10^{-2}$

$\log 5 = \quad 0.70$

$\log 10^{-2} = -2.00$

$\log [H^+] = -1.30$

Since $pH = -\log [H^+]$, $pH = 1.30$

Example 2 Calculate the pH of 0.01 M $Ca(OH)_2$ solution, assuming 100% ionization.

$$Ca(OH)_2 = Ca^{+2} + 2OH^-$$

$$[Ca(OH)_2] = 0.01. \text{ Therefore } [OH^-] = 0.02 = 2 \times 10^{-2}$$

Two possible methods for calculating pH are possible: (1) calculate $[H^+]$ from $[OH^-]$, and (2) calculate pH from pOH. The starting point is the ion product of water: $[H^+][OH^-] = 10^{-14}$.

(1) $(2 \times 10^{-2})[H^+] = 10^{-14}$

$[H^+] = 5 \times 10^{-13}$

$\log 5 = \quad 0.70$

$\log 10^{-13} = -13.00$

$\log [H^+] = -12.30$

$pH = 12.30$

(2) $pH + pOH = 14$

Since $[OH^-] = 2 \times 10^{-2}$,

$pOH = -\log 2 \times 10^{-2}$

$\log 2 = \quad 0.30$

$\log 10^{-2} = -2.00$

$\log [OH^-] = -1.70$

$pOH = 1.70$

$$\begin{array}{r} 14.00 \\ 1.70 \\ \hline pH = 12.30 \end{array}$$

Example 3 Calculate the pH of a 0.1 M acetic acid solution. The ionization constant for acetic acid is 1.8×10^{-5}.

Write the simple equation for the dissociation of HOAc and the expression for the equilibrium constant.

$$HOAc = H^+ + OAc^-$$

$$K_{HOAc} = \frac{[H^+][OAc^-]}{[HOAc]} = 1.8 \times 10^{-5}$$

According to the equation, $[H^+] = [OAc^-]$. Since we don't know $[H^+]$ and $[OAc^-]$, let x equal these quantities. In order to produce x moles of H^+ and x moles of OAc^-, we must have used up x moles of HOAc, leaving $(0.1 - x)$ moles of HOAc at equilibrium:

$$HOAc = H^+ + OAc^-$$
$$(0.1 \mp x) \quad x \qquad x.$$

Make a mole table as shown and assume 1 liter of solution.

Specie	*Moles at Equilibrium*	*Concentration in Moles per Liter*
HOAc	$0.1-x$	$(0.1-x)$
H^+	x	x
OAc^-	x	x

Plug the molar concentration of each specie into the equilibrium constant. The equation takes the form of a quadratic equation. We can make an approximation, however, since we know that x is small compared to 0.1, and write a simpler equation, which we can solve with little difficulty.

$$K = \frac{x^2}{0.1-x} = 1.8 \times 10^{-5}$$

$$\frac{x^2}{0.1} = 1.8 \times 10^{-5}$$

Solving for x: $x^2 = 1.8 \times 10^{-6}$

$$x = 1.35 \times 10^{-3} = [H^+]$$

$$-\log[H^+] = pH = 2.9$$

Example 4 Calculate the ionization constant of a weak acid, HA, if a 0.1 molar solution of HA has a pH of 2.0.

Write the expression for the dissociation and the expression for the equilibrium constant. We know from the stoichiometry that $[H^+] = [A^-]$. Since the pH = 2.0, $[H^+] = 10^{-2}$.

$$HA = H^+ + A^-$$
$$(0.10-0.01) \quad 0.01 \quad 0.01$$

$$[HA] = 0.09 = 9\times10^{-2}$$
$$[H^+] = 0.01 = 10^{-2}$$
$$[A^-] = 0.01 = 10^{-2}$$

$$K = \frac{[H^+][A^-]}{[HA]} = \frac{(10^{-2})(10^{-2})}{9 \times 10^{-2}} = 1.1 \times 10^{-3}$$

Example 5 Calculate the concentration of silver ion in a saturated solution of Ag_2CrO_4 if the solubility product of Ag_2CrO_4 is 1.0×10^{-12}.

Let x represent the moles of CrO_4^{-2} ions produced in 1 liter of solution.

$$Ag_2CrO_4 = 2\,Ag^+ + CrO_4^{-2}$$
$$— \qquad 2x \qquad x$$

$$[Ag^+] = 2x \qquad KSP = [Ag^+]^2 [CrO_4^{-2}] = 10^{-12}$$
$$[CrO_4^-] = x \qquad 4x^3 = 10^{-12} = 1000 \times 10^{-15}$$
$$x^3 = 250 \times 10^{-15}$$
$$x = 6.3 \times 10^{-5}$$
$$2x = [Ag^+] = 1.3 \times 10^{-4} \text{ moles per liter}$$

Example 6 Calculate the solubility product of AgI if its solubility is 9.2×10^{-9} moles per liter.

Let x represent the moles of Ag^+ ions per liter of solution.

$$AgI = Ag + I^-$$
$$— \quad x \quad x$$

We know that 9.2×10^{-9} moles of AgI produces 9.2×10^{-9} moles of Ag^+ and I^- ions per liter of solution. Therefore

$$x = 9.2 \times 10^{-9} \text{ and } KSP = [Ag^+] [I^-] = x^2$$
$$x^2 = 8.5 \times 10^{-17} = KSP$$

Example 7 A 2-liter container was charged with 0.200 moles of SO_2 gas and 0.200 moles of O_2 gas, which react to produce SO_3 gas. The system was allowed to come to equilibrium, and 0.150 moles O_2 remained unchanged. The equation for the reaction is

$$2\,SO_2 + O_2 = 2\,SO_3$$

Calculate the value for the equilibrium constant.

Make a mole table and use the mole ratios given in the equation to establish the number of moles of each substance present before and after equilibrium has been reached. Calculate the molar concentration of each substance (moles at equilibrium/2 liters). Substitute into the expression for K.

Substance	*Moles at Start*	*Moles Used*	*Moles at Equil.*	*Molar Conc.*
SO_2	0.200	0.100	0.100	0.050
O_2	0.200	(0.200 – 0.150) = 0.050	0.150	0.075
SO_3	—	—	0.100	0.050

$$K = \frac{[SO_3]^2}{[SO_2]^2 [O_2]} = \frac{(0.050)^2}{(0.050)^2 (0.075)} = 13.3$$

6

Interpreting the Properties of Solutions and Colloids

1. EXPLAINING THE GENERAL PROPERTIES OF SOLUTIONS

A solution might be defined as a homogeneous mixture consisting of a solvent and a solute. You should stress that this means a single phase, the composition is variable, the components retain their identities and can be separated by physical means, and therefore the solution can be classified as a mixture. Emphasize that the phase might be either solid, liquid, or gas. Give examples such as:

Phase	*Components*
gas	air: oxygen, nitrogen, etc.
gas	air and gasoline vapor
liquid	sea water
liquid	gasoline (mixture of hydrocarbons)
liquid	sugar in water
solid	alloys, such as brass and bronze, coin silver (silver and copper)

The solution appears homogeneous because the particle size is exceedingly small (less than 10 Angstroms in diameter). Solutions mix spontaneously by diffusion. Gases diffuse quite rapidly because the moving particles are relatively far apart, but liquids diffuse slowly because the particles are close together. Use the analogy of trying to cross Times Square on New Year's Eve for a liquid and crossing Times Square on a Sunday morning for a gas. Refer to the kinetic theory.

The driving force in diffusion is the increase in entropy; the solute tends to become more randomly distributed. (See sections 1.4 and 9.3.) Diffusion in solids is exceedingly slow. Show the students a rock in which different kinds of crystals are visible, mentioning that there is little evidence of spontaneous mixing. Refer to section 6 for a discussion of the colligative properties of solutions.

Demonstrations

1) Add a small amount of concentrated nitric acid to some copper turnings in a covered cylinder and observe the diffusion of brown NO_2 gas. Place a large crystal of chrome alum in the bottom of a covered cylinder filled with distilled water and let it stand undisturbed for several months. There is a marked difference in rate of diffusion.

2) To demonstrate that volumes of solutions are not additive, mix carefully-measured 50 ml volumes of distilled water and isopropanol. The "shrinkage" can be attributed to some of the space between molecules of one liquid being partially occupied by molecules of the other liquid.

To demonstrate extraction, shake the water-isopropanol solution with 50 ml carbon tetrachloride (separatory funnel) and permit the emulsion to separate. Measure the volumes of the two layers. Isopropanol is soluble in both water and carbon tetrachloride. Challenge the students to explain that!

2. EXPLORING FACTORS WHICH INFLUENCE SOLUBILITY

(a) *Nature of Solute and Solvent.* Correlate the types of attractive forces with bonding. (See sections 4.5 and 4.7). Ionic compounds in general have high lattice energy, and a suitable solvent is needed to separate the ions. Covalent compounds have less lattice energy. Compounds which are hydrogen bonded require solvents which also hydrogen bond in order to effect interaction between solvent and solute.

Polar solvents are more effective in dissolving polar substances and ionic compounds (salts), because of dipole-dipole and ion-dipole attraction. Use Coulomb's law to relate dielectric constant (which is high for polar solvents) to force of attraction between ions: $f = q_1q_2 / Dr^2$. D is the dielectric constant, r is the interionic distance, q_1 and q_2 are the charges of the ions, and f is the force of attraction between the ions. When D is large (water, for example, has a dielectric constant of about 80), the attractive force between ions is greatly diminished, resulting in greater solubility. The reason why highly-polar solvents dissolve ionic compounds is the phenomenon called *solvation* (in the case of water this is called *hydration*). Small, highly-charged ions have a high charge density, resulting in greater attraction for water dipoles than larger, singly-charged ions. Solubility of ionic compounds is largely determined by the predominance of one of the following factors over the other: lattice energy of the crystal versus the solvation energy. Another factor is that solute particles must wedge themselves between solvent molecules, and this requires energy.

Diagram the effect of solvation. Use a model of a crystal to show the point of attack of solvent molecules (the exposed corners), pointing out that the solvent molecules envelop the ions and actually tear the crystal apart.

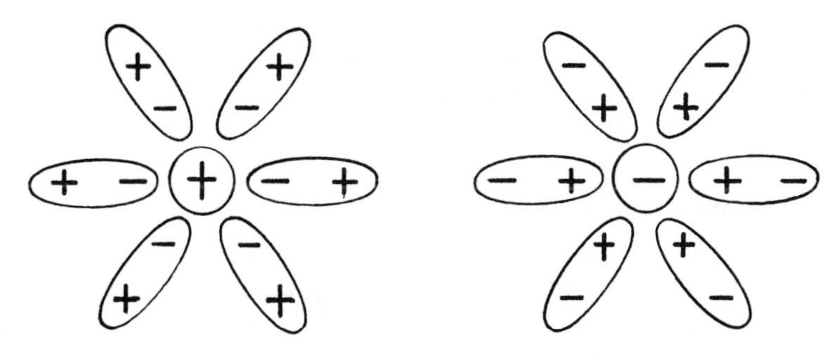

Ions solvated by dipoles

Demonstrations

1) To demonstrate the rule that polar solvents dissolve polar and ionic substances and non-polar solvents dissolve non-polar substances, add some carbon tetrachloride to some very dilute potassium permanganate solution containing a small amount of sulfuric acid. Shake and permit the liquids to separate. Add a small amount of sodium iodide solution and shake. Permanganate should be reduced and iodide ion oxidized. The purple permanganate did not dissolve in the carbon tetrachloride, but the free iodine dissolved readily.

2) Dissolve some ammonium chloride crystals in water and measure the temperature change with a thermometer. The drop in temperature can be attributed to the lattice energy of the ammonium chloride being greater than the hydration energy of the ions.

3) Dissolve some anhydrous sodium carbonate in water and explain the temperature rise in terms of the hydration energy being greater than the lattice energy.

4) Place a small puddle of water on a block of wood and a small beaker on the puddle. Put some ice water in the beaker and add a spoonful of fine ammonium nitrate crystals, with stirring. Sufficient energy is absorbed by the dissolving ammonium nitrate to freeze the beaker to the block of wood.

Why don't carbon tetrachloride and water mix? Water molecules are highly associated by hydrogen bonding (see section 4.7). Water is polar, and CCl_4 is non-polar. CCl_4 does not hydrogen bond and will not associate with water molecules, since CCl_4 molecules will not "hold hands" with water molecules. Sugar molecules contain many hydroxyl groups (hydrophilic group) and can hydrogen bond, so sugar dissolves readily in water, despite its covalent nature and large molecular size. Simple polar molecules, such as HCl and NH_3, are very soluble in water, but non-polar molecules, such as CH_4, are not soluble in water.

The CHEM Study film "Shapes and Polarities of Molecules" provides a good explanation for solubility effects.

b) *Size of Solute Particles.* Capitalize on the idea that a reaction between two phases proceeds at the interface. Illustrate the case of a cube 1 cm on an edge. The surface area is 6 cm for a volume of 1 cm. Subdivide the cube into eight half centimeter cubes, giving a total surface area of 12 cm^2. Generalize that the smaller the particles are for a given amount of material, the larger the surface area, and this tends to speed up the process of interaction between the two phases which are in contact. Powdered sugar dissolves more rapidly than coarse granular sugar.

c) *Stirring and Mixing.* Correlate the idea of rates of reaction depending on concentration (see sections 3 and 8.1) with the necessity of having fresh solvent in contact with the solute being dissolved. A good demonstration of mixing of solutions to hasten the rate of dissolving consists of placing a large crystal of copper sulfate at the bottom of a cylinder filled with water. In a second cylinder full of water, place a large crystal of copper sulfate in a wire screen cradle located at the top of the cylinder. In the first cylinder the solution process slows down as the solution around the crystal becomes concentrated and approaches saturation, but the solution produced in the second cylinder sinks to the bottom, permitting fresh solvent to make contact with the crystal. It dissolves more rapidly than the crystal at the bottom of the first cylinder. Point out the oily appearance of the denser solution as it sinks to the bottom. The "oiliness" is due to a change in refractive index as the solution becomes more concentrated.

d) *Effect of Temperature.* You can capitalize on the kinetic theory by pointing out that molecules move faster at a high temperature, and therefore a reaction should proceed more rapidly. The solution process is generally hastened by raising the temperature. The extent of solubility can be predicted by using Le Chatelier's principle. If the dissolving process is endothermic, the solubility should increase with temperature, and if the dissolving process is exothermic, the solubility should decrease with a rise in temperature.

$$\text{energy} + \text{solid solute} \rightleftharpoons \text{solute in solution}$$

Solution process is favored by increasing the energy.

3. UNSATURATED, SATURATED, AND SUPERSATURATED SOLUTIONS

Explore the rate of dissolving, using a diagram with arrows representing rates of crystallization and dissolving. Since rate is proportional to concentration, and also temperature, analyze the situation in the following manner: at a given temperature the rate of dissolving of a crystal is constant, since the concentration of the solid is constant. The crystal dissolves at its own merry rate, and as solute particles begin to accumulate in the solution, the reverse process (crystallization) begins to become apparent. At first the

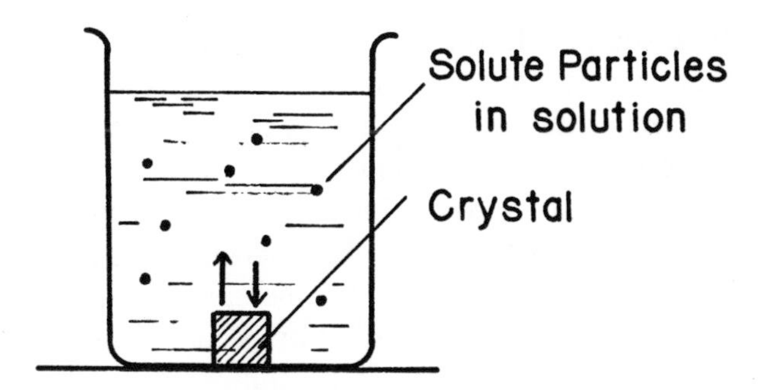

rate of crystallization is zero (concentration of dissolved solute is zero), but this rate increases as the concentration of dissolved solute increases. At equilibrium (see sections 8.1 and 8.2) the two rates become equal, and there is no longer any change in the system. The solution is said to be *saturated.* Emphasize that this is a dynamic process: solid is dissolving as fast as solute is crystallizing. The CHEM Study film "Equilibrium" treats the dissolving process and formation of a saturated solution very effectively.

An unsaturated solution and a supersaturated solution do not represent conditions of equilibrium, however. Solute will dissolve in an unsaturated solution until equilibrium is reached. In the case of a supersaturated solution, the solute is present in solution in a higher concentration than is normal for that temperature, and this represents an unstable condition. The reason that some substances tend to supersaturate is that there is no nucleus on which solute particles may build a crystal. This is especially true of substances such as sodium acetate, in which the acetate ion is unsymmetrical (see illustration, next page). In order to fit into the crystal lattice, these ions must have a particular orientation. They are randomly oriented in the solution and must have a nucleus on which to collect and form a crystal.

Demonstration: Make a supersaturated solution of sodium acetate in a 500-ml Erlenmeyer flask by dissolving solid sodium acetate in distilled water at an elevated temperature. Permit the solution to cool to room temperature,

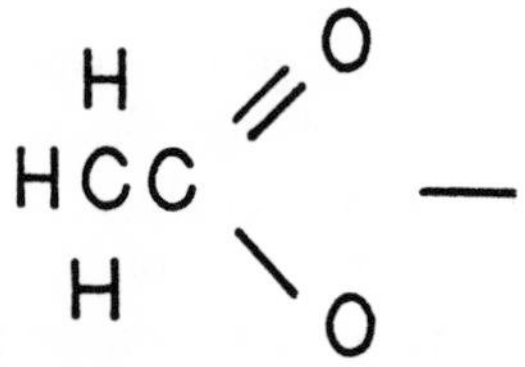

```
 H   //O
HCC        —
 H   \O
```

acetate ion

covered and undisturbed. Introduce a thermometer and drop a small seed crystal of sodium acetate into the solution. The marked rise in temperature as solute crystallizes is due primarily to the release of lattice energy. Excess solute has come out of solution, producing a saturated solution. Equilibrium between dissolved and undissolved solute has been attained. An understanding of solution equilibrium is essential to the students when they come to formation and dissolution of precipitates and the concept of solubility product (section 8.7). Emphasize that when a solution becomes supersaturated, excess solute is precipitated, leaving a saturated solution.

4. DETERMINING SOLUBILITY AND INTERPRETING SOLUBILITY CURVES: CRYSTALLIZATION

In a sense, solutions have a definite composition. Emphasize that a saturated solution has a fixed composition at a given temperature and that the composition is temperature dependent. This composition is what is meant by *solubility,* which is often expressed in grams of solute per 100 grams solvent. In more sophisticated work, solubility is expressed in terms of molarity or molality.

A worthwhile laboratory exercise is the determination of solubility. [See Experiment 8 in *Enrichment Experiments in Basic Chemistry*. (Olmsted), Hayden Publishing Co., 1966.] A saturated solution of a substance such as potassium chloride is made by heating an excess of crystals and water, permitting the solution to cool to a certain temperature, decanting into a tared vessel, determining the weight of the solution, evaporating to complete dryness, determining the weight of solute, and calculating grams of solute per 100 grams solvent. The solubility at different temperatures is determined in this manner and a solubility curve is plotted (grams solute per 100 grams solvent versus temperature).

By referring to solubility curves, you can determine the solubility of a substance at different temperatures and predict the amount of material that would come out of solution if a solution of known composition was cooled to a certain temperature.

An experiment based on the idea of relative solubilities at different temperatures involves the preparation of potassium nitrate from a solution of sodium nitrate and potassium chloride. The problem of preparing potassium nitrate, starting with a half a mole of each of the starting materials, introduces the student to the idea of per cent yield (actual yield over theoretical yield times 100 = per cent yield), as well as laboratory techniques. The student should consult the solubility curves of potassium chloride, sodium nitrate, and potassium nitrate, as well as sodium chloride (which should remain in solution). He should take the minimum amount of water needed to retain all the sodium chloride in solution. Cooling to a low temperature (ice bath or refrigerator) causes crystallization of potassium nitrate, because this is the least soluble combination of the ions present at the low temperature. Filtration using a filter flask, water aspirator and Buchner funnel, followed by recrystallization from a small amount of water, produces rather pure potassium nitrate.

During this experiment the student may observe that the crystal size is dependent upon the rate of crystallization. Rapid crystallization leads to small crystals, and slow crystallization leads to large crystals. This idea can be used to advantage in accounting for the size of snow crystals, which are larger at higher temperatures and smaller at lower temperatures. Precipitation (rain, snow, dew, etc.) occurs when the atmosphere becomes supersaturated with respect to water vapor. Honey represents a supersaturated solution of sugar (sugar supersaturates readily if impurities are present), which sometimes crystallizes on standing.

5. SOLUTIONS OF GASES IN LIQUIDS

The solubility characteristics of gases in liquids can be explained in terms of kinetic theory and Le Chatelier's principle. Henry's law states that the amount of gas dissolved in a liquid is proportional to the pressure on the

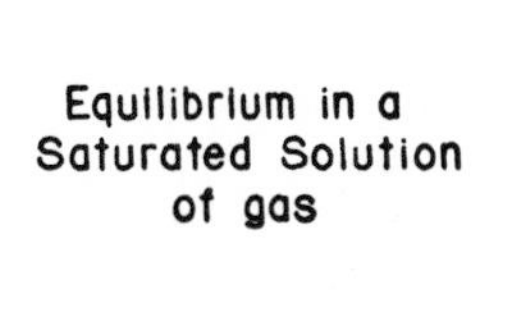

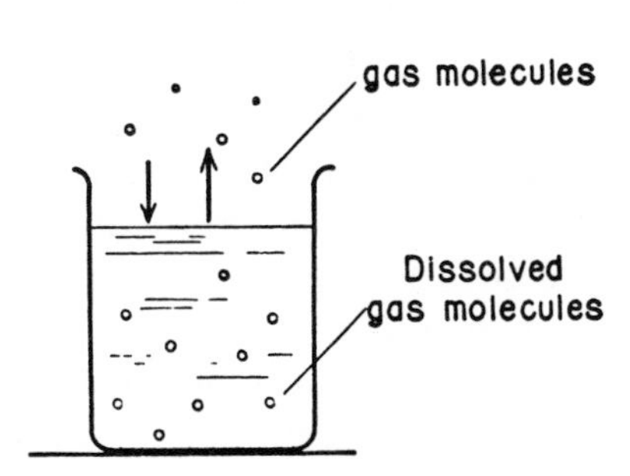

system. Increasing the concentration of gas by raising the pressure causes the rate of dissolving to increase. This results in more gas dissolving. Another way of explaining the increase of solubility with pressure is to apply Le Chatelier's principle: to relieve the stress created by increasing the pressure some gas enters the liquid phase. The effervescence produced by opening a bottle of soda water illustrates the effect of lowering the pressure on the solution of a gas in water. The solubility of a gas decreases as the temperature is increased. Since molecules contain more energy at a higher temperature, gas molecules will leave the liquid phase at a faster rate than at a low temperature. They contain sufficient energy to overcome attractive forces.

6. EXPLAINING COLLIGATIVE PROPERTIES OF SOLUTIONS

Colligative properties refer to properties of solutions which depend upon the number of particles present and not upon the kind. These properties include vapor pressure lowering, boiling point elevation, freezing point depression, and osmotic pressure. Solution concentration is expressed in terms of molality rather than morarity when dealing with these phenomena, because the concept of molality involves a definite number of particles of solute and solvent, which is not the case when using molarity. You can explain these properties on the molecular level as follows.

a) *Vapor Pressure Lowering*. Capitalize on the idea that rate is proportional to concentration and use a diagram showing molecules at the surface of a liquid. The students should have a clear idea of the concept of

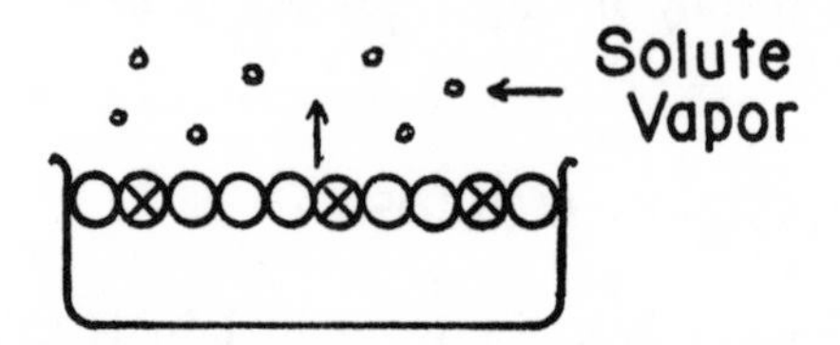

vapor pressure (see section 2.6) before proceeding. At a given temperature the rate of evaporation for the pure liquid is given by the arrow pointing up. Introduction of solute particles (marked *X*) reduces the concentration of liquid at the surface and therefore reduces the rate of evaporation, lowering the vapor pressure (make the arrow shorter). The relative number of solute and solvent particles determines the amount of vapor pressure lowering. This accounts for Raoult's law, which may be stated mathematically: (vapor pressure of pure solvent) (mole fraction of solvent) = vapor pressure of solution. The mole fraction is the ratio of number of moles of one component to the total number of moles in solution. The bigger the mole fraction of solute, the smaller the mole fraction of solvent, and the lower the vapor pressure.

b) *Boiling Point Elevation and Freezing Point Depression.* A phase diagram (see section 2.6) can be used to account for these phenomena. The phase diagram for water is shown, and the dotted line shows the vapor pressure curve and solid-liquid boundary for a solution:

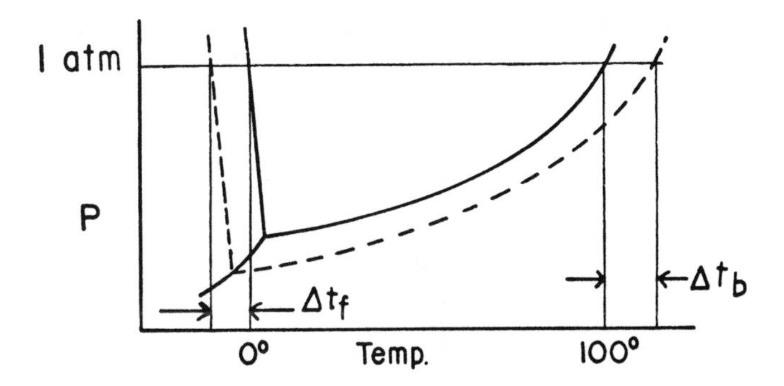

In order to have the vapor pressure equal to the atmospheric pressure (boiling point), the temperature must be higher than 100°C, which accounts for the boiling point elevation. The ice-liquid temperature at 1 atmosphere is below 0°C, accounting for the freezing point depression.

Another approach to the freezing point depression is to consider the rates of melting and freezing in a solution, represented by arrows in the diagram.

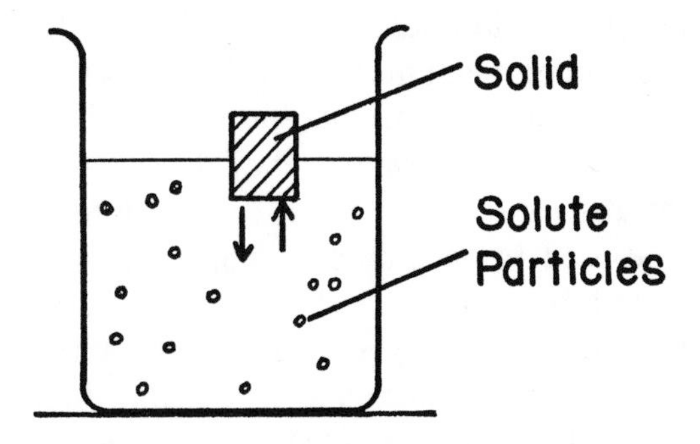

[See sec. 2.5] At the melting point of the pure solvent, equilibrium exists between solid and liquid, meaning that the rate of freezing is equal to the rate of melting. Rate is proportional to concentration, and the concentration of a solid is constant. If solute particles are mixed with the liquid solvent, the concentration of solvent is reduced in proportion to the mole fraction of solute. Since the rate of freezing is thereby decreased, there is no longer equilibrium, and some solid melts. The temperature decreases, accompanied by a decrease in the rate of melting. Equilibrium is reestablished at a lower temperature.

Applications of the freezing point lowering property of solutions are antifreeze for automobiles and the use of salt to melt ice and snow.

c) *Osmotic pressure.* Osmosis is selective diffusion through a semi-permeable membrane, as opposed to ordinary diffusion through a membrane. Use a diagram to account for the difference in diffusion rates of water across a membrane permeable to water but not to solute molecules (marked *X*).

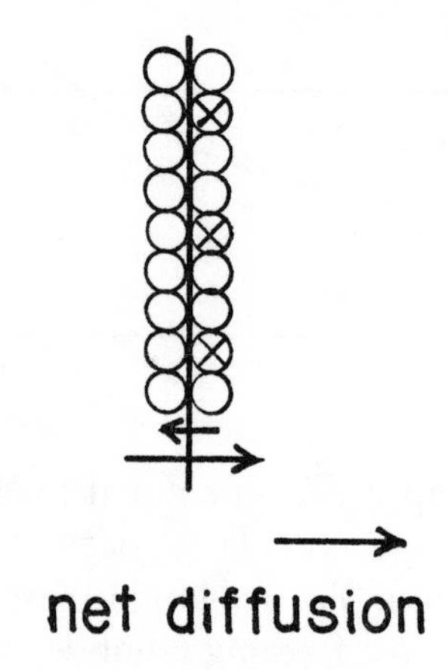

Again, rate is proportional to concentration, and so pure water diffuses faster than water which has been diluted by solute molecules. Since there is a difference in rates of diffusion across the membrane, there is a net pressure built up. This phenomenon accounts for blood cells swelling or shrinking when placed in salt solutions of different concentrations. If the salt is too concentrated, there is a net diffusion of water out of the cell, resulting in shrinkage. If the salt concentration is too low, water diffuses into the cell, causing it to swell. This may be used to account for people passing out from excessive perspiration followed by too much drinking without readjusting osmotic pressure of body fluids by taking salt tablets. Isotonic solutions have the same osmotic pressure across a particular type of membrane. Ask the students to explain why aqueous solutions injected into the body usually contain some salt. Osmosis plays a major role in biological processes.

Demonstrations:

1) Dissolve the shell off an egg with dilute hydrochloric acid and permit the egg to stand in water for a while. Diffusion of water into the egg causes it to swell.

2) Place some sugar syrup containing a trace of methylene blue (for color) in a thistle tube and stretch a piece of cellophane across the opening. Secure in place with rubber bands (make sure they are tight), invert into beaker

of water. The tube can be lengthened by attaching an extra piece of glass tubing. Colored liquid will rise in tube because of osmotic pressure.

7. INTERPRETING DIFFERENCES BETWEEN SOLUTIONS OF ELECTROLYTES AND NON-ELECTROLYTES

The abnormal colligative properties of electrolytes can be accounted for in terms of ions (see section 7.1). Present data of this type:

		Aqueous Solutions	
Solute	*Molality*	*Freezing Point*	*Conductivity*
alcohol	0.1	–0.184	none
urea	1.0	–1.86	none
glucose	1.0	–1.85	none
NaCl	0.1	–0.345	high
KOH	0.01	–0.0353	high
$Mg(NO_3)_2$	0.1	–0.551	high

Analysis of these data reveals that one mole of non-electrolytes must contain the same number of particles, since the freezing point depression is about the same in each case. In the case of NaCl and KOH (electrolytes) one mole of solute produces nearly two moles of particles (2×1.86), and one mole of $Mg(NO_3)_2$ produces nearly three moles of particles (3×1.86). Such information was used by Arrhenius in formulating his theory of ionization (section 7.1).

8. DISTINGUISHING BETWEEN COLLOIDS, SOLUTIONS AND SUSPENSIONS

Solutions, colloids and suspensions are mixtures (see section 1.5). Emphasize that the fundamental differences between these categories are due to particle size. The particles in a solution are molecular or ionic, ranging up to about 10 Angstroms in diameter. Since the material in a solution is subdivided into individual molecules or ions, one mole of solute must contribute at least one mole of particles, which accounts for the properties of solutions already discussed.

The size of colloidal particles ranges somewhere between about 10 and 10,000 Angstroms in diameter, which implies that colloidal particles usually contain a number of molecules. Therefore, one mole of material colloidally suspended contains considerably less than one mole of particles. Colloidal dispersions in liquid do not exhibit the colligative properties of true solutions to nearly the same extent. Colloidal particles tend to disperse, however, as do solution particles. Reasons for this are: (1) Brownian motion and (2) electrical properties of colloidal particles (see next section). Colloidal particles do not tend to settle, as do the particles in a coarse suspension. The word colloid was coined by Thomas Graham around 1860 and is derived from the Greek word *Kolla,* meaning glue. He had found that substances such as glue, gelatin, albumin, starch, etc., diffuse much more slowly than ordinary solutions.

Emphasize that macro-molecules (proteins, etc.) lie in the range of colloidal particles. Give examples of colloids: liquid in gas (fog), solid in gas (smoke), gas in liquid (foam), liquid in liquid (cream), solid in liquid (glue), gas in solid (Ivory soap), liquid in solid (jelly), solid in solid (colored glass).

Suspensions consist of particles which settle on standing. Give examples: dust, muddy water. The larger the particle size, the faster the rate of settling. Liquid-liquid suspensions are called emulsions.

9. EXPLAINING ADSORPTION, LIGHT-SCATTERING, AND OTHER PROPERTIES OF COLLOIDS

The relationship of surface area to volume was covered in section 2b. Emphasize that some properties of colloids are due to the large surface area available. *Adsorption* is such a property. Distinguish clearly between adsorption and absorption by using a sponge as an illustration of the latter and dust sticking to furniture as an illustration of the former. Any surface attracts certain other materials which stick to that surface. Colloidal particles selectively adsorb certain materials, such as colored impurities in brown sugar. Use is made of activated charcoal in refining sugar for this reason, and gas mask cannisters are filled with activated charcoal. Contact catalysts and adsorbents in chromatography columns depend on this surface phenomenon. Explain that in the process of making activated charcoal, adsorbed gases must be driven off by heat, usually under reduced pressure.

Electrically-charged particles, such as ions, may be selectively adsorbed on colloidal surfaces, which accounts for colloidal particles remaining dispersed (like charges repel). To precipitate colloids requires the neutralization of adsorbed charges. Examples: Cottrell precipitator, adding an electrolyte to colloidal dispersions, such as adding acid to curdle milk.

Explain light-scattering properties of colloids in terms of particle size. Visible light ranges in wave length from about 4000 to 7000 Angstroms, which is within the range of colloidal particle size. Waves are diffracted (scattered) by objects which have about the same diameter as the length of the wave being affected. The red sky at sunset, or the red sun seen through smoke are the results of red light being scattered by larger colloidal particles, and the blue sky is the result of blue light being scattered by smaller colloidal particles in the atmosphere. Monochromatic light is scattered by relatively few particles, and so fog lights are usually made yellow, affording better penetration and visibility. The Tyndall effect and observation of Brownian motion can be explained as light-scattering phenomena.

Soap and detergents are used to emulsify dirt and grease. The soap and detergent particles are ionic, but they also contain large non-polar groups, which mix with the grease. Since the ionic portion is attracted to water, these ions solubilize the dirt and grease, forming a permanent emulsion.

Demonstrations:

1) The CHEM Study film "Crystals and Their Structure" includes a good demonstration of diffraction of waves in a ripple tank.

2) Dissolve a very small amount of sodium thiosulfate in about 1 liter of distilled water, add some hydrochloric acid. Colloidal sulfur is produced. Shining a beam of light through the solution produces the effect of a red "sunset," caused by the colloidal particles growing larger and scattering light of longer wave length.

3) Decolorize a dilute solution of methylene blue, using activated charcoal. Two or three small crystals of methylene blue are dissolved in water, some animal charcoal is added, the mixture is stirred and filtered, producing a colorless filtrate.

4) Coagulate some skimmed milk as follows: dilute skimmed milk with about an equal volume of water and place the mixture in a cylinder. Add some acetic acid and look for precipitation, which occurs after several minutes of waiting.

5) Dissolve a small amount of ferric chloride in distilled water (very dilute solution), add a little sodium acetate as a buffer, and heat the solution. The red-brown color is due to colloidal particles of hydrated ferric hydroxide.

7

Developing Acid-Base Concepts and Ionization Theory

1. HOW ARRHENIUS INTERPRETED PROPERTIES OF SOLUTIONS AND ELECTROLYTES

Svante Arrhenius proposed his ionization theory around 1887 in order to explain the properties of solutions of electrolytes. He was aware of the colligative properties of solutions (see section 6.6) and the abnormal behavior of electrolytes in freezing point depression and boiling point elevation (see section 6.7). The conductivity of solutions of electrolytes could be explained simply by assuming the existence of ions, which migrate toward the oppositely-charged electrodes and react. Arrhenius was more interested in offering a quantitative explanation for the abnormal behavior of electrolytes.

Show your students data such as found in the table in section 6.7 and analyze the results as follows. The freezing point lowering is dependent upon the number of particles of solute, not upon the kind. An aqueous solution containing 0.1 moles of solute particles should freeze at $-0.186°$. A 0.1 M NaCl solution freezes at $-0.345°$, however, indicating that there are 0.345/0.186, or 1.85 moles of particles per mole of NaCl. Arrhenius assumed that NaCl was composed of molecules which dissociated into Na^+ and Cl^- ions in aqueous solution. Furthermore, NaCl molecules were in equilibrium with the ions as shown in the equation

$$NaCl \rightleftharpoons Na^+ + Cl^-$$

If 1 mole of NaCl produces x moles of Na^+ and x moles of Cl^- ions, leaving $(1-x)$ moles of NaCl molecules, the total number of moles of particles would be $(1-x) + x + x$, or $1 + x$ particles. Therefore, $1 + x = 1.85$, or $x = 0.85$ moles of Na^+ and Cl^- ions, leaving 0.15 moles of NaCl molecules. Evidently, 0.1 M NaCl is about 85% dissociated into ions.

The freezing point of 0.1 M acetic acid is depressed by 0.192°. This means that there are 0.192/0.186, or 1.03 moles of particles produced from 1 mole of HOAc. Using the same argument as in the case of NaCl, show your students that 0.1 M HOAc is about 3% ionized. Arrhenius assumed that HOAc is only slightly dissociated into ions, as shown in the equation

$$HOAc \rightleftharpoons H^+ + OAc^-$$

The presence of few ions in the solution is consistent with the fact that acetic acid is a weak electrolyte (lower conductivity than strong electrolytes).

To support this argument, demonstrate the conductivity of several solutions, using an apparatus consisting of a light bulb in series with two electrodes immersed in the solution. Test aqueous solutions of NaCl, H_2SO_4, KOH, KNO_3, sugar, alcohol, acetic acid, and ammonia. Arrhenius assumed that all of these substances were composed of molecules which dissociated to greater or lesser extents into ions in aqueous solution. He also assumed that molecules of common acids dissociated into H^+ and negative ions, but did not react with water in the process. Some of his ideas had to be changed in the light of new evidence. Arrhenius made a great step forward in chemical theory, but he was limited by insufficient information.

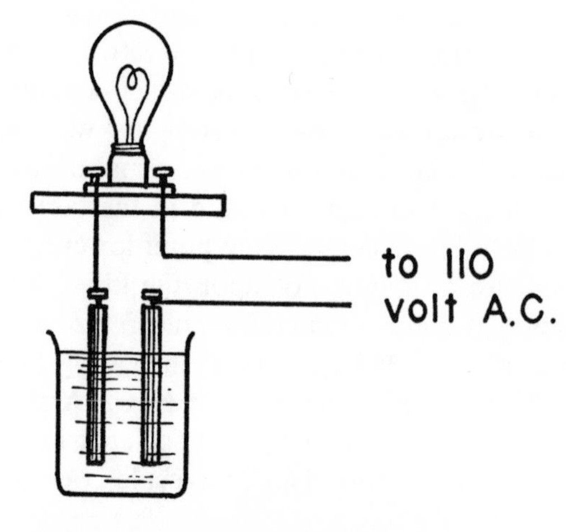

Wiring Diagram for
Conductivity Apparatus

2. ACCOUNTING FOR PROPERTIES OF SOLUTIONS OF ELECTROLYTES IN MODERN TERMS

We now know that salts are ionic compounds (X-ray studies show salt crystals are ionic lattices) and are not made of molecules. Molten salts conduct electricity as opposed to molecular compounds. We also know that acids (molecular compounds) react with water to produce ions. Modern acid-base concepts will be developed later in this chapter. Arrhenius explained the apparently incomplete ionization in terms of an equilibrium between molecules and ions formed by the dissociation of the molecules in solution. This assumption is not consistent with the idea that salts are composed of ions.

Review the process of hydration of ions (section 6.2) and Coulomb's law. Present the following data [from Noyes and Falk, *J. Am. Chem. Soc., 32,* 1011 (1910)], explaining that as the dilution increases, the apparent degree of ionization increases.

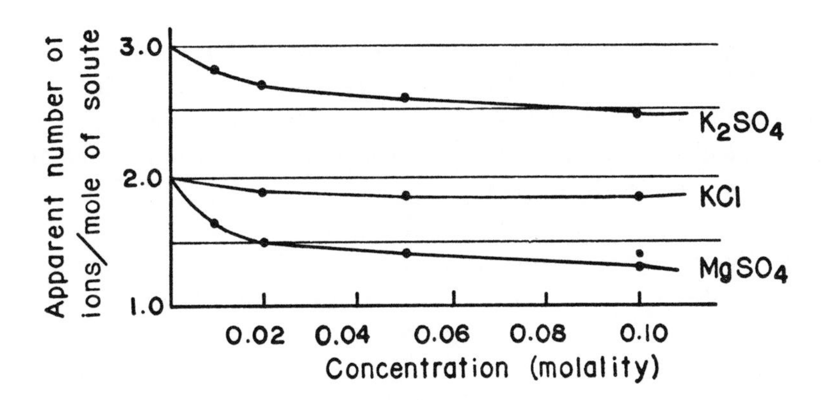

As the solution becomes more dilute, the distance between the ions increases. This results in less attraction between oppositely-charged ions, and consequently they are acting more independently. In concentrated solutions, the ions attract each other, with the result that clusters of ions are formed. This decreases the effective number of independent particles in the solution, producing a lower apparent degree of ionization. A theory of interionic attraction was proposed by Debye and Huckel in 1923 to account quantitatively for the deviation from ideal behavior of solutions of electrolytes.

Point out the interesting features revealed in the graph above, relating the phenomena to Coulomb's law. A solution of KCl does not seem to deviate much from ideal behavior, since the charge density of K^+ and Cl^- ions is relatively small. There is greater attraction between Mg^{+2} and SO_4^{-2} ions however, resulting in a greater deviation from ideal behavior. The apparent degree of ionization of $MgSO_4$ is less than that of KCl. Likewise, there is more interionic attraction between K^+ and SO_4^{-2} ions than between K^+ and Cl^- ions. At infinite dilution, however, the interionic attraction approaches zero, and the compounds are apparently 100% ionized.

Point out to your students that the development of the ionization theory is a good illustration of the interdependence of discoveries and changing ideas in science. In the 1830's Faraday differentiated between electrolytes and non-electrolytes and inferred that conductivity of solutions was due to charged particles, which he called ions. Raoult investigated the colligative properties of solutions and published his findings around 1884, and these led to Arrhenius's theory of ionization. This theory was then modified in accordance with later discoveries regarding the nature of salts. In the next sections, we will investigate the development of more modern concepts of acids and bases.

3. DEVELOPING THE BRONSTED ACID-BASE CONCEPT

According to Arrhenius, an acid is a substance that produces H^+ ions in water solution, and a base produces OH^- ions in water solution. These definitions are very limited, since many acid-base reactions occur in non-aqueous media. He assumed that molecules of an acid were in equilibrium with the ions formed by dissociation:

$$HCl \rightleftharpoons H^+ + Cl^-$$

One big objection to this is that H^+ ions (bare protons) do not exist in chemical systems (the charge density of a proton is extremely high, as discussed in section 4.2). A proton must be attached to a larger specie by coordinating with a pair of electrons. This leads to a lower charge density. The reason that ammonia solution is basic, according to the Arrhenius concept, is that ammonia reacts with water to form molecules of ammonium hydroxide, which then dissociate into NH_4^+ and OH^- ions. Challenge your students to write a satisfactory structure for molecules of ammonium hydroxide, satisfying the valence requirements of all the atoms. Perhaps the closest thing to ammonium hydroxide molecules would be an ammonia molecule hydrogen bonded to a water molecule:

```
    H
    ..        ..
  H:N:......H:O:
    ..        ..
    N         H
```

A more appropriate explanation of the ionization of acids and bases in solution was offered independently by Bronsted and Lowry in 1923; protons may be transferred from one substance to another. In other words, an acid is a proton donor, and a base is a proton acceptor. Demonstrate that the reaction between solvent and solute leads to ion formation by testing the conductivity of aqueous HCl and aqueous acetic acid, comparing these results with those of HCl gas dissolved in benzene and acetic acid dissolved in benzene. No ions are present in the benzene solutions. Water has reacted with the acids to produce ions, as shown in the equations

$$H_2O + HCl \rightleftharpoons H_3O^+ + Cl^- \text{ (many ions)}$$
$$H_2O + HOAc \rightleftharpoons H_3O^+ + OAc^- \text{ (few ions)}$$

Water has accepted protons from the acids and acted as a base, and the hydrogen chloride and acetic acid acted as acids by donating protons to the water.

Ammonia, on the other hand, acts as a base by accepting a proton from the water, which acts as an acid (proton donor):

$$HOH + NH_3 \rightleftharpoons NH_4^+ + OH^- \text{ (few ions)}$$

The arrows show the proton transfer. If we examine the reverse reaction, NH_4^+ ion can donate a proton to OH^- ion to produce NH_3 and H_2O. This reaction proceeds extensively whenever a strong base (containing many OH^- ions in aqueous solution) is added to an ammonium compound.

Students sometimes have difficulty with the terminology used in the Bronsted acid-base concept: conjugate acid-base pairs. Show them a number of examples of proton transfer reactions (protolysis), such as the ones above, pointing out the conjugate acid-base relationship between the species shown.

acid	*base*
HCl	Cl^-
HOAc	OAc^-
HOH	OH^-
NH_4^+	NH_3
H_3O^+	H_2O
NH_3	NH_2^-
OH^-	O^{-2}

Point out that protolysis reactions involve an acid and a base reacting to produce another acid and another base. Example:

$$\underset{acid_1}{HNO_3} + \underset{base_1}{H_2O} \rightleftharpoons \underset{acid_2}{H_3O^+} + \underset{base_2}{NO_3^-}$$

Any protolysis reaction is reversible. The question to raise once the students buy the ideas already discussed is "How do we predict the extent of the reaction?" Before attempting to answer this, however, point out the feature in a base that permits it to accept a proton: an unshared pair of electrons to which a proton may cling.

Give your students two rules vital to the proton transfer concept:

(1) The stronger the acid, the weaker the conjugate base; the stronger the base, the weaker the conjugate acid.

(2) The stronger acid reacts with the stronger base to produce the weaker acid and weaker base.

Interpret the first rule in the following manner. An acid is composed of a proton riding on a pair of electrons belonging to the base. If the base is weak, the proton is lost easily (the acid is strong). If the base is strong, the proton is lost with difficulty (the acid is weak). Acid-base reactions depend upon competition for a proton. Return to the case of ammonia and water to illustrate the proton competition between ammonia and hydroxide ion for H^+:

$$H{:}\ddot{N}{:}H \ (\text{with H above}) \longleftarrow \textcircled{H^+} \longrightarrow :\ddot{O}{:}H^-$$

Hydroxide ion is a stronger base than ammonia. Therefore, most of the protons end up with the hydroxide ion, forming water. This explains the extensive reaction between NH_4^+ and OH^- and the very slight reaction between NH_3 and HOH.

In the case of HCl, there is competition between water and chloride ion for the proton:

$$H{:}\ddot{O}{:}H \longleftarrow \textcircled{H^+} \longrightarrow :\ddot{Cl}{:}^-$$

Since water is a much stronger base than Cl^- ion, most of the protons go to H_2O, producing H_3O^+ and Cl^- ions. This explains why HCl reacts extensively with water to form H_3O^+ and Cl^- ions. Hang a chart of relative strengths of acids and bases in your classroom, and make sure your students have a chart in their texts or notebooks. Give them practice in predicting the extent of reaction between acids and bases, using the chart.

Ask them to explain why metal oxides are basic. Since these compounds contain oxide ion, which is a stronger base than OH^- ion, water donates protons extensively to the oxide ion, producing hydroxide ions:

$$:\ddot{O}{:}^{-2} + HOH \longrightarrow :\ddot{O}H^- + :\ddot{O}H^-$$

Metal hydrides are very strong bases, since the $H{:}^-$ ion is a stronger base than OH^- ion. When a metal hydride is placed in water, a vigorous reaction occurs, producing hydrogen and OH^- ion:

$$H{:}^- + HOH \longrightarrow H{:}H + :\ddot{O}H^-$$

The reaction between sodium hydride and water makes a good demonstration. An easy way to make limewater is to carefully add some calcium hydride to water. (NaH and CaH_2 may be obtained from the Ventron Corporation, Beverly, Mass. They are dangerous chemicals and must be handled and stored using proper precautions.) Demonstrate the great base strength of hydride ion by adding NaH to methanol and isopropanol, comparing the speed of reaction between the alcohols and water. The general reaction is

$$ROH + :H^- \longrightarrow H_2 + :\ddot{\underset{\cdot\cdot}{O}}R^-$$

Isopropoxide ion is a stronger base than methoxide ion, which is a stronger base than hydroxide ion. Metallic sodium liberates hydrogen from methanol, but does not react as vigorously as with water. Point out that alcohols are similar to water in many respects. They have a polar group and a replaceable (acidic) hydrogen. Demonstrate the reaction between benzoic acid (weak acid) and aqueous NaOH. The benzoic acid dissolves and may be reprecipitated by adding an excess of a strong acid, such as aqueous HCl.

$$C_6H_5COOH + OH^- \rightleftharpoons C_6H_5COO^- + HOH$$
$$C_6H_5COO^- + H_3O^+ \rightleftharpoons C_6H_5COOH + HOH$$

Hydrolysis reactions involve the comsumption of water. Certain ions may act as acids or bases when dissolved in water, resulting in the production of H_3O^+ or OH^- ions. Sodium carbonate, for example, produces a basic solution:

$$CO_3^{-2} + HOH \rightleftharpoons HCO_3^- + OH^-$$

The reaction from left to right proceeds only to a slight extent, since CO_3^{-2} ion is a weaker base than OH^- ion. Another example of hydrolysis of a salt is the slight acid reaction of ammonium chloride in aqueous solution:

$$NH_4^+ + HOH \rightleftharpoons NH_3 + H_3O^+$$

This reaction proceeds only to a slight extent, since H_3O^+ is a stronger acid than NH_4^+ ion. Salts containing hydrated ions, such as $Cu(H_2O)_4^{+2}$, $Fe(H_2O)_6^{+3}$, and $Al(H_2O)_6^{+3}$, generally produce an acid solution because the hydrated ion donates protons to water. The case of hydrated aluminum ion is discussed in the next section. Other examples of hydrolysis reactions will be discussed in Chapters 11 and 13.

Certain anions containing hydrogen (ions present in acid salts) may act as either acids or bases, depending upon the situation. Such substances are amphiprotic (amphoteric). Bicarbonate ion, for example, reacts with water to a slight extent to produce a weakly basic solution:

$$HCO_3^- + HOH \rightleftharpoons H_2CO_3 + OH^-$$

In this case, bicarbonate ion acts as a weak base. In the presence of a stronger base, however, this ion may donate protons and act as an acid:

$$HCO_3^- + OH^- \rightleftharpoons CO_3^{-2} + HOH$$

Since OH^- is a stronger base than CO_3^{-2} ion, the forward reaction proceeds extensively.

An important consequence of the rule that the stronger acid reacts with the stronger base to produce the weaker acid and the weaker base is the leveling effect. In the case of water, the strongest acid which can exist in the solution is the H_3O^+ ion, and the strongest base is the OH^- ion. If HCl is dissolved in water, the predominant reaction is the one producing H_3O^+ and Cl^- ions, since HCl is a stronger acid than H_3O^+.

$$\underset{\text{stronger acid}}{HCl} + \underset{\text{stronger base}}{H_2O} \rightleftharpoons \underset{\text{weaker acid}}{H_3O^+} + \underset{\text{weaker base}}{Cl^-}$$

The result is that very little molecular HCl exists in aqueous solution. When sodamide is dissolved in water, a vigorous reaction occurs, producing ammonia and hydroxide ions.

$$\underset{\text{stronger base}}{NH_2^-} + \underset{\text{stronger acid}}{HOH} \rightleftharpoons \underset{\text{weaker base}}{OH^-} + \underset{\text{weaker acid}}{NH_3}$$

Since virtually all the amide ion reacts with water the strongest base that can exist in an aqueous solution of $NaNH_2$ is the OH^- ion.

Proton transfer may occur in solvents other than water. In liquid ammonia, for example, protolysis may occur. A neutralization reaction in water involves the transfer of a proton from H_3O^+ ion to OH^- ion. The analogous reaction in ammonia is the transfer of a proton from the NH_4^+ to the NH_2^- ion.

$$\begin{array}{ccccccc} H_3O^+ & + & OH^- & \rightleftharpoons & HOH & + & HOH \\ NH_4^+ & + & NH_2^- & \rightleftharpoons & NH_3 & + & NH_3 \\ \text{stronger acid} & & \text{stronger base} & & \text{weaker acid} & & \text{weaker base} \end{array}$$

An example of the leveling effect in liquid ammonia is the reaction between imide ion and ammonia to produce amide ion. This is analogous to the reaction between oxide ion and water.

$$\begin{array}{ccccccc} NH^{-2} & + & NH_3 & \rightleftharpoons & NH_2^- & + & NH_2^- \\ O^{-2} & + & HOH & \rightleftharpoons & OH^- & + & OH^- \\ \text{stronger base} & & \text{stronger acid} & & \text{weaker base} & & \text{weaker acid} \end{array}$$

The next section will discuss the strengths of acids and bases in greater detail. Since the Bronsted acid-base concept is such a useful one, give your students plenty of practice in applying these ideas. Their understanding and appreciation of this concept will gradually develop as they encounter more applications.

4. RELATING STRUCTURE AND ELECTRONIC EFFECTS TO STRENGTHS OF ACIDS AND BASES

Compare the acid-base character of NaOH with that of HOCl, interpreting the difference in behavior as a consequence of the electronegativity of the Na and Cl atoms. Draw the structures:

$$\overset{+}{Na}\,\}\!:\!\ddot{\underset{\cdot\cdot}{O}}\!:\ \ \overset{-}{H} \qquad\qquad H\,\}\!:\!\ddot{\underset{\cdot\cdot}{O}}\!:\,:\!\ddot{\underset{\cdot\cdot}{Cl}}\!:$$

$$\xrightarrow{\hspace{1cm}} \qquad\qquad\qquad \xrightarrow{\hspace{1cm}}$$

electrons electrons

The electronegativity of Na is low, and the electrons belong almost entirely to the oxygen atom (which is highly electronegative). The compound is essentially ionic (the sodium salt of water), and so the compound is highly basic by virtue of containing a hydroxide ion. In hypochlorous acid, however, Cl and O share electrons, and since Cl is highly electronegative, the electron density on oxygen is somewhat reduced. The hydrogen atom finds itself in a rather unhappy situation, since the electrons spend most of their time between the oxygen and chlorine atoms. Hydrogen, therefore, feels no qualms about leaving his electron with the oxygen and transferring as a proton to another pair of electrons. A molecule of HOCl acts as an acid.

Compare the relative acid strengths of hypochlorous and chlorous acids. The oxidation number of Cl in HOCl is $+1$, and in HOClO its oxidation number is $+3$. Draw structures and point out the electronic distribution around the oxygen to which H is attached.

$$\overset{(+1)}{H\,\}\!:\!\ddot{\underset{\cdot\cdot}{O}}\!:\!\ddot{\underset{\cdot\cdot}{Cl}}\!:} \qquad\qquad \overset{(+3)}{H\,\}\!:\!\ddot{\underset{\cdot\cdot}{O}}\!:\!\ddot{\underset{\cdot\cdot}{Cl}}\!:\!\ddot{\underset{\cdot\cdot}{O}}\!:}$$

$$\xrightarrow{\hspace{1cm}} \qquad\qquad\qquad \xrightarrow{\hspace{1cm}}$$

electrons electrons

(I) (II)

The electron density around O in (I) is higher than that around O in (II). The second O attached to Cl in (II) helps pull the electrons away from the hydrogen atom, which results in a more discontented hydrogen atom. (II) is a stronger acid than (I). In general, the higher the oxidation number of the central atom in a hydroxy compound, the stronger the acid. In the case of the chlorine acids, the order of increasing acid strength is $HOCl < HOClO < HOClO_2 < HOClO_3$. Perchloric acid is the strongest Bronsted acid known, since it loses protons more easily than any other compound. Another way of correlating the oxidation number of the central atom to acid strength is to say that the higher the + charge in the central atom, the greater the repulsion on a proton.

The electronegativity and charge density of the central atom is a factor in the acid strength of hydroxy compounds on non-metals. Perchloric acid (III) is a stronger acid than periodic acid (IV).

```
       :Ö:                        :Ö:
H :Ö: (Cl) :Ö:             H :Ö:(  I  ):Ö:
       :Ö:  (III)                 :Ö:  (IV)
```

Point out that Cl is a smaller and more highly electronegative atom than iodine. Both atoms have an oxidation number of +7. The charge density on Cl is higher than that on I, and so the electrons are pulled away from the hydrogen more in the case of Cl than in the case of I. Another viewpoint is that a proton is repelled more by the atom with the higher positive charge density.

Consider the case of the hydrated aluminum ion. The Al^{+3} ion is small and multiply charged, which means that its positive charge density is quite high. Aluminum is next to the dividing line between metals and non-metals, which means that it has a higher electronegativity than most metals. The Al^{+3} ion bonds six water molecules quite strongly, as shown by the structural formula. Hydration reduces the charge density by making the volume larger.

```
          H   H
           \ /
    H       O       H
     \      |      /
      O     |     O
     /  \   |   /  \
    H      Al       H
    H\   /  |  \   /H
      O     |     O
    H/      O      \H
           / \
          H   H
```
$$\left[Al(H_2O)_6 \right]^{+3}$$

A proton is readily lost by one of the water molecules (electrons pulled toward the aluminum, or the high positive charge density of the central atom repels the protons). The hydrated aluminum ion is acidic in water solution, donating a proton to water:

$$Al\,(H_2O)_6^{+3} + H_2O \rightleftharpoons Al\,(H_2O)_5\,(OH)^{+2} + H_3O^+$$

Upon making the solution more basic, more protons are lost successively, producing uncharged $Al\,(H_2O)_3\,(OH)_3$, which precipitates. On adding more base, another proton is lost, producing aluminate, $Al(H_2O)_2\,(OH)_4^-$ ions.

These repel each other, and the precipitate disssolves. Aluminum hydroxide has acted as an acid, and it can act as a base by accepting protons and regenerating the positively-charged species. Such a substance is amphiprotic (amphoteric). More interesting aspects of the chemistry of aluminum will be discussed in Chater 13.

Discuss the nitride, imide, amide ions, and ammonia as bases, pointing out the differences in electron density and charge.

$$:\ddot{\underset{\cdot\cdot}{N}}:^{-3} \qquad :\ddot{\underset{\cdot\cdot}{N}}H^{-2} \qquad :\overset{H}{\underset{\cdot\cdot}{N}}H^{-} \qquad :\overset{H}{\underset{H}{N}}H$$

$$\xrightarrow{\hspace{6em}}$$

decreasing electron density
decreasing charge on ion
decreasing base strength

Magnesium nitride (produced easily by heating magnesium turnings in an open crucible) reacts vigorously with water, producing ammonia and magnesium hydroxide, because of the following reactions:

$$N^{-3} + HOH \longrightarrow NH^{-2} + OH^-$$
$$NH^{-2} + HOH \longrightarrow NH_2^- + OH^-$$
$$NH_2^- + HOH \longrightarrow NH_3 + OH^-$$

$$\text{net reaction: } N^{-3} + 3\,HOH \longrightarrow NH_3 + 3OH^-$$

A number of transition metals form acids when they have a high oxidation number. Chromic acid, for example, is analogous to sulfuric acid (Cr and S have an oxidation number of + 6). Since the chromium atom has a high positive charge density, it forms bonds with oxygen atoms (by means of *d* orbitals). Since the positive charge of the central atom is high, protons are repelled, or electrons are attracted toward the central atom. The hydrogen atoms find themselves in an environment of low electron density and therefore leave when a more favorable pair of electrons becomes available. Chromium is considerably less electronegative than sulfur, however, and so chromic acid is a weaker acid than sulfuric acid.

Consider the relative strengths of HF, HCl, HBr, and HI. In this series, the weakest acid is HF and the strongest is HI, which is contrary to expectation. Hydrogen fluoride has the most ionic character, and hydrogen iodide is the most covalent of these compounds, so we would expect HF to be the strongest acid. We must consider the conjugate bases of these acids to account for their strengths, however. The fluoride ion is the smallest, and the iodide ion is the largest in size. Therefore F^- ion has the highest electron density and attracts protons to a greater extent than the increasingly larger ions in the series. The strength of the conjugate bases decreases from F^- to I^-, and so the acid strength increases.

5. CORRELATING ACID-BASE PROPERTIES WITH CHEMICAL PERIODICITY

Several trends were discussed in the previous section. In the case of hydroxy compounds, acid strength increases as the electronegativity of the central atom increases. Acid strength increases as the oxidation number of the central atom increases. In the case of binary compounds of hydrogen, acid strength increases as the electronegativity of the element combined with hydrogen increases. Sodium hydride, for example, is a very strong base, by virtue of the high base strength of the H^- ion. Ammonia is a stronger base and is therefore a weaker acid than water. Hydrogen fluoride, however, is a stronger acid than water (fluoride ion is a weaker base than hydroxide ion). The trend in the periodic table in going from left to right is that the acid strength of the hydrides and hydroxy compounds increases.

Illustrate the above trend using the hydrides of the elements in the second period:

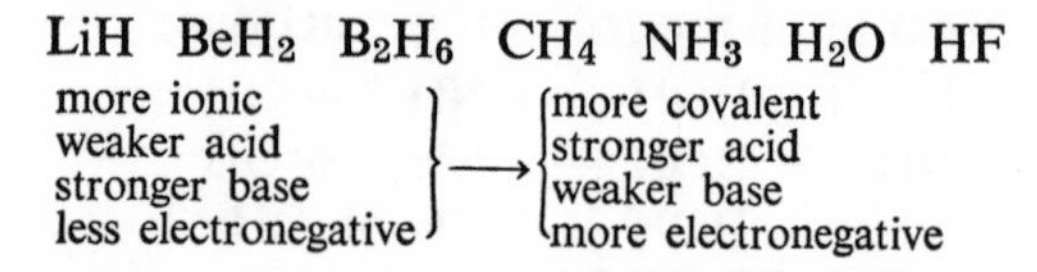

The same trend can be illustrated in the case of hydroxy compounds of the elements in their highest oxidation states, using those of the third period:

$NaOH$ $Mg(OH)_2$ $Al(OH)_3$ $(HO)_2CO$ $(HO)_3PO$ $(HO)_2SO_2$ $HOClO_3$

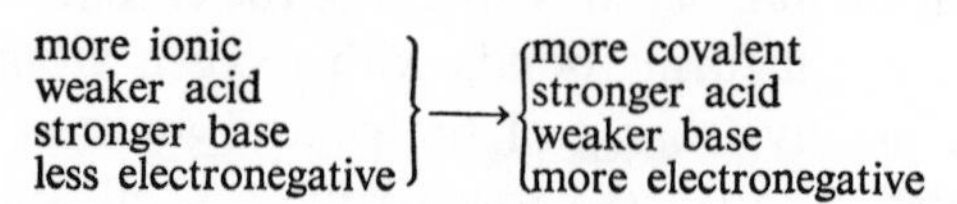

The trend within a chemical family can be illustrated in the same manner. Consider the elements in Group V:

Element	*Hydroxy Compound*	*Hydride*
N	$HONO_2$	NH_3
P	$(HO)_3PO$	PH_3
As	$(HO_3)AsO$	AsH_3
Sb	$(HO)_3SbO$	SbH_3
Bi	$[(HO)_3BiO]$*	BiH_3
↓ increasing size, decreasing electronegativity	↓ decreasing acid strength, increasing base strength	↓ increasing acid strength, decreasing base strength

*Existence not definitely established

The trends shown above hold for other chemical families, too. When discussing these, refer to the rule regarding the relative strengths of conjugate acid-base pairs: the stronger the acid, the weaker the conjugate base, and the stronger the base, the weaker the conjugate acid. Use the descriptive chemistry of the elements to illustrate the acid-base properties of their compounds (see Chapter 13). Reinforce the acid-base concept whenever the opportunity presents itself.

6. USING THE LEWIS ACID-BASE CONCEPT

The Bronsted concept of acids and bases is far more useful than the Arrhenius concept, since it applies to many situations which are not covered by the Arrhenius concept. It is limited, however, by the necessity for considering a porton transfer. Shortly after the advent of the Bronsted concept, G. N. Lewis focused his attention on what was really happening and realized that the lowly proton was seeking a pair of electrons. He therefore proposed that a base is an electron pair donor (nucleophile), and an acid is an electron pair acceptor (electrophile). The reaction of an acid with a base involves the formation of a coordinate-covalent bond:

$$A + :B \longrightarrow A:B$$

The resulting specie is called a coordinated complex. This view does away with the cumbersome idea of conjugate acid-base pairs and also permits us to consider many reactions which do not involve the transfer of a proton. For these reasons it is a more general, elegant, and useful concept than the Bronsted idea of proton transfer.

An example of an acid-base reaction which does not involve a proton is one between metal and non-metal oxides:

$$CaO + CO_2 \longrightarrow CaCO_3$$

In this reaction the oxide ion is attracted toward the slightly positive carbon atom in CO_2(the C=O bond is polar and C becomes positive in a resonance form of CO_2):

$$O::C::O \longleftrightarrow (+)\ C(:O:^{(-)})(:O:) \longleftarrow :O:^{(-2)} \Longrightarrow [C(:O:)(:O:)(:O:)]^{(-2)}$$

The result is the formation of a coordinate-covalent bond between the oxide ion (base) and the carbon atom in CO_2 (acid). The carbonate ion is a coordinated complex.

Many Lewis acid-base reactions can be considered base displacement reactions, as opposed to the Bronsted interpretation which involves a stronger acid reacting with a stronger base to produce a weaker acid and weaker base. In Lewis terminology all we must think about is the stronger base displacing the weaker base. Contrast the Bronsted and Lewis interpretations of the following types of reactions:

(1) *Neutralization:*

(a) Bronsted: $H_3O^+ + OH^- \longrightarrow H_2O + H_2O$
stronger acid, stronger base, weaker acid, weaker base

(b) Lewis: $HO{:}^- \curvearrowright H \{ :\ddot{O}{-}H^+ \longrightarrow HO{:}H + :\ddot{O}{-}H$ (with H bonded below each O)
stronger base, coordinated complex A, coordinated complex B, weaker base

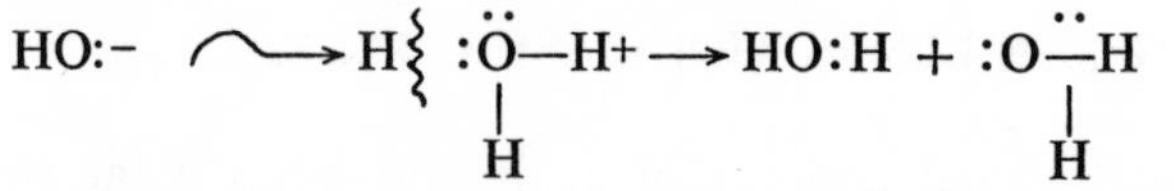

(2) *Ionization:*

(a) Bronsted: $HCl + H_2O \longrightarrow H_3O^+ + Cl^-$
stronger acid, stronger base, weaker acid, weaker base

(b) Lewis: $H{-}\ddot{O}{:} \curvearrowright H \{ :\ddot{Cl}: \longrightarrow H{-}\ddot{O}{:}H^+ + :\ddot{Cl}{:}^-$ (with H bonded below each O)
stronger base, coordinated complex A, coordinated complex B, weaker base

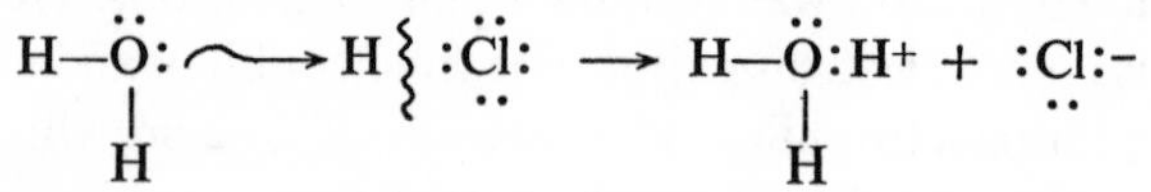

(3) *Hydrolysis:*

(a) Bronsted: $NH_4^+ + H_2O \rightleftharpoons NH_3 + H_3O^+$
weaker acid, weaker base, stronger base, stronger acid

(b) Lewis: $H{-}\ddot{O}{:} \curvearrowright H \{ :N{-}H^+ \rightleftharpoons H{-}\ddot{O}{:}H^+ + :N{-}H$ (with H bonded below each O and above and below each N)
weaker base, coordinated complex A, coordinated complex B, stronger base

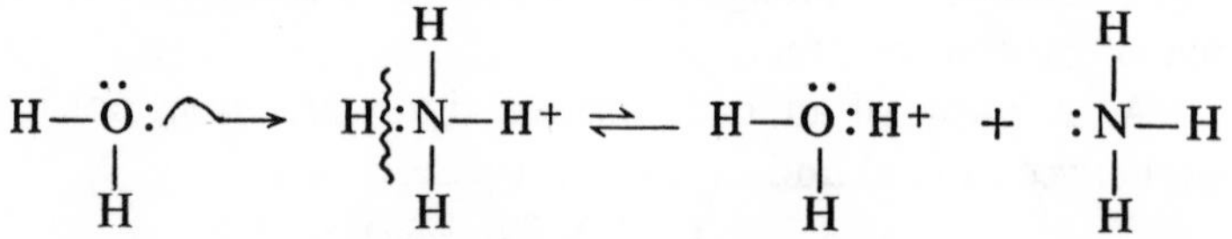

The vast majority of organic reactions can be interpreted in terms of the Lewis concept, since most of these proceed by means of a polar mechanism. The base-catalyzed of an organic halide, for example, involves the displacement of a halide ion by the OH^- ion:

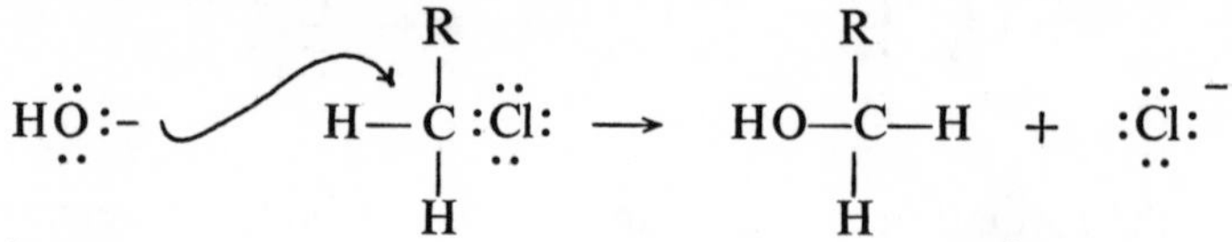

$$H\ddot{O}{:}^- \curvearrowright H{-}C(R)(H){:}\ddot{Cl}{:} \longrightarrow HO{-}C(R)(H){-}H + :\ddot{Cl}{:}^-$$

stronger base, weaker base

The Lewis acid-base concept is of utmost value to organic chemists for interpreting and predicting reactions. More examples of organic reactions will be discussed in Chapter 11.

Another important use of the Lewis concept is the interpretation of complex ion formation. A metal ion with empty orbitals acts as a Lewis acid, accepting a pair of electrons from the ligand (coordinating group) to form a coordinated complex. Water, for example, can form a complex with Cu^{+2} ion:

$$4H-\underset{\underset{\displaystyle H}{|}}{\ddot{O}}: \;+\; Cu^{+2} \longrightarrow \left(\begin{array}{ccccc} & H & & H & \\ & | & & | & \\ H- & O & & O & -H \\ & & \diagdown \;\; \diagup & & \\ & & Cu & & \\ & & \diagup \;\; \diagdown & & \\ H- & O & & O & -H \\ & | & & | & \\ & H & & H & \end{array}\right)^{+2}$$

The hydrated copper ion reacting with ammonia involves base displacement (NH_3 is a stronger base than H_2O), and a more stable complex ion is produced:

$$4\,H_3N: + Cu\,(H_2O)_4{}^{+2} \longrightarrow Cu\,(NH_3)_4{}^{+2} + 4H_2O:$$

Transition metals are notorious complex ion formers, since they have readily available *d* orbitals which can hybridize with *s* and *p* orbitals to produce dsp^2 or d^2sp^3 hybrids. These can accept pairs of electrons from the complexing ligands.

Perhaps the Lewis concept is a luxury, but your better students would benefit from exposure to these ideas. An excellent reference on the subject is Vander Werf's *Acids, Bases, and the Chemistry of the Covalent Bond* (Reinhold Publishing Corporation, 1961).

7. TEACHING THE WRITING OF IONIC EQUATIONS

Before your students begin to master the art of writing ionic equations, they should realize that salts have two sets of properties: each of the two ions has its own properties. An ionic equation usually describes a reaction of only one of these ionic species. Your students should also be able to determine the principal species in a system. A principal specie is one which is present in a reasonably high concentration (in the order of about 0.1 molar).

An aqueous solution labeled "ammonium hydroxide" contains a relatively high concentration of NH_3 and only a trace of $NH_4{}^+$ and OH^- ions. The principal specie in such a solution is NH_3. An aqueous solution of NaOH, however, contains a reasonably high concentration of Na^+ and OH^- ions, which are considered principal species. An aqueous solution of HCl contains H_3O^+ and Cl^- as principal species (HCl is highly ionzied), but an aqueous solution of acetic acid, HOAc, contains very few H_3O^+ and OAc^- ions. The principal specie in aqueous acetic acid is HOAc.

The molecular equation for the reaction between NaCl and $AgNO_3$ in aqueous solution is

$$NaCl_{(aq)} + AgNO_{3(aq)} \longrightarrow AgCl_{(s)} + NaNO_{3(aq)}$$

In this reaction AgCl is precipitated. In writing the ionic equation for this reaction, we must know what principal species are in the solution and what new substances are produced. In this case, the new substance is AgCl (solid). The equation may be written

$$Na^+ + Cl^- + Ag^+ + NO_3^- \longrightarrow AgCl + Na^+ + NO_3^-$$

Examination of this equation reveals that the essential reaction occurs only between Ag^+ and Cl^-ions to produce solid AgCl. The other ions (which cancel in the above equation) are not involved in the principal reaction and remain in solution. They are called *spectator ions* and are omitted from the net ionic equation:

$$Ag^+ + Cl^- \longrightarrow AgCl$$

Point out that the net ionic equation is a more accurate description of the change in the system than the molecular equation. The ionic equation states, whenever Ag^+ and Cl^- ions are placed in the same solution, AgCl is precipitated, regardless of what other ions are present.

In the reaction between aqueous ammonia and hydrochloric acid, the principal species are NH_3, H_3O^+, and Cl^- ions. The reaction occurs between H_3O^+ ions (which donate protons) and NH_3 molecules (which accept protons). The Cl^- ions are not involved and are spectators. We can write the net ionic equation:

$$NH_3 + H_3O^+ \longrightarrow NH_4^+ + H_2O$$

When aqueous NaOH (containing Na^+ and OH^- ions as principal species) and aqueous nitric acid (containing H_3O^+ and NO_3^- ions as principal species) are mixed, the net reaction produces water by means of a proton transfer. Since Na^+ and NO_3^+ ions do not react, they are omitted from the net ionic equation:

$$H_3O^+ + OH^- \longrightarrow 2\,H_2O$$

This equation describes the essential process involved when a strong acid and strong base neutralize each other in aqueous solution.

The three examples already discussed reveal what happens in a reaction: reacting species are consumed, and new species are produced. These new species may be in the solution or may precipitate. A third possibility is the formation of a gas. Aqueous sodium carbonate, when treated with hydrochloric acid, produces carbon dioxide gas. The reason is that CO_3^{-2} ions are basic and accept protons to produce H_2CO_3. Since carbonic acid is unstable, the decomposition products CO_2 and H_2O are produced. Since Na^+ and Cl^-ions remain in the solution, they are omitted from the net ionic equation:

$$2\,H_3O^+ + CO_3^{-2} \longrightarrow 3H_2O + CO_2$$

For simplicity we may use H^+ instead of H_3O^+:

$$2\,H^+ + CO_3^{-2} \longrightarrow H_2O + CO_2$$

Before students proceed any further, give them a rule regarding solids: a solid specie is represented by its formula. When writing the net ionic equation for the reaction between calcium carbonate and nitric acid, for example, we are describing

$$CaCO_{3(s)} + HNO_{3(aq)} \longrightarrow Ca(NO_3)_{2(aq)} + H_2O_{(l)} + CO_{2(g)}$$

The net ionic equation (omitting spectator ions) is

$$CaCO_3 + 2\,H^+ \longrightarrow Ca^{+2} + H_2O + CO_2$$

Calcium ions are produced in aqueous solution at the expense of the slightly soluble $CaCO_3$, and nitrate ion is not involved. In order to predict what species are not considered soluble in water, the students should memorize the solubility rules for aqueous solutions, which can be correlated with the periodic table.

Anions Nitrates, acetates: generally all soluble (except AgOAc, which is slightly soluble).

Halides (chlorides, bromides, iodides): generally soluble except those of Ag^+, Pb^{+2}, Hg_2^{+2} ($PbCl_2$ slightly soluble in cold water, quite soluble in hot water)

Sulfates: generally soluble except $BaSO_4$, $SrSO_4$, $PbSO_4$ ($CaSO_4$ is borderline)

Sulfides, hydroxides, carbonates, phosphates: generally insoluble except those of the alkali metals and ammonium (alkaline earth metal sulfides and hydroxides are slightly soluble)

Cations Alkali metal and ammonium compounds generally soluble.

Summarize the rules for predicting whether or not a reaction occurs. The criterion for a reaction is the consumption of species and the formation of new species. These may be produced in the form of a precipitate (predictable from solubility rules), the formation of a gas, or the formation of a new specie in solution. A solid reactant or product is represented by its formula, and the formulas for the principal species in solution are used. Spectator ions are omitted from net ionic equations. A beginner may determine what these are by writing the formulas for all the principal species present before and after reaction and then cancelling out the spectator ions. Remind your students that reactions between ions involve the application of Coulomb's law. In simple ionic reactions, therefore, oppositely-charged ions generally interact. Give your students plenty of practice, using examples such as the following:

$BaCl_{2(aq)}$ and $Na_2SO_{4(aq)}$ are mixed:

$Ba^{+2} + SO_4^{-2} \longrightarrow BaSO_4$ (precipitate produced)

$HOAc_{(aq)}$ and $KOH_{(aq)}$ are mixed:

$HOAc + OH^- \longrightarrow H_2O + OAc^-$ (principal reacting specie is HOAc, and H_2O is produced)

$Cu^{+2}_{(aq)}$ and $NH_{3(aq)}$ are mixed:

$Cu^{+2} + 4\,NH_3 \longrightarrow Cu(NH_3)_4^{+2}$ (new specie, a complex ion, is produced in solution)

$FeS_{(s)}$ and $HCl_{(aq)}$ are mixed:

$FeS + 2H^+ \longrightarrow Fe^{+2} + H_2S$ (FeS not soluble, Fe^{+2} new specie in solution, gaseous H_2S produced)

$NaNO_{3(aq)}$ and $KBr_{(aq)}$ are mixed:

No reaction, since no species are consumed and no new ones are produced

$NaNH_{2(s)}$ and water are mixed:

$NaNH_2 + H_2O \longrightarrow Na^+ + OH^- + NH_3$ (amide ion is a very strong base, accepting protons from water: new species are produced in solution, some NH_3 gas escaping)

Demonstrate the generality of the following reaction by placing some zinc metal (strips or granulated) in three test tubes. Add aqueous cupric nitrate to the first, cupric sulfate to the second, and cupric chloride to the third. The same reaction occurs in each case:

$$Cu^{+2}_{(aq)} + Zn_{(s)} \longrightarrow Cu_{(s)} + Zn^{+2}_{(aq)}$$

The generality of the reaction between Ag^+ and Cl^- ions can be demonstrated by adding $AgNO_3$ solution to solutions of NaCl, $NaNO_3$, $CuCl_2$, $CuSO_4$, $ZnCl_2$, $Zn(NO_3)_2$, as well as CCl_4. Ask your students why no precipitate is produced when $AgNO_3$ solution is shaken with CCl_4.

The formation of a complex ion (highly colored) may be demonstrated by adding aqueous ammonia to several different solutions containing cupric ions. Evolution of a gas occurs when different carbonates are treated with different acids. In each case the reaction is between hydronium ion and the carbonate.

8. PREDICTING ELECTRODE REACTIONS IN ELECTROLYSIS CELLS

Predicting the feasibility of a redox reaction was already discussed in section 5.8, and this subject will be discussed again in Chapter 10. Consider simple reactions occurring at the electrodes in an electrolysis cell. The favored reaction at the anode is the one in which electrons are more easily lost (higher E° value), and the favored reaction at the cathode is the one in which electrons are more readily accepted (lower E° value). In many cases there is competition between two or more possible reactions, including the oxidation or reduction of H_2O. Before proceeding any further, define the *anode* as the electrode at which oxidation (loss of electrons) occurs and the *cathode* as the electrode at which reduction (gain of electrons) occurs.

Consider the case of electrolyzing fused anhydrous calcium chloride, in which Ca^{+2} and Cl^- ions are moving around in the liquid state. These are the only species present, and so the reactions at the electrodes are easy to predict:

(1) The anion is attracted by the anode and is oxidized:

$$2Cl^- \longrightarrow Cl_2 + 2e^-$$

(2) The cation is attracted by the cathode and is reduced:

$$Ca^{+2} + 2e^- \longrightarrow Ca$$

The products are chlorine gas and calcium metal.

Consider the case of the elctrolysis of aqueous sodium chloride, in which the principal species are H_2O, Na^+, and Cl^- ions. Water dipoles are attracted toward both anode and cathode, where they may gain or lose electrons. A competition between H_2O and Na^+ ions exists at the cathode. The $E°$ values (oxidation potentials) are:

$$H_2 + 2\,OH^- = 2\,H_2O + 2e^- \qquad + 0.41 \text{ volts}$$
$$Na = Na^+ + e^- \qquad + 2.71 \text{ volts}$$

Writing these half-reactions as reductions, the sign of the $E°$ value changes, indicating that the favored reduction reaction is the one involving water. Sodium ions are not affected. The cathode reaction is:

$$2\,H_2O + 2\,e^- \longrightarrow H_2 + 2\,OH^-$$

The competing anode reactions are:

$$2\,H_2O = O_2 + 4\,H^+ + 4\,e^- \qquad - 0.82 \text{ volts}$$
$$2\,Cl^- = Cl_2 + 2\,e^- \qquad - 1.36 \text{ volts}$$

The observed reaction is the oxidation of chloride ion, but the predicted one is the oxidation of water. The reason that water is not decomposed is a phenomenon called *overvoltage,* which is beyond the scope of an elementary course. It can be explained qualitatively by considering the reactions occurring at the surfaces of the electrodes. Apparently oxygen gas is selectively adsorbed on the suface of the electrode in this cell, inhibiting the oxidation of water. In order to discharge water, a greater voltage than the $E°$ value is needed, and so the chloride ion is discharged.

Water may be electrolyzed by using sulfuric acid as a catalyst. The principal species in the solution are H_2O, H^+, HSO_4^-, and SO_4^{-2} ions. The H^+ ion is easily discharged, producing hydrogen gas. Since the two anions shown are very stable and require a considerably higher voltage than that needed to oxidize water, oxygen is produced by the oxidation of H_2O. The electrode reactions are:

$$\text{anode: } 2H_2O \longrightarrow O_2 + 4\,H^+ + 4\,e^-$$
$$\text{cathode: } 2\,H^+ + 2e^- \longrightarrow H_2$$

Since the electrons must balance, the cathode reaction is doubled, accounting for the production of two moles of hydrogen and one mole of oxygen. Point out that hydrogen ions are replenished by the anode reaction and sulfate ions are not consumed.

Water may also be electrolyzed by using a stable salt, such as KNO_3, which produces K^+ and NO_3^- ions in solution. Water is preferentially discharged at both anode and cathode, since K^+ ions are difficult to reduce and NO_3^- ions are very stable and resist being oxidized. The electrode reactions are:

$$\text{anode: } 2\,H_2O \longrightarrow O_2 + 4\,H^+ + 4\,e^-$$
$$\text{cathode: } 2\,H_2O + 2\,e^- \longrightarrow H_2 + 2OH^-$$

In order to balance the electrons, the cathode reaction is doubled, accounting for the two moles of hydrogen and one molè of oxygen produced. Equal numbers of H^+ and OH^- ions are produced, which neutralize each other. Since K^+ and NO_3^- ions are not consumed, the KNO_3 acts as a catalyst.

Don't make the mistake of telling your students that during the electrolysis of aqueous NaCl or KNO_3 the active metal ions are discharged and the resulting metal reacts with water to produce hydrogen and hydroxide ions. Likewise, don't tell them that nitrate or sulfate ions are discharged and react with water to produce oxygen and hydronium ions. No evidence for such reactions exists. Another common misconception is that H^+ and OH^- ions are discharged from a neutral (pH 7) solution. Since these ions are present in such low concentrations, it is very unlikely that their discharge could account for the reactions observed.

A good demonstration of the production of hydrogen and hydroxide ions at the electrodes consists of using a Hoffman apparatus and a solution of KNO_3, $NaNO_3$, or some other neutral salt of an active metal and stable anion. Place an indicator such as bromthymol blue in the solution, adjusting the pH to the neutral color of the indicator. Electrolysis of this solution produces the color changes at the electrodes, indicating the production of H^+ ions at the anode and OH^- ions at the cathode. These are produced by the discharge of water.

Other aspects of electrolysis are discussed in Chapter 10. The effect of concentration on voltage is also discussed and related to Le Chatelier's principle.

9. USE OF IONIZATION CONSTANTS, pH, ACID-BASE INDICATORS

An acid-base indicator is a weak organic acid which can donate a proton and produce a conjugate base (anion) having a different color than the molecular acid. The pH (see section. 5.9) at which the molecular form of the indicator donates a proton depends upon the strength of the acid. A strong acid donates a proton at a low pH (a low concentration of OH^- ion is needed to remove the proton), and a weaker acid does not donate a proton until the pH is relatively high (a higher concentration of OH^- is needed). Show your students the CHEM Study film "Acid-Base Indicators" and discuss the use of ionization constants and indicators.

Use bromthymol blue as an example. The molecular form of this indicator (HIn) is yellow at a pH below 6.0 and has donated protons completely by the time the pH reaches 7.6, producing the blue anions, In^-.

$$\underset{\text{yellow}}{HIn} \rightleftharpoons H^+ + \underset{\text{blue}}{In^-}$$

The ionization constant (see sections 5.9 and 8.5) for the above reaction is

$$K = \frac{[H^+][In^-]}{[HIn]}$$

During the middle of the color change, the concentrations of the molecular and ionic species are equal, resulting in a greenish color. Since [HIn] = [In], these terms in the ionization constant expression cancel and we can say that the ionization constant of bromthymol blue is equal to the hydronium ion concentration at a pH of about 7, or $K = 10^{-7}$. If the concentration of hydrogen ion increases, the reaction producing yellow HIn is favored, and if the hydrogen ion concentration is decreased, the reaction producing blue In^- ion is favored (apply Le Chatelier's principle).

The same argument can be used to determine the ionization constant of any acid-base indicator. In general, the stronger the acid, the larger the ionization constant. Since the ionization constant of an indicator is equal to the hydrogen ion concentration when equal concentrations of the molecular and ionic species are present, we can select an indicator for a particular job if we know the pH range in which we want the color to change.

Consider the titration of a strong acid with a strong base. The essential reaction is the one between H_3O^+ and OH^-ions producing water, and the pH at the end point is 7. An indicator which changes color around pH 7 is needed for the job. In the reaction between ammonia, a weak base, and a strong acid produces NH_4^+ ions and water. Since the ammonium ion is the conjugate acid of a weak base, NH_4^+ ion is acidic in water solution:

$$NH_3 + H_3O^+ \longrightarrow NH_4^+ + H_2O \text{ (neutralization)}$$
$$NH_4^+ + H_2O \rightleftharpoons NH_3 + H_3O^+ \text{ (hydrolysis)}$$

The solution at the end point is acidic. Therefore an indicator such as methyl orange (pH range 3.0–4.2) is needed to determine the end point. In the case of titrating acetic acid (weak acid) with a strong base, a basic solution results, since the acetate ion produced at the end point gives a slightly basic solution.

$$HOAc + OH^- \longrightarrow H_2O + OAc^- \text{ (neutralization)}$$
$$OAc^- + H_2O \rightleftharpoons HOAc + OH^- \text{ (hydrolysis)}$$

When titrating a weak acid with a strong base, therefore, use an indicator which changes color above pH 7. Phenolphthalein (pH range 8.3–10) indicates the end point in such a titration. Among the three indicators mentioned, methyl orange is the strongest and phenolphthalein is the weakest acid.

A universal indicator, such as pH paper, consists of a mixture of several indicators which change color over different pH ranges. The result is a spectrum of color changes, permitting the chemist to make a rough estimate of the pH of a solution. Demonstrate the pH of several solutions using wide-range pH paper. A solution of NH_4Cl is slightly acidic, and a solution of NaOAc is slightly basic because of the hydrolysis of the ammonium and acetate ions. A solution of ammonium acetate is neutral, since the two ions hydrolyze to the same extent. Test a solution of sodium hydrogen sulfate with methyl violet (pH range 0-2). The blue solution indicates that the pH is about one, revealing that HSO_4^- donates protons extensively (strong acid). Other examples of hydrolysis will be presented in Chapter 13.

8

Explaining the Concepts of Kinetics and Equilibrium

1. INTERPRETING THE FACTORS WHICH INFLUENCE RATES OF REACTIONS

Review the assumptions of the kinetic theory before discussing the factors which influence rates of reactions. Convince your students that reacting species must collide in order to react. Having set the stage, you are now ready to discuss the effects of temperature and concentration. Gas pressure determines the concentration of a gas, and so we can consider this factor under the heading of concentration. Refer to Chapters 1 and 2 for a discussion of concentration, rate of reaction, and the kinetic theory.

The rate of a reaction depends upon the frequency of collisions of the reacting species. Since molecules move faster at higher temperatures, the rate of reaction increases with temperature. The concept of activation energy will be developed in section 3. As the concentration of reacting species increases, the frequency of collision increases. This leads us to the idea that the rate of reaction is proportional to the concentration of reactants. More about this will be said in section 5. The effect of a catalyst will be discussed in section 3.

2. HOW WE RECOGNIZE AND EXPLAIN EQUILIBRIUM

The idea that equilibrium is a state of balance in which a system does not appear to change was developed in section 1.4. Show your students the

CHEM Study film "Equilibrium," which does an excellent job of showing that equilibrium can be recognized by observing a constant set of macroscopic properties. Such properties include color, pressure, pH, or some other measurable characteristic. One of the laws of nature is that all systems tend toward equilibrium, or a condition where no more net change in the composition or condition of the system occurs.

Although no net change in the composition of a chemical system occurs at equilibrium, opposing reactions are taking place at the same rate. This is called dynamic equilibrium. The CHEM Study film on equilibrium shows some experiments involving radioactive isotopes which reveal that many systems in equilibrium consist of opposing reactions. Give your students a few illustrations of this idea. Use a simple chemical reaction, such as the system containing a mixture of gaseous iodine, hydrogen, and hydrogen iodide. The equation showing the opposing reactions is

$$I_2 + H_2 \rightleftharpoons 2\,HI$$

If we add a small amount of radioactive iodine, some of this will be incorporated into the HI. If we add a small amount of HI containing radioactive iodine, some radioactivity will be found in the elementary iodine. This reveals that the two reactions proceed, even though the system may be at equilibrium and the relative amounts of the species are not changing.

An easy demonstration to perform in your classroom (although the results are not detectable for several days) involves placing some sodium chloride crystals in a saturated solution. The size of some of the crystals can be seen to change over a period of days, although the total amount of solid appears to remain constant. There must have been a dynamic equilibrium between dissolved and undissolved solute. If the dissolving process proceeds at the same rate as the crystallizing process, there is no net change in the amount of NaCl in the solid and solution.

3. USING THE CONCEPTS OF ACTIVATION ENERGY, COLLISION THEORY, AND REACTION COORDINATES

A rule of thumb used by chemists is that the rate of a chemical reaction doubles when the temperature rises 10°. If the rate of reaction were dependent only upon the frequency of collisions, the temperature rise would have to be much greater than 10° to account for doubling the rate. We know that the average kinetic energy of molecules varies directly with absolute temperature, or $mv^2 = cT$. This means that the square of the velocity of gas molecules varies directly with the absolute temperature. Therefore T should be quadrupled when v is doubled. The frequency of collisions should be directly proportional to the velocity of molecules, which means that if we double the frequency of collisions, the absolute temperature would have to increase fourfold. Experiments tell us that this does not happen, since only a slight increase in the absolute temperature doubles the rate of reaction. There must be another factor contributing to the rate of a chemical reaction. The dilemma can be resolved by assuming that only those collisions with sufficient energy lead to reaction. In other words, molecules must have sufficient kinetic energy if they are to react.

The above argument leads to the concepts of activation energy and the activated complex, which is an unstable, short-lived, high-energy specie produced when colliding molecules combine. The activated complex may decompose to give either the original reactants or products. In order to form products, reacting species must collide and produce an activated complex. Most collisions of reactants are not sufficiently energetic to produce such an activated complex, however, and the particles rebound without reacting.

The kinetic theory leads us to believe that energy is transferred with each collision, with the result that molecules in a system do not all have the same kinetic energy. A few molecules move very slowly, and some move rapidly. The result is that there is a distribution of kinetic energy among the molecules in a system. This may be represented by a graph (Maxwell-Boltzmann distribution). When the temperature is raised (dotted curve), the average kinetic energy of the molecules increases. The minimum energy needed for reaction forming the activated complex is called the activation energy, or energy barrier. Only those molecules with sufficient energy (shaded area) react. When the temperature is raised, more molecules have sufficient energy to react, and the reaction rate increases. The effect of a small rise in temperature is twofold:

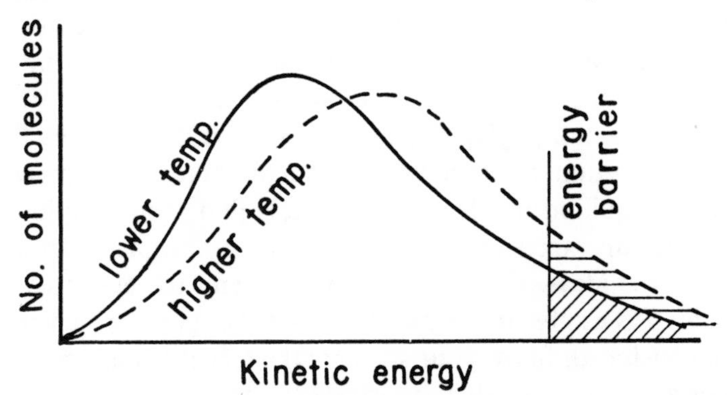

there is a higher frequency of collisions, and there is a greater percentage of successful collisions. The result is that a small rise in temperature greatly speeds up a chemical reaction. Practical applications of this principle are the refrigerator and freezer, in which the reactions leading to food spoilage are slowed down.

Another way of describing the interaction of colliding molecules is to use an energy diagram. The energy of the reactants is shown by the left part and that of the reactants by the right part of the curve. The peak indicates the energy barrier and the energy of the activated complex. As the molecules approach each other, the energy increases. If the molecules have sufficient energy, the activated complex (X) is formed, and this decomposes to produce either products or the original reactants. In the case of the reverse reaction, the same activated complex must be formed and the energy barrier crossed to produce

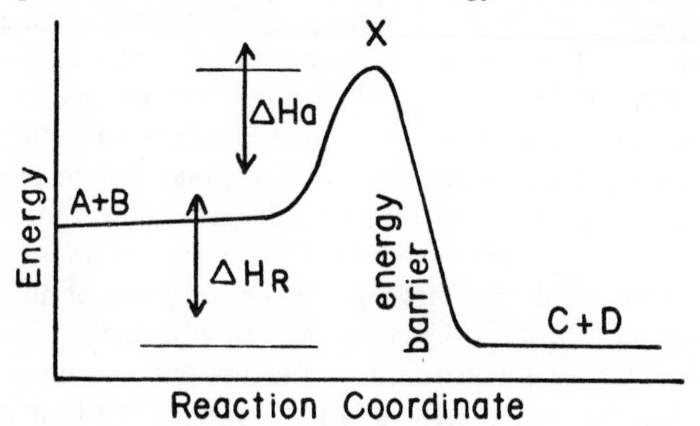

the original species. Examination of the diagram above suggests that the exothermic reaction is favored as opposed to the endothermic reaction. The energy needed to produce an activated complex is $\triangle H_a$, called the activation energy. The reaction coordinate describes the changing distance between the reacting species, A and B. This distance becomes zero when A and B merge to produce the activated complex. The remainder of the reaction coordinate describes the increasing distance between C and D after the activated complex has decomposed. We can deduce, on the basis of the energy (heat) of reaction, that the relative proportions of A, B, C, and D are influenced by the magnitude of the heat of reaction, $\triangle H_R$. When $\triangle H_R$ is large, there is very little A and B present at equilibrium, and when $\triangle H_R$ is small, there is an appreciable amount of A and B at equilibrium. The CHEM Study film "Introduction to Reaction Kinetics" does an excellent job of presenting, by means of animated graphs and models, the ideas of the collision theory and the activated complex.

A catalyst is a substance which increases the speed of a chemical reaction but is not consumed. Show your students the CHEM Study film "Catalysis," which uses animated models to illustrate the role of a catalyst in a reaction. The catalyst provides a different path from reactants to products by actually taking part in the reaction. The catalyst is consumed in the formation of an activated complex requiring less energy than would be used to form a complex without the catalyst. In other words, a catalyst lowers the energy barrier, permitting more molecules to react. When the activated complex decomposes to yield products, the catalyst is regenerated. Many examples of catalysis can be found in organic chemistry, such as enzymes in biochemical reactions or the acid or base-catalyzed hydrolysis of esters. Contact catalysts provide a surface on which a reaction may occur. The oxidation of ammonia in the Ostwald Process, for example, requires the use of platinum as a contact catalyst.

The role of a catalyst can be explained using energy diagrams. Diagram 1 shows the energy barriers with and without a catalyst. Since more molecules have sufficient energy to react in the presence of the catalyst, the reaction proceeds more rapidly. Diagram 2 shows the profile of a two-step reaction, in which a catalyst is incorporated in the activated complex, *X*. An intermediate product, *I*, is produced, and the catalyst is regenerated. The intermediate *I* undergoes another reaction by forming activated complex *Y*, which decomposes to produce the products C and D. Diagram 3 shows the reaction profile for the same reaction without the benefit of a catalyst. A different activated complex, *Z*, is produced, and this yields the products C and D. Since the activation energy is less in the catalyzed reaction, the reaction proceeds more rapidly.

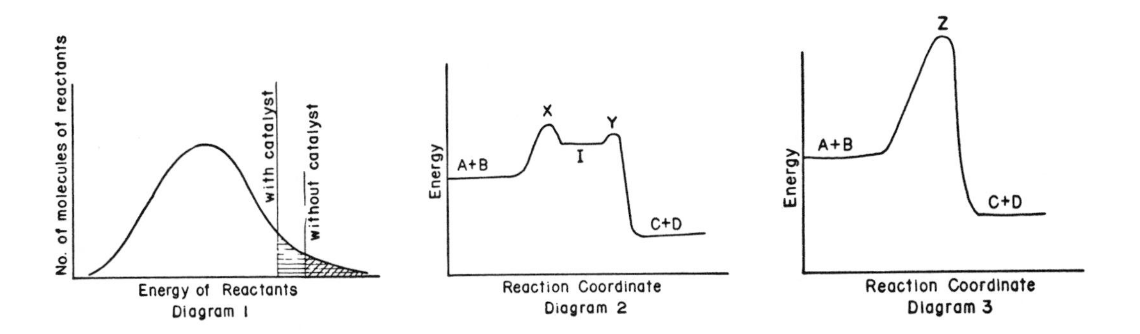

Some examples of catalysis and the concepts of activation energy are given in Chapters 11 and 13. The energetics of chemical reactions, including heats of reaction, will be discussed in Chapter 9, along with the criteria for equilibrium.

4. DETERMINING RATE LAWS EXPERIMENTALLY

In order to measure the rate of a reaction, one must select a measurable property of the system. In the hydrolysis of an organic chloride, for example, one of the products of the reaction is chloride ion. The progress of the reaction can be measured by determining the concentration of Cl^- ion present, and this may be used as a criterion for the rate of the reaction.

$$RCl + HOH \rightleftharpoons ROH + H^+ + Cl^-$$

Another way to measure the rate of the above reaction might be to measure the rate of increase of the hydrogen ion concentration.

Another example of a measurable property is the production or consumption of a gas. In the reaction of an unsaturated organic compound of hydrogen, for example, hydrogen gas is consumed. The reaction is usually carried out under pressure and in the presence of a catalyst. The rate of change in the pressure of hydrogen in the system serves as a criterion for the rate of hydrogen consumption.

The appearance or disappearance of a color may be used to measure reaction rates. A good demonstration of this is the famous iodine clock reaction, in which iodate ion is reduced to iodide ion in acid solution (using sulfite ion as the reducing agent). The excess iodate then oxidizes the iodide ion to free iodine after the sulfite has been consumed. A small amount of starch paste, prepared by boiling some corn starch with water, is used to produce a deep blue color when the free iodine is liberated.

$$IO_3^- + 3\,H_2SO_3 = I^- + 6\,H^+ + 3\,SO_4^{-2} \quad \text{(slow)}$$
$$IO_3^- + 6\,H^+ + 5\,I^- = 3\,H_2O + 3\,I_2 \quad \text{(slow)}$$
$$H_2O + I_2 + H_2SO_3 = 2\,I^- + SO_4^{-2} + 4\,H^+ \quad \text{(fast)}$$

Mix 25 ml 0.01 M KIO_3 solution, a few ml 2 M H_2SO_4, and a small amount of starch suspension. Dilute with water and add (stirring) 25 ml 0.01 M Na_2SO_3 solution. Determine the time required for the blue color to appear. Demonstrate the effect of temperature on the rate of reaction by varying the temperature of the reaction mixture. Your better students might be challenged by this reaction and wish to carry out a systematic study of rates by varying the concentrations of the different reactants.

Another intriguing demonstration is the "blue bottle" experiment, described in J. Arthur Campbell's paper in *J. Chem. Educ. 40,* 578 (1963) and in his excellent book *Why Do Chemical Reactions Occur?* (Prentice-Hall, Inc., 1965). A mixture of glucose, sodium hydroxide solution, and a small amount of methylene blue dissolved in methanol is shaken, producing a blue color which disappears on standing. Shaking the mixture causes the blue color to reappear. Your better students might be interested in the effect of varying the concentrations of sodium hydroxide, methylene blue, and glucose. Perhaps they might deduce that the reaction involves the reaction of oxygen from the air with methylene blue, which in turn reacts with glucoside ion (produced by the reaction between glucose and hydroxide ion) to produce a colorless form of methylene blue and a colorless oxidation product of glucose. Campbell's book is well worth reading. It provides a good discussion of reaction kinetics, equilibrium, and energy involved in chemical systems. Some good problems and answers are included with each chapter.

Complex chemical reactions usually involve several intermediate reactions. The chance of two molecules colliding is high, but the probability of three molecules colliding simultaneously is very low (as any billiard player realizes). Since collisions between more than two species are rare, most chemical reactions proceed by means of a series of steps. In the reaction of permanganate ion with iodide ion in acid solution, for example, it is inconceivable that ten iodide ions collide with two permanganate ions and sixteen hydronium ions simultaneously to produce the products shown in the equation, since the probability of such a multi-body collision is infinitesimally small.

$$2\,MnO_4^- + 10\,I^- + 16\,H_3O^+ = 2\,Mn^{+2} + 5\,I_2 + 24\,H_2O$$

Such a reaction must occur in a series of steps involving collisions between no more than two (seldom three) reacting particles.

Chemists postulate reaction mechanisms by considering the probability of collisions and the rate law for a reaction. The rate of the overall reaction is limited by the slowest step, just as the rate of any manufacturing process is limited by the slowest part of the assembly line. Give your students an example of a rate-determining step in the output of business letters in an office. Several people share one secretary, and she is suddenly swamped with a large number of letters to type. The letters can be produced no faster than the secretary can type. Her part in the operation is the rate-determining step. The output of dictation may be fast and the stuffing of envelopes and licking of stamps may be fast, but the rate-determining step is still the rate at which the secretary can turn out typed copies. The slow step in a series of reactions is the rate-determining step in the overall reaction.

The determination of the rate law for a reaction involves the systematic variation of the concentrations of the reactants and measuring the effect on the rate of reaction. In the reaction between A and B to produce C and D, for example, the stoichiometry is shown by the equation

$$2\,A + B = C + D$$

A series of experiments was performed, varying the concentrations of A and B, and the rate of increase in the concentration of C was measured. The following data were obtained:

Experiment	*Initial Molar Conc. x 10^{-2}* [*A*]	[*B*]	*Initial Rate, $\triangle$[C]*
1	1.00	1.00	10
2	1.00	2.00	20
3	1.00	3.00	30
4	2.00	3.00	60
5	3.00	3.00	90

Analysis of the data reveals that the rate of production of C (rate of reaction) is proportional to the concentration of A and the concentration of B, or

$$\text{rate} = k\,[\mathrm{A}]\,[\mathrm{B}]$$

This equation is called the rate law for the reaction, and k is called the rate constant.

Impress upon your students that the rate of a chemical reaction cannot be predicted from the stoichiometry of the reaction and the law of mass action (see next section). In the above reaction, for example, one might expect the rate to be proportional to $[\mathrm{A}]^2$ and [B], or rate $= k[\mathrm{A}]^2\,[\mathrm{B}]$. This is not the case, however. The rate law is not predictable and must be determined experimentally.

A possible mechanism for the reaction between A and B must involve at least two steps, and the rate-determining step (slow) must involve the interaction of A and B, forming an activated complex, AB^*. This activated complex then collides with a molecule of A to produce the products C and D (fast reaction).

$$\begin{array}{ll} \mathrm{A} + \mathrm{B} = \mathrm{AB}^* & \text{(slow)} \\ \mathrm{A} + \mathrm{AB}^* = \mathrm{C} + \mathrm{D} & \text{(fast)} \\ \hline 2\,\mathrm{A} + \mathrm{B} = \mathrm{C} + \mathrm{D} & \text{(net reaction)} \end{array}$$

This postulated mechanism does not involve collisions of more than two particles and is in agreement with the experimentally-determined rate law. Campbell's *Why Do Chemical Reactions Occur?* develops these ideas of chemical kinetics lucidly and gives some good examples.

The concept of reaction order is difficult to appreciate by students who have not had exposure to the calculus, since the functions plotted graphically are derived by integrating the rate law. Discussion of reaction order is not important at this level.

A reaction having the rate law rate $= k[\mathrm{A}]$ is a first-order reaction (monomolecular) and is dependent upon the concentration of only one reactant. An example of such a reaction is the decomposition of radioactive nuclei, or a reaction such as

$$\mathrm{A} = \mathrm{B} + \mathrm{C}$$

A second-order reaction (bimolecular) is proportional to the concentration of two reactants, [A] and [B], or to the square of a reactant. In the first case, rate $= k[\mathrm{A}]\,[\mathrm{B}]$, and the reaction is first order with respect to [A] and first order with respect to [B]. In the second case, rate $= k[\mathrm{A}]^2$, and the reaction is second order with respect to [A]. Third order reactions are rare.

5. USING THE LAW OF MASS ACTION TO WRITE EQUILIBRIUM CONSTANTS

The law of mass action was discovered by the Norwegian chemists Guldberg and Waage in 1864 and, in simple terms, states that the rate of a chemical reaction is proportional to the concentration of the reactants. In a chemical system in equilibrium, the rate of the forward reaction, r_1, is equal to the rate of the reverse reaction, r_2. Consider the system

$$aA + bB \rightleftharpoons cC + dD$$

The rates for the forward and reverse reactions are given by

$$r_1 = k_1 [A]^a [B]^b$$
$$r_2 = k_2 [C]^c [D]^d$$

Since $r_1 = r_2$, we can equate the two rate expressions and write

$$k_1 [A]^a [B]^b = k_2 [C]^c [D]^d$$

Rearranging so that the products appear in the numerator and the reactants in the denominator, we obtain

$$\frac{k_1}{k_2} = \frac{[C]^c [D]^d}{[A]^a [B]^b} = K$$

The equilibrium constant, K, is given by dividing k_1 by k_2. From the general case we can conclude that the expression for the equilibrium constant is given by writing the concentrations of the products (raised to the powers given by by coefficients in the equation) divided by the concentrations of the reactants (raised to the powers given by the coefficients).

If your students question why a concentration is raised to the power given by the coefficient, give them an example such as

$$2\,A + B \rightleftharpoons C + D$$

The equilibrium constant for this sytsem is

$$K = \frac{[C]\ [D]}{[A]^2\,[B]}$$

Since the equation states that two moles of A react with one mole of B, we can write

$$A + A + B \rightleftharpoons C + D$$

The denominator becomes [A] [A] [B], or $[A]^2$ [B].

Give your students some simple examples, such as

$$N_{2(g)} + 3H_{2(g)} \rightleftharpoons 2\,NH_{3(g)}$$

The equilibrium constant for this system, in which the concentrations of all the species are variable, is given by

$$K = \frac{[NH_3]^2}{[N_2]\,[H_2]^3}$$

In the case of ammonia dissolved in water, we have the system

$$NH_{3(aq)} + H_2O_{(l)} \rightleftharpoons NH_4^+{}_{(aq)} + OH^-{}_{(aq)}$$

The expression for the equilibrium constant is

$$K = \frac{[NH_4^+][OH^-]}{[NH_3][H_2O]}$$

Since water is the solvent, its concentration does not change significantly and may be omitted. The constant we obtain when we write the expression omitting the water concentration if the *ionization constant* for ammonia:

$$K_{NH_3} = \frac{[NH_4^+][OH^-]}{[NH_3]}$$

In the case of the thermal decomposition of solid calcium carbonate, the equation for the system is

$$CaCO_{3(s)} \rightleftharpoons CaO_{(s)} + CO_{2(g)}$$

The concentrations of the solid substances do not change (a solid occupies definite volume) and are omitted from the expression for the equilibrium constant:

$$K = [CO_2]$$

As a general rule, any specie whose concentration does not change (liquids acting as solvents or solid species) are omitted from the expression for the equilibrium constant.

Consider a saturated solution of a slightly-soluble solid, such as Ag_2CrO_4. The equation describing this system is

$$Ag_2CrO_{4(s)} \rightleftharpoons 2\,Ag^+_{(aq)} + CrO_4{}^{-2}{}_{(aq)}$$

The expression for the equilibrium constant in this case is called the *solubility product* constant for silver chromate:

$$KSP_{Ag_2CrO_4} = [Ag^+]^2[CrO_4{}^{-2}]$$

Give your students some practice in writing the expressions for equilibrium constants, ionization constants, and solubility products. Use examples such as the following:

$$2Pb(NO_3)_{2(s)} \rightleftharpoons 2\,PbO_{(s)} + 4\,NO_{2(g)} + O_{2(g)}$$

$$K = [NO_2]^4[O_2]$$

$$HOAc_{(aq)} + H_2O_{(l)} \rightleftharpoons H_3O^+_{(aq)} + OAc^-_{(aq)}$$

$$K = \frac{[H_3O^+][OAc^-]}{[HOAc]} \quad \text{(ionization constant)}$$

$$PbCl_{2(s)} \rightleftharpoons Pb^{+2}{}_{(aq)} + 2\,Cl^-_{(aq)}$$

$$KSP = [Pb^{+2}][Cl^-]^2 \quad \text{(solubility product)}$$

$$2H_3O^+_{(aq)} + CO_3{}^{-2}{}_{(aq)} \rightleftharpoons 3H_2O_{(l)} + CO_{2(g)}$$

$$K = \frac{[CO_2]}{[H_3O^+]^2[CO_3{}^{-2}]}$$

$$4\,NH_{3(g)} + 5O_{2(g)} \rightleftharpoons 4\,NO_{(g)} + 6H_2O_{(g)}$$

$$K = \frac{[NO]^4[H_2O]^6}{[NH_3]^4[O_2]^5}$$

6. USING LE CHATELIER'S PRINCIPLE AND EQUILIBRIUM CONSTANTS

The concepts of equilibrium and Le Chatelier's principle were developed in section 1.4. Your students should be able to make qualitative predictions regarding the relative amounts of different species present in a system when conditions are changed and the balance is upset. Le Chatelier's principle enables one to make such predictions, and the equilibrium constant enables the chemist to make a qualitative statement regarding the amounts of species present in a system at equilibrium. Your better students should be able to handle calculations involving equilibrium constants (see section 5.9).

Consider the system containing hydrogen, nitrogen, and ammonia at equilibrium. The reaction producing ammonia is exothermic. By examining the equation, which makes a statement about the relative volumes of gases present as well as the energy change involved, we can predict what will happen if the pressure, amount of material, or temperature are changed.

$$N_{2(g)} + 3\,H_{2(g)} \rightleftharpoons 2\,NH_{3(g)} + \text{energy}$$

Since all the species are gases, the nitrogen and hydrogen occupy a total of four volumes, and the ammonia occupies two volumes (from Avogadro's hypothesis). If the pressure is increased, the system is subjected to a stress and responds to relieve the stress by producing the substances which occupy less space. Therefore more ammonia is produced at the expense of some of the hydrogen and nitrogen. If the temperature is increased, energy is added to the system. The response to relieve the stress is to absorb the excess energy, producing hydrogen and nitrogen at the expense of ammonia. If more nitrogen or hydrogen is added, the increased concentration of the specie subjects the system to a stress, which is relieved by using up some of the excess material added. The formation of more ammonia is the system's response to relieve the stress.

The equilibrium constant can be used to predict the effect of changing concentrations of the species in a system qualitatively as well as quantitatively. Write the equilibrium constant expression for the synthesis of ammonia:

$$K = \frac{[NH_3]^2}{[N_2]\,[H_2]^3}$$

If the pressure is doubled, the volume of the gas mixture is halved (Boyle's law). This means that the concentration of each specie is doubled. The value of the numerator (concentration is squared) is increased by a factor of four, and the value of the denominator is increased by a factor of 2^4, or sixteen. The value of the entire expression, therefore, becomes considerably smaller than the value for K. This means that the system is no longer at equilibrium. In order for the system to reach equilibrium, the value of the expression must become equal to K. In this situation the value of the denominator must be decreased and that of the numerator increased in order to make the value of the expression again equal *K*. This is accomplished by using up some N_2 and H_2 to produce NH_3. Emphasize that the amounts of all species present at equilibrium must satisfy the equilibrium constant as well as the stoichiometry shown in the equation. A student who has a little bit of imagination should be able to follow this line of mathematical reasoning. Furthermore, he should be able to appreciate the fact that a quantitative prediction of the change in composition of the system can be made using the equilibrium constant expression, if the value of *K* is known. Actual calculations using equilibrium constants (see section 5.9) are beyond the scope of some students, however, so don't expect too much from your less able students.

We have already seen that temperature, pressure, and changes in the concentrations or amounts of some species upset a system at equilibrium, favoring one of the reactions and resulting in a new equilibrium having different proportions of species involved. The use of a catalyst favors both reactions equally and results in attaining equilibrium more rapidly. A catalyst does not change the proportions of species present at equilibrium, however. The value of the equilibrium constant is not affected by changes in concentration or pressure or the presence or absence of a catalyst. The only variable which affects the value for the equilibrium constant is temperature (see section 9.8). In the synthesis of ammonia, the value for *K* decreases as the temperature increases (apply Le Chatelier's principle).

7. RELATING SITUATIONS OF IONIC EQUILIBRIUM TO PRINCIPLES

Much of the laboratory work involved in elementary chemistry involves reactions between ions. This provides a student with a fertile field for investigating how the principles of equilibrium operate in actual practice. Give your students some examples of various ionic equilibria, including the hydrolysis of salts, the common ion effect, buffering, the solubility product principle, and the formation and dissolution of precipitates. Some of these effects are described in Olmsted's *Enrichment Experiments in Basic Chemistry* (Hayden Book Company, 1966).

Consider the system involving ammonia, ammonium ions, and hydroxide ions in aqueous solution. The equation for the system is

$$NH_3 + H_2O \rightleftharpoons NH_4^+ + OH^-$$

The ionization constant for the system and its value at 25° are:

$$\frac{[NH_4^+]\,[OH^-]}{[NH_3]} = 1.8 \times 10^{-5}$$

The small value for *K* reveals that at equilibrium the amount of NH_4^+ and OH^- ions is quite small compared to the amount of NH_3. Ask your students to smell a solution of NH_4Cl. No ammonia seems to be present. An aqueous solution of ammonia contains much NH_3, however. Add some hydroxide ions (NaOH solution) to the solution containing NH_4^+ ions. The odor of ammonia becomes apparent, indicating that the reaction proceeding toward the left has occurred to a significant extent. Whenever NH_4^+ and OH^- ions are brought together in the same solution, they react to produce ammonia and water. This is a case of a stronger acid and stronger base producing a weaker acid and a weaker base (see section 7.3).

Add some phenolphthalein to a 0.1 M ammonia solution. The pink color indicates the presence of an excess of OH^- ions, indicating that NH_3 and water have reacted. According to the equation, the concentration of NH_4^+ and OH^- ions are equal in aqueous ammonia. Now add some saturated NH_4Cl solution (a high concentration of NH_4^+ ions). The lightening of the pink color indicates a decrease in the OH^- ion concentration, due to the reaction between NH_4^+ and OH^- ions to produce ammonia. The equilibrium was upset, and to relieve the stress, the reaction forming ammonia was favored. This is an example of the common ion effect. Increasing the concentration of NH_4^+ ion caused the consumption of some of the OH^- ions.

A good demonstration of the common ion effect is the addition of a few drops of concentrated HCl (12 M) to a saturated solution of NaCl. Solid NaCl is precipitated. Review the equilibrium situation in a saturated solution (see section 6.3), pointing out that the balance was upset by increasing the Cl^- ion concentration. Addition of water dissolves the precipitated NaCl. Use this example when discussing the solubility product principle. Show the students the equation for this system:

$$NaCl_{(s)} \rightleftharpoons Na^+{}_{(aq)} + Cl^-{}_{(aq)}$$

We may write an expression for the solubility product of NaCl:

$$KSP = [Na^+][Cl^-]$$

The product of the concentration of the ions in a saturated solution (a condition for equilibrium between dissolved and undissolved solute) is equal to the value for *KSP*. Increasing the chloride ion concentration made the value of the expression larger than *KSP*, and to restore equilibrium some Na^+ and Cl^- ions had to be removed from the solution, resulting in the precipitation of NaCl. When water was added, the concentrations of the ions in solution was decreased, making the value for the expression less than *KSP*. To restore equilibrium, solid NaCl had to dissolve.

The solubility product principle is based on the idea of a saturated solution. In order to produce a precipitate, the ion concentrations in solution must be high enough so that the value for the expression is greater than *KSP* (the solution is oversaturated). In order to dissolve a precipitate, the value of the expression must be made smaller than *KSP* (the solution becomes unsaturated). This may be done by adding more solvent or by consuming one or more of the ionic species.

The ammonia equilibrium can be used to illustrate the effect of a buffer solution. Add some saturated NH_4Cl solution to a 0.1 M NaOH solution containing a few drops of phenolphthalein. The deep pink color becomes very light, because the addition of NH_4^+ ions caused the consumption of ionic species to produce ammonia. The result is a decrease in OH^- ion concentration, and the resulting solution becomes less basic. In general, a buffer contains an ion which acts as an acid or base, accepting or donating protons in such a way that the concentration of H_3O^+ or OH^- ion does not become excessive.

Another example of buffering is the addition of sodium acetate solution to a 0.5 M HCl solution containing methyl violet. The blue-green color becomes purple, indicating a rise in pH and the consumption of hydronium ions:

$$H_3O^+ + OAc^- \rightleftharpoons HOAc + H_2O$$

In this case the base, acetate ion, accepts a proton from the hydronium ion and prevents the solution from becoming excessively acid. A buffer which maintains the pH near 7 is ammonium acetate. Living organisms contain buffers, such as bicarbonate ion, which prevent a system from becoming excessively acidic or basic.

An interesting application of ionic equilibrium is the control of the concentration of sulfide ion in qualitative analysis. A number of metal ions may be precipitated as insoluble sulfides, using H_2S. By controlling the concentration of sulfide ion in the system one may selectively precipitate the least soluble sulfides in a group and leave the other metal ions in solution. Among the highly-insoluble sulfides of the acid hydrogen sulfide group are CuS, PbS, HgS, Bi_2S_3, and CdS. The most soluble of these is CdS, whose solubility product is about 10^{-28}. If a solution is 0.1 molar with respect to Cd^{+2} ion, the sulfide ion concentration at which CdS begins to precipitate is 10^{-27} moles per liter.

$$[Cd^+]^2 [S^{-2}] = 10^{-28}$$
$$(0.1) [S^{-2}] = 10^{-28}$$
$$[S^{-2}] = 10^{-27}$$

The least soluble sulfide in the basic hydrogen sulfide group (which does not precipitate with the sulfides already mentioned) is ZnS, whose solubility product is about 5×10^{-24}. If the Zn^{+2} ion concentration is about 0.1 molar, the sulfide ion concentration needed to begin precipitating ZnS is about 5×10^{-23}.

$$[Zn^{+2}] [S^{-2}] = 5 \times 10^{-24}$$

$$(0.1)\,[S^{-2}] = 5 \times 10^{-24}$$
$$[S^{-2}] = 5 \times 10^{-23}$$

If the sulfide ion concentration is adjusted to nearly 5×10^{-23}, CdS will precipitate, but ZnS will not. We can therefore separate the ions in the acid hydrogen sulfide group from those in the basic hydrogen sulfide group.

If your students have trouble at this point, write the equation for the complete ionization of H_2S and apply Le Chatelier's principle.

$$H_2S + 2H_2O \rightleftharpoons 2\,H_3O^+ + S^{-2}$$

If the hydrogen ion concentration is low, the sulfide ion concentration is relatively high, but if the hydrogen ion concentration is raised, the sulfide ion concentration decreases.

Hydrogen sulfide ionizes in two steps:

$$H_2S + H_2O \rightleftharpoons H_3O^+ + HS^-$$
$$HS^- + H_2O \rightleftharpoons H_3O^+ + S^{-2}$$

By multiplying the ionization constants for the two steps, we obtain the ionization constant for the reaction of H_2S producing S^{-2} ions:

$$K_1 = \frac{[H_3O^+]\,[HS^-]}{[H_2S]} = 1.1 \times 10^{-7}$$

$$K_2 = \frac{[H_3O^+]\,[S^{-2}]}{[HS^-]} = 1 \times 10^{-15}$$

$$K_1K_2 = \frac{[H_3O^+]^2\,[S^{-2}]}{[H_2S]} = 1.1 \times 10^{-22}$$

A saturated solution of H_2S is about 0.1 molar. Substitute this value for $[H_2S]$ and 5×10^{-23} for $[S^{-2}]$ in the expression for the overall ionization of H_2S to determine the hydrogen ion concentration needed to control the sulfide ion concentration.

$$\frac{[H_3O^+]^2\,(5 \times 10^{-23})}{10^{-1}} = 10^{-23}$$

$$[H_3O^+] = 0.45$$

Review pH (see section 5.9) and convert 0.45 molar hydrogen ion concentration to pH, which turns out to be about 0.3.

Discussing the selective precipitation of sulfides by controlling the pH of the solution may be a large dose of chemistry for some students, but it is an excellent example of the operation of the common ion effect and the solubility product principle. If your students can follow the argument qualitatively, omitting the arithmetic, they will begin to appreciate the meaning of Le Chatelier's principle.

Discuss the dissolution of AgCl by the addition of ammonia and the reappearance of AgCl on adding acid in the test for a chloride or silver ion. On mixing Ag^+ and Cl^- ions, the value for *KSP* is exceeded, and AgCl precipitates (the solution becomes oversaturated).

$$Ag^+ + Cl^- \rightleftharpoons AgCl$$
$$AgCl + 2\,NH_3 \rightleftharpoons Ag(NH_3)_2^+ + Cl^-$$
$$Ag(NH_3)_2^+ + 2\,H^+ + Cl^- \rightleftharpoons AgCl + 2\,NH_4^+$$

The addition of NH_3 takes some Ag^+ ions out of solution by converting them to diammine silver (I) ions. Since the silver ion concentration is reduced so that $[Ag^+][Cl^-]$ becomes less than *KSP*, the precipitate dissolves. The principal species in the solution are now $Ag(NH_3)_2^+$ and Cl^- ions and NH_3. Addition of acid (H^+) removes NH_3 from the solution, and the complex ion breaks up, regenerating Ag^+ ions. The concentration of Ag^+ ions increases so that the AgCl reprecipitates.

A good problem for your students is to account for the following observations:

> Aqueous NaOH is added to a solution of Cu^{+2} ions, producing a gelatinous pale blue precipitate $[Cu(OH)_2]$. Addition of saturated NH_4Cl solution dissolves the precipitate and produces a deep blue solution $[Cu(NH_3)_4^{+2}]$. Acidification of this solution produces a very pale blue solution (hydrated Cu^{+2}). Adding more NaOH produces the deep blue solution but not the precipitate.

Discuss the chemistry of this series of reactions with the students, analyzing the changes as follows. $Cu(OH)_2$ was precipitated upon the addition of OH^- ions:

$$Cu^{+2} + 2\,OH^- \rightleftharpoons Cu(OH)_2$$

The solution now contains some excess OH^- ions, which react with NH_4^+ ions to produce NH_3. The concentration of Cu^{+2} ions in equilibrium with the precipitate is reduced, because Cu^{+2} ions combine with NH_3 to produce the blue complex ion in solution $[Cu(NH_3)_4^{+2}]$. The reaction of OH^- ions with NH_4^+ ions also serves to reduce the concentration of OH^- ions. Since the concentration of these ions is reduced, the precipitate dissolves. Acidification breaks up the complex ion and neutralizes any excess OH^- ions, and aqueous copper ions are generated, producing the pale blue solution.

$$NH_4^+ + OH^- \rightleftharpoons NH_3 + H_2O$$
$$Cu^{+2} + 4\,NH_3 \rightleftharpoons Cu(NH_3)_4^{+2}$$
$$Cu(NH_3)_4^{+2} + 4\,H^+ \rightleftharpoons Cu^{+2} + 4NH_4^+$$

Since the principal species in solution are Cu^{+2} and NH_4^+ ions, the addition of OH^- ions produces NH_3, which converts Cu^{+2} to $Cu(NH_3)_4^{+2}$ ions, causing the dark blue solution to reappear.

8. APPLYING PRINCIPLES TO INTERPRET NON-IONIC EQUILIBRIUM

Solubility equilibria were discussed in sections 6.3 and 6.5, and the synthesis of ammonia was discussed in section 6. There are essentially two types of equilibria: homogeneous (single phase) and heterogeneous (more than one phase). The synthesis of ammonia and ionic equilibria occurring in solution are examples of homogeneous equilibrium, and situations involving precipitates (dissolved and undissolved solute) and solutions of gases (liquid and gas phases) are examples of heterogeneous equilibrium.

Consider the system consisting of calcium carbonate in equilibrium with calcium oxide and carbon dioxide.

$$\text{energy} + CaCO_{3(s)} \rightleftharpoons CaO_{(s)} + CO_{2(g)}$$

The two solid phases do not change in concentration (solids have definite volume), but the concentration of CO_2 depends upon the pressure. Increasing the pressure decreases the volume, making $[CO_2]$ greater. The equilibrium constant for this system is

$$K = [CO_2]$$

If $CaCO_3$ is placed in a sealed container and the temperature is increased, the favored reaction is the one producing CaO and CO_2 (energy is consumed).

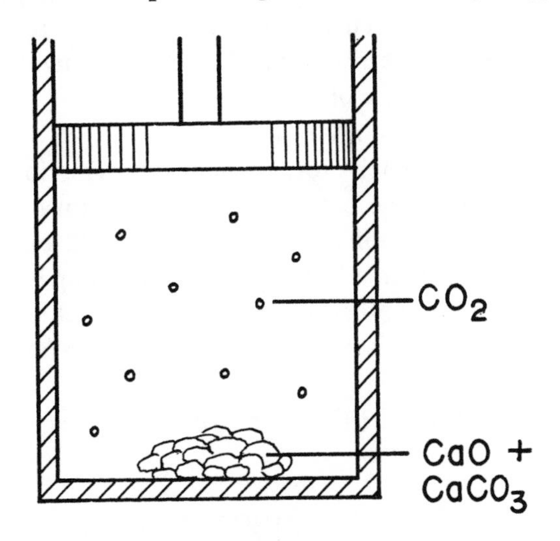

The concentration of CO_2 is increased, and the value of K increases. Keep the temperature constant and decrease the volume by pushing down on the movable piston. The concentration of CO_2 increases, favoring the reaction producing $CaCO_3$. Another way of explaining this is to consider the value of K. Decreasing the volume makes $[CO_2]$ larger than K, and the system is no longer in equilibrium. The concentration of CO_2 must decrease in order to restore equilibrium, and so CO_2 and CaO are consumed and $CaCO_3$ is produced, as predicted by Le Chatelier's principle. In the production of calcium oxide by heating limestone in a kiln, the carbon dioxide is swept away by hot air in order to minimize the reverse reaction.

Review the synthesis of ammonia, which was discussed in section 6. In the industrial process (Haber Process), a catalyst is used to speed up the reactions, and a high pressure is used to favor the reaction producing ammonia (which occupies a smaller volume than the other gases). Since reactions proceed at a faster rate at higher temperatures, a moderately high temperature is used, but a high temperature decreases the conversion of nitrogen and hydrogen to ammonia (the reverse reaction is favored, since energy is absorbed). The speed of reaction must be balanced against conversion to ammonia, and the optimum temperature must be determined to achieve the highest efficiency.

The oxidation of ammonia to produce nitric acid (Ostwald Process) involves the use of a catalyst.

$$4\,NH_{3(g)} + 5O_{2(g)} \rightleftharpoons 4\,NO_{(g)} + 6\,H_2O_{(g)} + \text{energy}$$

The products occupy a larger volume than the reactants, and so a low pressure is used. The reaction occurs on the surface of a catalyst and provides sufficient heat to supply the activation energy. The reactants are removed quickly in order to minimize the reverse reaction. The next step involves the oxidation of NO to NO_2, with the release of energy.

$$2\,NO_{(g)} + O_{2(g)} \rightleftharpoons 2NO_{2(g)} + \text{energy}$$

The reaction mixture is cooled in order to favor the formation of NO_2. Air and NO_2 are admitted through the bottom of an absorption tower, and water is added from the top. The reaction takes place on the surface of an inert packing (the large surface area leads to a faster reaction). Cooling is applied, since the formation of nitric acid is exothermic. Since the product is continually being removed, the reverse reaction is minimized. Pressure also favors the formation of nitric acid.

$$4\,NO_{2(g)} + O_{2(g)} + H_2O_{(l)} \rightleftharpoons NHO_{3(aq)} + \text{energy}$$

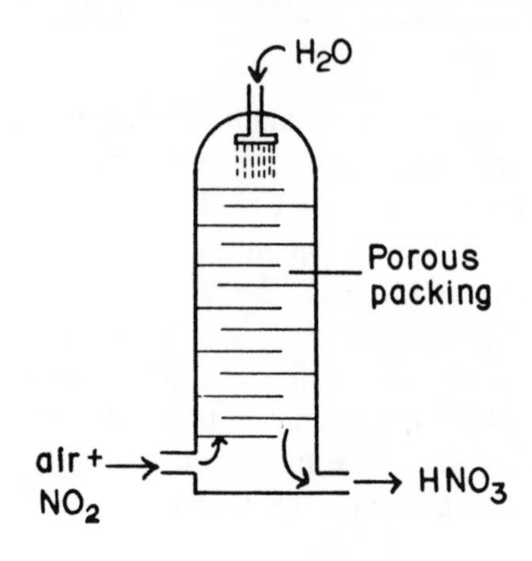

Point out that the decomposition of nitric acid occurs when the concentrated acid is heated or exposed to sunlight. The brown color of concentrated nitric acid is caused by NO_2 dissolved in the acid. Commercial concentrated nitric acid is usually 70% by weight HNO_3 and 30% water in order to stabilize the material. One hundred per cent (fuming) nitric acid is rather unstable and extremely reactive, acting as a powerful oxidizing agent.

Many industrial processes have been designed for efficient production of chemicals, using the principles of reaction kinetics and equilibrium. Relate these principles to any reactions encountered when discussing the preparation of materials and descriptive chemistry. More examples will be discussed in Chapter 13.

9

Developing the Concept of Energy

1. EXPLAINING THE DIFFERENT VARIETIES OF ENERGY

The idea of energy was introduced in section 1.4, which mentioned mechanical, electrical, radiant, and chemical energy and how their transfer is recognized. The nature of heat energy as molecular motion was developed in section 2.2. Electrical energy consists of a movement of charges due to a difference in potential. Radiant energy (heat and light transmitted through space) is carried by electromagnetic waves, or photons, moving through space. Chemical energy is due to chemical bonding, which in turn is dependent upon Coulomb's law. We know from experimental observation that energy is conserved and can be converted from one form to another. In the final analysis, however, energy implies that a force is moving through a distance (kinetic energy) or is in a position to move through a distance (potential energy).

Review the energy relationships between solids, liquids, and gases with your students. Changes in temperature are related to the kinetic energy of molecules being changed by adding or removing heat energy. When a solid changes to a liquid at the melting point, no change in temperature occurs. The energy absorbed in this phase change is called latent (hidden) heat of fusion and increases the potential energy of the material. The latent heat of vaporization increases the potential energy of the material in going from liquid to vapor (the molecules are farther apart).

On the atomic level, a quantum of light energy excites an atom by moving an electron from a lower to a higher energy level. The potential energy of the electron has been increased, since it is in position to fall back to the lower energy level and emit radiant energy. Work must be performed on the electron to overcome the attractive force of the nucleus and remove it from the atom to produce an ion. Ionic lattices are held together by coulombic forces. Ions which are separated come together to form a crystal lattice with the release of much potential energy (lattice energy). Atoms which form chemical bonds release energy in the process, since the nuclei and electrons of the atoms attract each other (see section 4.2). Emphasize that chemical energy is, in the final analysis, based upon Coulomb's law and the idea of potential and kinetic energy.

2. DEVELOPING THE CONCEPT OF CHEMICAL ENERGY

The criterion for a chemical change is the formation of new substances, and this is usually accompanied by a change in energy (generally in the form of heat, evidenced by a temperature change). Relate the idea of heat of reaction to the result of breaking old and making new chemical bonds during a chemical change. Energy must be supplied to break bonds (related to activation energy?), and energy is released in making new ones. Most of the energy change in a chemical system is related to the difference between the energy needed to break old bonds and the energy released when new ones are made. Other factors which enter into the picture are the work the system performs on its surroundings (a gas produced has to push air out of the way) or any changes in state which may absorb or emit energy.

The study of energy changes in chemical reactions is a part of chemical thermodynamics. Some of the basic ideas of this subject can be understood and appreciated by beginning students, as long as the mathematics involved is limited to simple algebra. One of the basic ideas to stress is that the absolute energy content of the starting materials and products is difficult to determine, since the starting point would have to be at absolute zero. However, the difference in energy between the initial and final states of a system is not difficult to measure, using a calorimeter. The calculation of the change in energy of a system is based upon the law of conservation of energy: in an insulated system (in which no energy is added or removed from the system), the total amount of heat released or absorbed by a process is equal to the total amount of heat absorbed or released by the surroundings. Before proceeding any farther, the students should have some idea of how to calculate the heat absorbed or released in a process. This is based on the law of conservation of energy, or "heat in = heat out." Begin by giving them simple examples and explanations, as shown below.

Example 1 Calculate the amount of heat needed to change 10 g ice at 0°C to steam at 100°C.

The process consists of (1) melting the ice at 0°, (2) warming the liquid water from 0°to 100°, and (3) changing the water to steam at 100°. A change of state occurs at constant temperature, and the amount of heat involved is given by

$$\text{calories} = (\text{mass})\left(\text{heat of } \begin{matrix}\text{fusion or} \\ \text{vaporization}\end{matrix}\right)$$

The heat of fusion is the amount of heat needed to change 1 g of solid to liquid at a constant temperature, and the heat of vaporization is the heat needed to change 1 g of liquid to vapor at constant temperature. When no change in state occurs, the temperature changes, and the amount of heat needed to do this is found by using the relationship

$$\text{calories} = (\text{mass})\ (\text{specific heat})\ (\text{temperature change})$$

Specific heat may be defined as the amount of heat needed to change the temperature of 1 g of substance 1°C. You might point out that the molar heat capacity of a substance is the amount of heat needed to change the temperature of 1 mole of substance 1°C.

The three steps involved are:

(1) melt ice at 0°:	$(10\ g)\ (80\ cal\ g^{-1})$	= 800 cal
(2) heat liquid water from 0° to 100°:	$(10\ g)\ (1\ cal\ g^{-1}\ deg^{-1})\ (100\ deg)$	= 1000 cal
(3) vaporize water at 100°:	$(10\ g)\ (540\ cal\ g^{-1})$	= 5400 cal
	total energy needed	= 7200 cal

Example 2 When 10.7 g (0.2 mole) NH_4Cl crystals was added to 100 g water contained in a 50 g beaker (specific heat of glass is 0.20 cal g^{-1} deg^{-1}), the temperature dropped from 20.5° to 13.4°. Calculate the heat of solution per mole of NH_4Cl. Since the temperature dropped, heat must have been absorbed in dissolving the ammonium chloride (see section 6.2). The heat absorbed by the ammonium chloride dissolving is equal to the heat released by the water and beaker when they are cooled.

$(100\ g)\ (1\ cal\ g^{-1}\ deg^{-1})\ (7.1\ deg)$	= 710 cal
$(50\ g)\ (0.20\ cal\ g^{-1}\ deg^{-1})\ (7.1 deg)$	= 71 cal
heat absorbed by 0.2 mole $NH_4\ Cl$	= 781 cal

$$\frac{781\ \text{cal}}{0.2\ \text{mole}} = 3.9\ \text{Kcal (molar heat of solution of } NH_4Cl)$$

Example 3 The heat of combustion for benzene was determined by placing 0.78 g (0.01 mole) benzene and excess oxygen in a bomb calorimeter immersed in water. The reaction was started by means of a spark, and the temperature rose from 12.0° to 27.0°. The calorimeter constant (heat needed to change the temperature of the apparatus plus water 1°) for the bomb, water, and container was 522 cal deg^{-1}.

The heat produced in the reaction was absorbed by the calorimeter.

$$(522 \text{ cal deg}^{-1})(15.0 \text{ deg}) = 7800 \text{ cal for burning 0.01 mole}$$

$$\frac{7800 \text{ cal}}{0.01 \text{ mole}} = 780 \text{ Kcal mole}^{-1}$$

The three examples above should convince the students that energy changes can be measured experimentally. What is actually being measured is the change in energy going from the initial to the final states of the system, not the absolute energies. In more advanced work, a distinction is made between two types of energy in a system: E represents the total energy of the system, and H represents the enthalpy (heat content) of the system. An elementary course need not distinguish between these, however. If you have some curious students and the time, develop the ideas of total energy and enthalpy.

The law of conservation of energy really states that the change in the total energy of a system ($\triangle E$) is equal to the sum of the heat added to the system (Q) and the work performed on the system (W):

$$\triangle E = Q + W \qquad (1)$$

Assuming that the only work performed on the system is the reverse of expansion (in the case of gases), then $W = -\triangle PV$. If a reaction is carried out at constant volume (in a bomb calorimeter, for example), there is no work performed on the system, since $\triangle V = 0$. Therefore,

$$\triangle E = Q_v \qquad (2)$$

Most reactions are carried out at constant pressure, however, which means that when a gas is produced, the system does work on the surroundings (work performed by the system $= -\triangle PV$). A new function, the change in enthalpy, must be introduced to account for the change in energy of a system at constant pressure.

$$\triangle H = \triangle E + \triangle PV \qquad (3)$$

Combining equations (1) and (3) produces a new relationship:

$$\triangle H = Q + W + \triangle PV \qquad (4)$$

Since the work performed on the system is $= -\triangle PV$, we can substitute this quantity for W and obtain

$$\triangle H = Q + (-\triangle PV) + \triangle PV \qquad (5)$$

Simplifying, we obtain the relationship between enthalpy and the heat added to a system at constant pressure:

$$\triangle H = Q_p \qquad (6)$$

The difference between $\triangle E$ and $\triangle H$ for an ideal gas is given by substituting nRT for PV in equation (3):

$$\triangle H = \triangle E + \triangle nRT \qquad (7)$$

Since the temperature is almost constant and R is a constant, the only variable in the last term is the number of moles, n, and so we may rewrite equation (7):

$$\triangle H = \triangle E + RT\triangle n \qquad (8)$$

At 25° C, the value of RT is relatively small:

$$RT = (1.99 \text{ cal mole}^{-1} \text{ deg}^{-1})(298 \text{ deg}) = 594 \text{ cal mole}^{-1}$$
$$= 0.59 \text{ Kcal mole}^{-1}$$

When $\triangle n$ is zero, $\triangle H = E$. When $\triangle n$ is a small number, as it usually is, the difference between $\triangle H$ and $\triangle E$ is quite small. In determining $\triangle H$, using a bomb calorimeter, the experimenter is really measuring $\triangle E$, which he can convert to $\triangle H$ by using equation (8).

3. EXPLAINING HEAT CONTENT, ENTROPY, FREE ENERGY

Follow up the development of the notion of calculating differences in energy from experimental data using a calorimeter by introducing Hess' law. The generality was discovered by G. H. Hess around 1840 and is really a corollary of the law of conservation of energy. It states that the net change in energy in any reaction is independent of the path taken from the initial to the final state of a system, regardless of how many intermediate steps are involved. Use the analogy of going from New York to Los Angeles. The elevation of the two cities is about the same (sea level), and the change in potential energy going from New York to Los Angeles is about zero, whether one goes by plane, train, auto, or ship. Diagram the possible route using a potential energy diagram. When taking a plane, the "activation energy" is high, but the

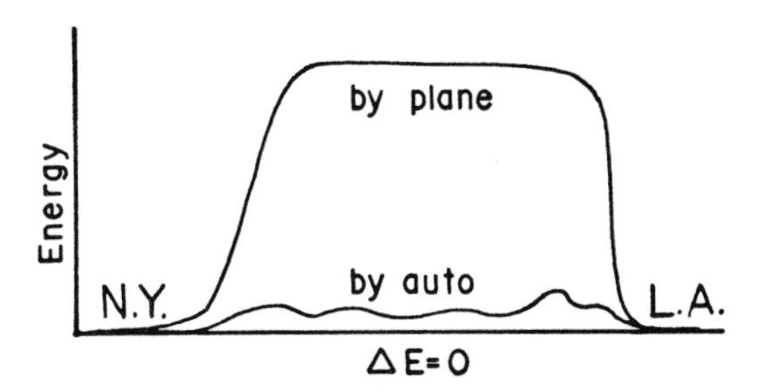

difference between the initial and final states of the system is the same as when going by train across the Rockies or by ship through the Panama Canal. The change in energy of any system is given by the difference in energy between the final and initial states. The heat of reaction (enthalpy) is equal to the energy of the products minus the energy of the reactants:

$$\triangle H = H_{products} - H_{reactants}$$

The consequence of this relationship is that $\triangle H$ is negative for exothermic reactions and positive for endothermic reactions, as shown in the energy diagrams, page 176. Remind your students that if less energy is contained in a system, the more stable the system.

One of the functions used by chemists in calculating heat of reaction is the heat of formation. This is defined as the energy change when a substance is produced from the free elements at 25° C and 1 atmosphere pressure and is represented by $\triangle H_f$. The heats of formation for all chemical elements at their standard state (natural state at 25° and 1 atm) is defined as $\triangle H_f = O$. Heats of formation of compounds or elements not at their standard state are determined experimentally, using a calorimeter, or by calculation using Hess' law (see section 4). The stability of compounds is related to their heats of formation. A compound having a large negative $\triangle H_f$ is very stable, and one which has a small negative $\triangle H_f$ or a positive $\triangle H_f$ is generally unstable and easily decomposed. Hydrogen iodide, for example, has a heat of formation of $+6.2$ Kcal mole^{-1}(unstable), and carbon dioxide has a heat of formation of -94.0 Kcal mole^{-1}(stable). Calculations involving heats of formation and heats of reaction will be discussed in the next section.

The two natural tendencies for all processes are to change to a state of lower energy and to increase in entropy (see sections 1.4 and 2.6), which results in the system reaching a state of equilibrium. Entropy may be described in numerous ways, among which are: the measure of order in a system, and the organization energy of a system. Consider a change of state, such as the melting of ice. The solid state represents a highly-organized state which becomes less organized upon melting. The liquid water at 0° C contains more potential energy than ice at 0° (represented by the heat of fusion), although the average kinetic energy of the two phases is the same. Water melts spontaneously because at 0° the increase in entropy outweighs the increase in the energy of the system. The two tendencies oppose each other. When water freezes, energy is needed to organize the crystal structure of ice. This energy is released when the ice melts, even though the reaction appears to be endothermic. How to resolve the conflict between the natural tendency to increase entropy and to decrease the energy content of the system necessitates a new function: free energy.

Free energy may be regarded as the useful work performed by a system when it proceeds to a state of equilibrium. An electrochemical cell, for example, provides electrical energy which can perform useful work (free energy) as well as energy which cannot be harnessed. The change in free energy ($\triangle G$) is the difference between the change in heat content and the change in organization energy (entropy) at a given temperature:

$$\triangle G = \triangle H - T\triangle S$$

You might clarify the meaning of free energy and its relation to entropy and heat content by showing your students the following equation, pointing out the meaning of each term:

G	$+$	TS	$=$	H
free energy (available)		organization energy (not available)		total energy of system

The change in free energy of a system can be calculated from the free energies of formation, using Hess' law, just as the change in enthalpy of a system is calculated from the heats of formation. A system which produces available energy has a negative free energy change (difference between the free energy of the final state minus the free energy of the initial state of the system) and proceeds spontaneously to a state of equilibrium. The criterion for a reaction that is feasible, therefore, is the sign of $\triangle G$. A reaction proceeds spontaneously when $\triangle G$ is negative, but is not feasible when $\triangle G$ is positive. In the case of an endothermic reaction ($\triangle H > 0$), the useful work ($\triangle G < 0$) comes from the release of organization energy ($\triangle S > 0$). The driving force behind any system undergoing a change (physical or chemical) is a decrease in free energy.

Use an example such as the water-gas reaction to develop this idea.

$$\text{energy} + C_{(s)} + H_2O_{(g)} = H_{2(g)} + CO_{(g)}$$

According to Le Chatelier's principle, the reaction producing hydrogen and carbon monoxide is favored by an increase in temperature. The heat of reaction may be calculated from the heats of formation of the reactants minus the heats of formation of the products:

$$\begin{aligned}\triangle H_R &= (\triangle H_{H_2} + \triangle H_{CO}) - (\triangle H_C + \triangle H_{H_2O})\\ &= [0 + (-26.4 \text{ Kcal})] - [O + (-57.8 \text{ Kcal})]\\ &= +31.4 \text{ Kcal}\end{aligned}$$

Since the value for $\triangle H_R$ is positive, the reaction is endothermic and should not proceed spontaneously. We can qualitatively predict the change in the entropy of the system, however, by examining the degree of order of the reactants and products. Solid carbon is highly ordered. The most ordered of the gases is water vapor (triatomic), as opposed to hydrogen and carbon monoxide, which are diatomic gases. The system, therefore, is proceeding toward greater randomness by forming carbon monoxide and hydrogen. Since the entropy is increasing, the sign of $\triangle S$ is positive. Considering the relationship $\triangle G = \triangle H - T\triangle S$ and the signs of $\triangle H$ and $\triangle S$, a large value for T would make $\triangle G$ negative. A reaction proceeds spontaneously when $\triangle G$ is negative (free energy is released), and so the water-gas reaction can proceed when the temperature is sufficiently high, in spite of the fact that the enthalpy is increasing. The criterion for whether or not a reaction proceeds is the sign of $\triangle G$. Whenever $\triangle G$ is negative, a reaction is feasible, but when $\triangle G$ is positive, the reaction does not proceed spontaneously. An excellent development and discussion of chemical thermodynamics can be found is Strong and Stratton's *Chemical Energy* (Reinhold Publishing Company, 1965).

Although quantitative treatment of entropy and free energy is a bit beyond the average student of elementary high school chemistry, an understanding of the concepts is most desirable. The ideas of heats of formation and heats of reaction should certainly be included in the form of simple problems, as discussed in the next section. Your better students might explore the subject more deeply and would benefit from reading Strong and Stratton's *Chemical Energy.*

4. TEACHING ENERGY CALCULATIONS

The calculation of the heat of reaction for the water gas reaction was illustrated in the previous section. Such calculations are based on Hess' law, which states that the net amount of energy involved when a system proceeds from the initial to the final state is the algebraic sum of all the steps. This may be done graphically (see section 6) or simply by using the relationship

$$\triangle H_R = \sum \triangle H_{products} - \sum \triangle H_{reactants}$$

You should give your students examples of calculating heats of reaction and heats of formation using Hess' law. Calculation of bond energy and lattice energy will be discussed in section 6, using energy diagrams.

Example 1 Calculate the heat of reaction for the combustion of one mole of propane gas at 25°, producing CO_2 gas and H_2O liquid.

$$C_3H_{8(g)} + 5O_{2(g)} = 3CO_{2(g)} + 4H_2O_{(l)}$$

Having written the balanced equation, the next step is to look up the heats of formation of the reactants and products at 25° C. Sum up the total heats of formation of the products and subtract the total heats of formation of the reactants. The algebraic sum is the heat of reaction for one mole of propane.

3 moles $CO_{2(g)}$ = 3(− 94.0 Kcal) = − 282.0 Kcal

4 moles $H_2O_{(l)}$ = 4(− 68.4 Kcal) = − 273.6

Sum of heats of formation of products = − 555.6 Kcal

5 moles $O_{2(g)}$ = 5(0 Kcal) = 000.0 Kcal

1 mole $C_3H_{8(g)}$ = 1(−24.8 Kcal) = − 24.8

Sum of heats of formation of reactants = − 24.8 Kcal

$$\text{Heat of reaction} = -555.6 \text{ Kcal} - (-24.8 \text{ Kcal})$$
$$= -530.8 \text{ Kcal}$$

Point out that the enthalpies are multiplied by the number of moles involved, just as masses or volumes in chemical reactions depend upon the number of moles of materials.

Example 2 Calculate the molar heat of formation of ethane gas at 25° C from the heat of reaction and the heats of formation found in a table. Assume that the water produced is in the liquid state.

$$C_2H_{6(g)} + 3.5\ O_{2(g)} = 2CO_{2(g)} + 3H_2O_{(l)}$$

Let x be the heat of formation of ethane. Sum up the heats of formation as in example 1 and take the difference.

$$2 \text{ moles of } CO_{2(g)} = 2(-94.0 \text{ Kcal}) = -188.0 \text{ Kcal}$$
$$3 \text{ moles of } H_2O_{(l)} = 3(-68.4 \text{ Kcal}) = -205.2$$

Heat of formation of products	-393.2 Kcal
Heat of formation of reactants	$x + 0$ Kcal
Heat of reaction	-372.8 Kcal

$$-393.2 - (x + 0) = -372.8$$
$$x = -20.4 \text{ Kcal/mole}$$

Example 3 Calculate the heat of formation of carbon monoxide gas from the heats of combustion of carbon monoxide and carbon. This illustrates the calculation of a quantity that cannot be measured directly, since it is next to impossible to react a mole of carbon with half a mole of oxygen to produce one mole of carbon monoxide (considerable CO_2 is also produced). If we write the equations for the reactions and include the heats of reaction, we can subtract the second from the first and obtain the net reaction producing CO from the elements.

$$C_{(s)} + O_{2(g)} = CO_{2(g)} + 94.0 \text{ Kcal}$$
$$-(CO_{(g)} + 0.5\ O_{2(g)} = CO_{2(g)} + 67.6 \text{ Kcal})$$
$$C_{(s)} + 0.5\ O_2 = CO_{(g)} + 26.4 \text{ Kcal}$$
$$\text{Heat of formation of } CO_{(g)} = -26.4 \text{ Kcal/mole}$$

Example 4 When 0.700 g ethene gas was burned in excess oxygen, 8.43 Kcal was produced. Calculate the heat of formation of ethene at 25° C. Calculate the heat of reaction per mole of ethene consumed. Then sum up the enthalpies, letting x represent the heat of formation of ethene.

$$\frac{0.700\text{g } C_2H_6}{28\text{g mole}^{-1}} = 0.025 \text{ mole } C_2H_6$$

$$\frac{-8.43 \text{ Kcal}}{0.025 \text{ mole}} = -337.2 \text{ Kcal/mole} \left\{ \begin{array}{l} \text{exothermic reaction,} \\ \text{therefore sign of} \\ \triangle H_R \text{ is negative} \end{array} \right.$$

$$C_2H_{4(g)} + 3O_{2(g)} = 2CO_{2(g)} + 2H_2O_{(l)}$$

$$2(-94.0) + 2(-68.4) - (x + O) = -337.2 \text{ Kcal}$$
$$x = +12.4 \text{ Kcal/mole}$$

Example 5 Calculate the heat produced or absorbed when 3.50 g ethene is hydrogenated to produce ethane at 25° C.

$$C_2H_{4(g)} + H_{2(g)} = C_2H_{6(g)}$$

Calculate the heat of reaction per mole of ethene. The sign of $\triangle H_R$ indicates whether the reaction is exothermic or endothermic.

$$\frac{3.50\text{g } C_2H_4}{28 \text{ g mole}^{-1}} = 0.125 \text{ mole } C_2H_4$$

$$\triangle H_R = -20.4 - (+12.4 + O) = -32.8 \text{ Kcal/mole}$$
$$(-32.8 \text{ Kcal/mole})(0.125 \text{ mole}) = 4.10 \text{ Kcal produced}$$

If your students have difficulty in learning to calculate energy changes as illustrated above, show them how to do it graphically, as illustrated in section 6. Give them a variety of problems involving the mole concept as well as heats of formation and reaction.

5. RELATING FREE ENERGY TO ELECTRICAL ENERGY IN ELECTROCHEMICAL REACTIONS

The electrical energy obtained from an electrochemical cell can be harnessed to perform useful work. Therefore, the electrical energy from an electrochemical reaction is equal to the free energy of the reaction. Electrical energy consists of a charge being moved by an electromotive force (electrical potential, or voltage). Relate this idea to Coulomb's law, using a simple diagram of an electron between two charged plates. The coulombic force which makes the electron move from the negative toward the positive plate is caused by the difference in charge (difference in potential) between the plates. This difference in potential is measured in volts. The voltage multiplied by the amount of charge is equal to electrical energy: joules = (volts) (coulombs).

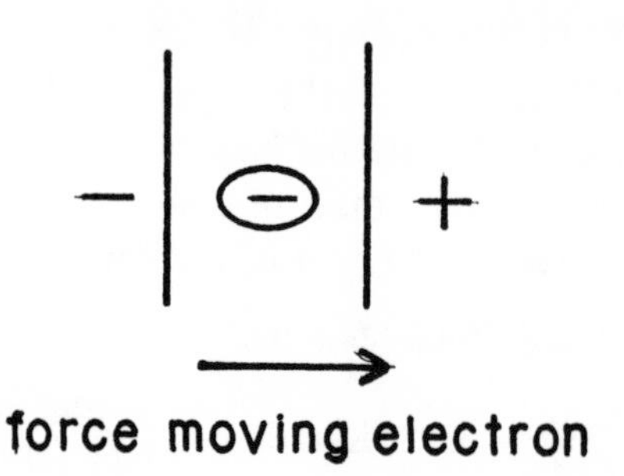

Since electrical energy is a positive number and change in free energy is negative, the equation relating the two must include a negative sign. The standard free energy change, $\triangle G°$, is equal to minus the number of moles of electrons transferred, *n*, times the faraday, *F* (charge of one mole of electrons), times the standard voltage of the cell, $E°$. The standard quantities, denoted by the superscript zero, are measured at 25° C, 1 atmosphere pressure, and a concentration of 1 molar (really at unit activity, which is beyond the scope of an elementary high school chemistry course).

$$\triangle G° = -nFE^0$$

In principle, therefore, it is possible to calculate the standard free energy change of any redox system from the $E°$ value for the reaction.

Example 1 Calculate the standard free energy change for the reaction between zinc and 1 molar hydrochloric acid at 25° C. Write the half-reactions for the oxidation and reduction steps and determine the $E°$ value for the net reaction. The number of moles of electrons transferred is the value used for *n*, and the faraday is 9.65×10^4 coulombs.

$$Zn = Zn^{+2} + 2e^- \quad + 0.76 \text{ volts}$$
$$2H^+ + 2e^- = H_2 \quad 0.00 \text{ volts}$$
$$Zn + 2H^+ = Zn^{+2} + H_2 + 0.76 \text{ volts}$$
$$\triangle G° = -(2)(9.65 \times 10^4 \text{ coulombs})(0.76 \text{ volts})$$
$$= -1.47 \times 10^5 \text{ joules}$$

Convert to calories using the conversion factor 4.183 joule = 1 calorie.

$$\triangle G° = \frac{-14.7 \times 12^4 \text{ joule}}{4.183 \text{ joule cal}^{-1}} = -3.51 \times 10^4 \text{ calories}$$
$$= -35.1 \text{ Kcal}$$

Example 2 Calculate the standard free energy of the reaction between 1 molar nitrate ion, 1 molar hydronium ion, and copper, producing 1 molar copper (II) ions and nitric oxide gas at 25° C and 1 atmosphere pressure. Write the half-reactions (see Chapter 10) and $E°$ values, then balance the net equation to determine the number of electrons transferred. Solve for $\triangle G°$.

$$2(NO_3^- + 4H^+ + 3e^- = NO + 2H_2O) + 0.96 \text{ volts}$$
$$3(Cu = Cu^{+2} + 2e^-) \quad -0.34 \text{ volts}$$
$$3Cu + 2NO_3^- + 8H^+ = 3Cu^{+2} + 2NO + 4H_2O + 0.62 \text{ volts}$$

Since 6 moles of electrons are transferred, the value for *n* is 6.

$$\triangle G° = -(6)(9.65 \times 10^4 \text{ coul})(0.62 \text{ volt}) = -3.58 \times 10^5 \text{ joule}$$
$$= \frac{-35.8 \times 10^5 \text{ joule}}{4.183 \text{ joule cal}^{-1}} = -8.57 \times 10^4 \text{ cal}$$
$$= -85.7 \text{ Kcal for 3 moles Cu}$$

Emphasize that the free energy change for a reaction changes with the concentrations (activities) and conditions of the reaction. This means that the electrical energy available from a cell depends upon the concentrations of the species as well as the amounts of reactants consumed. The voltage depends upon concentration, too. As the reactants in a cell are consumed, their concentrations decrease. We may write an equation relating the free energy change for a system not at its standard state in regard to concentrations:

$$\Delta G = -nFE$$

In a more advanced course, the calculation of the voltage of a cell not at its standard state may be calculated using the Nernst equation. The relationship of standard free energy to the equilibrium constant and the $E°$ value of a system can also be developed. These topics, however, are beyond the scope of an elementary course. If you can leave your students with the appreciation of a relationship between free energy and electrical energy, they will be in a better position to pursue the subject at greater depth.

6. THE USE OF ENERGY DIAGRAMS AND THE BORN-HABER CYCLE

The algebraic summation of enthalpies using Hess' law can be made more meaningful by using energy diagrams. A student can also gain a greater appreciation of some concepts previously studied by re-examining the steps involved in the formation of sodium chloride from the elements (see section 4.2), using the Born-Haber cycle. The method used by chemists to calculate bond energies can be more clearly understood if the steps used are related by use of an energy diagram.

For the benefit of the students who had difficulty in understanding the calculations of heats of reaction and formation described in section 4, show them the graphical determination of the heat of reaction for the water gas reaction. In this case, the heat of formation of water (gaseous state) is −57.0 Kcal/mole. The algebraic sum of the heats of formation in the graph is the heat of reaction, which turns out to be +30.6 Kcal/mole.

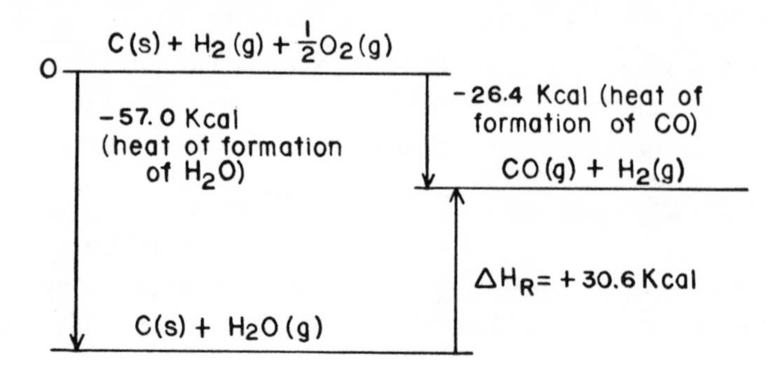

Show your students how they may use a graph to calculate the heat of formation of ethane gas (see example 2, section 4).

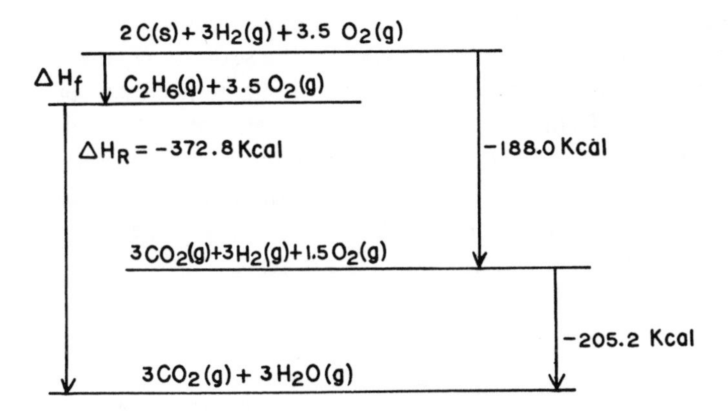

The heat of formation turns out to be – 20.4 Kcal/mole. Point out that the steps postulated for the reaction leading from the free elements at their standard states to the final products include the formation of ethane.

Show your students how the bond energy of the C-H bond may be calculated from the heat needed to vaporize carbon, the bond energy of the H-H bond, and the heat of formation of methane.

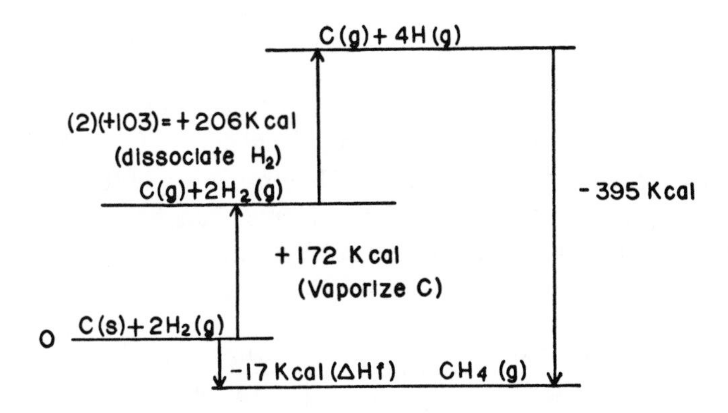

The energy released when four hydrogen atoms become bonded to one carbon atom is 395 Kcal. Dividing this number by four gives the energy released when one atom of hydrogen becomes bonded to one atom of carbon. Therefore, the energy of the C-H bond is about –99 Kcal/mole. Other bond energies may be calculated in a similar fashion.

The lattice energy of sodium chloride can be calculated by algebraically summing up all the steps involved in going from one mole of solid sodium and a half mole of chlorine gas to one mole of sodium chloride crystals, using the Born-Haber cycle. The energy for each step can be determined experimentally: (1) the energy needed to melt and vaporize the sodium, (2) the energy needed to dissociate chlorine into atoms, (3) the ionization energy of sodium, the electron affinity of chlorine, (4) the heat of reaction. These changes can be shown graphically, and the change from gaseous sodium and chloride ions to solid sodium chloride (lattice energy) can be evaluated. Since, by convention, the heats of formation of the free elements at their standard states is zero, the energy of the starting materials is zero.

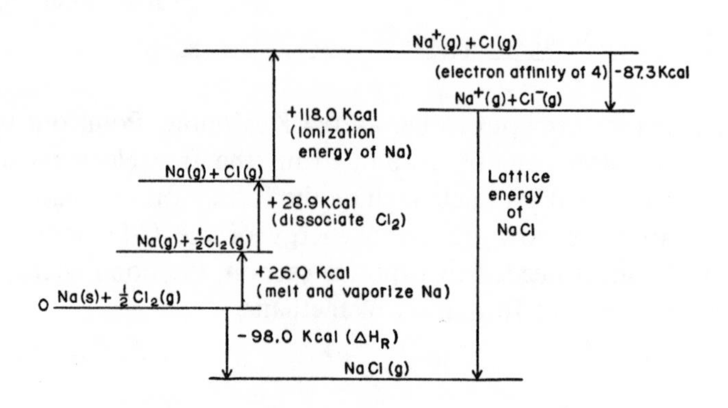

The lattice energy turns out to be – 183.8 Kcal/mole.

The energy of hydration of ions can be calculated from the lattice energy of the crystal and the heat of solution. Determination of the latter quantity is relatively easy (see section 2), and the former can be calculated using the Born-Haber cycle. Compare the heats of hydration of LiCl and NaCl:

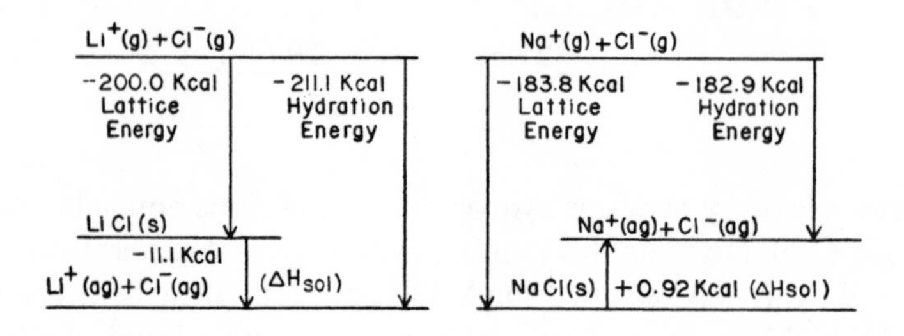

Remind your students that the ions dispersed in aqueous solution are analogous to ions in the gaseous state. Considerably more energy is released when Li^+ ions are hydrated than in the case of Na^+ ions. The explanation can be found when we consider the difference in charge densities. Since lithium ions are considerably smaller, they have a higher charge density than sodium ions. Consequently, Li^+ ions have a greater attraction for water dipoles, and more energy is released when Li^+ ions are hydrated. Give your students similar types of calculations until they understand the idea behind Hess' law of heat summation.

7. USE OF FREE ENERGY AS CRITERION FOR FEASIBILITY OF A REACTION

Free energy was discussed in section 3, which also pointed out that in order for a reaction to proceed, the free energy change must be negative (useful work can be performed). When the free energy change of a reaction is positive, the reaction does not proceed as written, but the reverse reaction (negative $\triangle G$) is favored. Consider the reaction involving the formation of water from the gaseous elements:

$$H_{2(g)} + 0.5\, O_{2(g)} = H_2O_{(l)}$$

The reaction proceeds extensively and explosively, releasing 68.4 Kcal per mole of liquid water formed at 25° C. If we examine the order of the products and reactants, we can conclude that the product, triatomic water, is considerably more ordered than the diatomic gases from which it was formed. The change in entropy, therefore, is negative, which makes the term $-T\triangle S$ positive. Examination of the equation and using the value for $\triangle H$ reveals that the free energy change is less negative then $\triangle H$:

$$\triangle G = \triangle H - T\triangle S$$
$$\triangle G = -\ 68.4 \text{ Kcal} + \text{number}$$

Some of the energy of the system must have been used to organize the water molecules, leaving less energy available for performing useful work. Nevertheless, the change in free energy is quite large, as evidenced by the extent of the reaction.

If we raise the temperature sufficiently, however, the value of the number added to $\triangle H$ will become larger, and eventually the sign of the free energy change will become positive. At very high temperatures, water will decompose into the elements, since the sign of $\triangle G$ for the reverse reaction is changed from positive to negative.

Return to the example of the water gas reaction, which was discussed in section 3:

$$C_{(s)} + H_2O_{(l)} = CO_{(g)} + H_{2(g)}$$

The value of $\triangle H$ for this reaction was found to be + 31.4 Kcal at 25° C. The free energy change can be found:

$$\triangle G = 31.4 \text{ Kcal } - T\triangle S$$

At low temperatures, $\triangle G$ is positive, and no CO and H_2 are produced when steam is blown through charcoal. The change in entropy is positive, and so $T\triangle S$ is positive. If T is sufficiently high, however, the value of $\triangle G$ will become negative, and the forward reaction will proceed.

The unknown terms in the above equations are the values for $\triangle S$ and $\triangle G$. The value for $\triangle G$ can be determined by measuring the value for the equilibrium constant, and this will be discussed in the next section. The value for $\triangle S$ can be determined using the values for $\triangle G$ and $\triangle H$. At this point, your students should have assimilated the idea that a chemist can predict whether or not a reaction will proceed as written by determining the value and sign of $\triangle G$. If $\triangle G$ is positive, the reaction as written is not feasible, but the reverse reaction is favored. When $\triangle G$ is negative, the reaction is feasible, and the reverse reaction is not favored. The next question to explore is some of the ramifications of $\triangle G = 0$, the condition for equilibrium.

8. RELATION OF FREE ENERGY TO EQUILIBRIUM

As was already intimated, the condition for a system in equilibrium is that no more useful work can be obtained from the system: $\triangle G = 0$. The natural tendency of any system is to decrease its free energy to a minimum (i.e., become zero), and this explains why all systems tend toward equilibrium. A dry cell produces electrical energy by means of a redox reaction, but as the reaction proceeds and the reactants are consumed, the voltage drops and becomes zero when equilibrium is reached. Examination of the relationship between $\triangle G$ and electrical energy shows that this is true:

$$\triangle G = -nFE$$

When $E = 0$, $\triangle G = 0$.

Examination of the equation relating $\triangle G$, $\triangle H$, and $\triangle S$ reveals that at equilibrium, when $\triangle G = 0$, $\triangle = H T\triangle S$, or

$$\frac{\triangle H}{T} = \triangle S$$

The relationship permits one to calculate $\triangle S$ for a system at equilibrium. Consider the vaporization of water at 100° C (both phases are in equilibrium at 1 atmosphere pressure). We must calculate the molar heat of vaporization of water ($\triangle H$).

$$(540 \text{ cal g}^{-1})(18 \text{ g mole}^{-1}) = 9700 \text{ cal mole}^{-1}$$

Dividing this value by the absolute temperature gives us the change in entropy of vaporization for water:

$$\triangle S = \frac{9700 \text{ cal mole}^{-1}}{373 \text{ deg}} = 26 \text{ cal deg}^{-1} \text{ mole}^{-1}$$

The entropy of vaporization for most substances is about 21 cal deg^{-1} mole^{-1}. The high value for water reveals that water is a highly-ordered liquid. Relate this to hydrogen bonding. The interesting relationship between heat of vaporization and boiling point is known as Trouton's rule:

$$\triangle S_{vap} = \frac{\triangle H_{vap}}{T_b} \cong 21 \text{ cal deg}^{-1} \text{ mole}^{-1}$$

Your more mathematically inclined students might appreciate the relationship between the standard free energy, $\triangle G°$, for a reaction and the value for the equilibrium constant. The free energy for a system is given by the relationship

$$\triangle G = \triangle G° + RT \ln Q$$

The term $\ln Q$ is the natural logarithm of the mass action expression for the reaction (see section 8.5), and this may be converted to base 10 logarithm by using the conversion factor 2.303:

$$\triangle G = \triangle G° + 2.303\, RT \log Q$$

Since the value for $\triangle G$ is zero at equilibrium and Q is the equilibrium constant, K, we may write

$$\triangle G° = -\, 2.303\, RT \log K$$

This equation suggests a relationship between the equilibrium constant and temperature. Combining this equation with $\triangle G° = \triangle H° - T\triangle S°$ gves us the relationship

$$2.303 \log K = -\frac{\triangle H°}{RT} + \frac{\triangle S°}{R}$$

The Van't Hoff equation relating the logarithm of K to temperature is derived from the above using calculus.

We can also relate the value of K to the $E°$ value for a reaction.

$$\triangle G° = -\, nFE^0$$
$$= -\, 2.303\, RT \log K$$
$$2.303\, RT \log K = nFE°$$

This equation permits us to calculate the equilibrium constant of a reaction from the $E°$ value.

Example Calculate the solubility product of AgCl at 25° C. We must first find appropriate half-reactions and their $E°$ values in a table of standard oxidation potentials. Summing up the half-reactions gives the desired equation and its $E°$ value.

$$
\begin{array}{ll}
AgCl_{(s)} + e^- = Ag^\circ + Cl^- & + 0.22 \text{ volts} \\
Ag^\circ = Ag^+ + e^- & - 0.80 \text{ volts} \\
\hline
AgCl = Ag^+ + Cl^- & - 0.58 \text{ volts}
\end{array}
$$

Point out that since E° is negative, the reaction as written is not favored, but the reaction forming the precipitate of AgCl is highly favored. The next step involves solving for log K. Use the value R = 8.314 joule deg^{-1} $mole^{-1}$, since joule = coul × volt.

$$
\begin{aligned}
\log K &= \frac{n F E^\circ}{2.303RT} \\
&= \frac{(1)(9.65 \times 10^4 \text{ coul mole}^{-1})(-0.58 \text{ volt})}{(2.303)(8.314 \text{ coul volt deg}^{-1} \text{ mole}^{-1})(298 \text{ deg})} \\
&= -10 \\
KSP &= 10^{-10}
\end{aligned}
$$

A good many students may not be able to follow and understand all of the material discussed in the last several sections. Hopefully, however, most of them will be able to perform simple energy calculations. Use your discretion in regard to the other material discussed. Most of them should be able to understand the concept of free energy and entropy in a qualitative way. If they can see the connection between equilibrium and free energy and realize that all sorts of interesting results can be calculated using the principles of chemical thermodynamics, your students will have a better understanding of chemical as well as physical processes. More applications of some of these ideas will be discussed in Chapter 13.

10

Teaching Oxidation-Reduction and Electrochemistry

1. DEVELOPING THE CONCEPT OF REDOX

Give your students the historical and modern definitions of the terms *oxidation* and *reduction* and develop the modern concept from the historical viewpoint. Years ago, oxidation referred to combination with oxygen (operational definition), and reduction referred to removal of oxygen. Start with simple examples such as

(1) $2H_2 + O_2 = 2H_2O$ (hydrogen is oxidized)
(2) $2Cu + O_2 = 2CuO$ (copper is oxidized)
(3) $4Al + 3O_2 = 2Al_2O_3$ (aluminum is oxidized)

These are combination reactions. Give your students a couple of combination reactions not involving oxygen and point out the similarities to the first three examples.

(4) $H_2 + Cl_2 = 2HCl$
(5) $2Al + 3Br_2 = 2AlBr_3$

The last two examples are quite obviously similar to the first three, and this suggests a process common to all of the above examples. The unifying concept is the oxidation number, which is a bookkeeping device for determining which atoms have gained or lost control of electrons.

Consider the electron-dot formulas for hydrogen, chlorine, water, and hydrogen chloride (see section 4.3). The two hydrogen atoms share a pair of electrons equally, since there is no difference in electronegativity. In order to assign "ownership" of the electrons, we must split the pair down the middle.

Each hydrogen atom controls one electron, which means that neither hydrogen atom has gained or lost any electrons in the process. If we define *oxidation number* as the number of electrons gained or lost in a bonding situation (whether covalent or ionic), the oxidation number of free hydrogen is zero. Examination of the structure of a chlorine molecule leads to a similar conclusion. Since neither chlorine atom has gained or lost control of any electrons

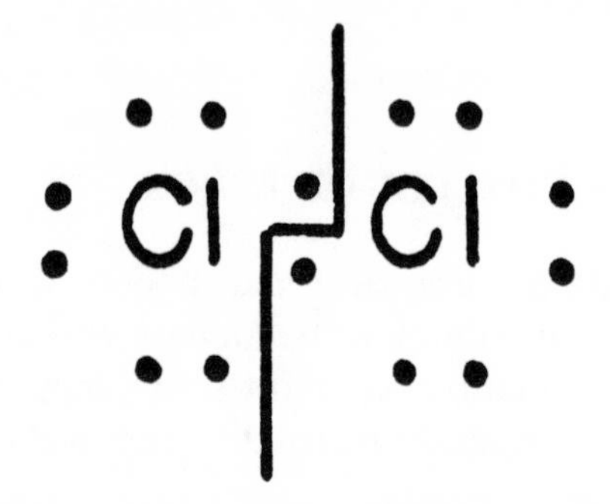

(no difference in electronegativity), the oxidation number of free chlorine is zero. In general, the oxidation number of any free element is zero.

If we examine the electron-dot formulas for hydrogen chloride and water, in which hydrogen is the less electronegative element, we come to the conclusion that the hydrogen atoms have lost control of one electron apiece,

+1 H :Cl: −1

+1 H :O: −2
H +1

giving the hydrogen an oxidation number of +1. Chlorine has acquired one electron at the expense of the hydrogen atom, since it is more electronegative than hydrogen. The oxidation number of chlorine is −1. Oxygen, on the other hand, has gained control of two additional electrons, giving it an oxidation number of −2. More examples of determining oxidation numbers will be discussed in the next section.

Now we may define oxidation conceptually as an increase in oxidation number by virtue of an atom losing control of one or more electrons. Reduction, on the other hand, is defined as a decrease in oxidation number by virtue of an atom gaining control of one or more electrons. In example (1), the oxidation number of hydrogen changed from 0 to +1 (increase), and so hydrogen was oxidized. Since the oxidation number of oxygen changed from 0 to −2, reduction of oxygen occurred. In example (4), hydrogen was oxidized and chlorine was reduced. Emphasize that oxidation and reduction always occur simultaneously, since one or more electrons must be transferred in the process. Point out that the electron transfer does not necessarily lead to the formation of ions, and remind your students that the oxidation number concept is merely a device used to keep track of which atom controls the electrons in a bonding situation.

Give your students some more simple examples of electron transfer, such as the reaction between magnesium and hydrochloric acid (displacement):

$$Mg + 2HCl = MgCl_2 + H_2$$

Show them how magnesium metal loses electrons to form ions and how hydrogen ions gain electrons to form the free element. Label the half-reactions as either oxidation or reduction.

oxidation:	$Mg = Mg^{+2} + 2e^-$
reduction:	$2H^+ + 2e^- = H_2$
net reaction:	$Mg + 2H^+ = Mg^{+2} + H_2$

Point out the electron transfer from the magnesium to the two hydrogen ions. More sophisticated examples will be discussed in section 3.

Many students have difficulty with the terminology of redox. They seem to resist the idea that the oxidizing agent is reduced and the reducing agent is oxidized. Point out that the oxidizing agent causes something to be oxidized by accepting electrons and is therefore reduced in the process. The reducing agent, on the other hand, causes something to be reduced by giving away electrons, which results in its being oxidized in the process. A simple example, such as the reduction of copper oxide by hydrogen, serves as a good starting point for introducing the terminology.

$\overset{+2\ -2}{CuO}$	+	$\overset{0}{H_2}$	=	$\overset{0}{Cu}$	+	$\overset{+1\ -2}{H_2O}$
oxidizing agent: Cu is reduced going from+2 to O		reducing agent: H is oxidized going from O to + 1		each Cu gained 2 electrons		each H lost 1 electron; oxygen does not change

2. DETERMINING OXIDATION NUMBERS FROM A FORMULA

One general rule about oxidation numbers has already been given: the oxidation number of any free element is zero. Develop the other rules for assigning oxidation numbers by considering the difference in electronegativities of bonded atoms (see previous section and section 4.3). In the case of simple ionic compounds, the oxidation number of an element is the charge of its ion. Since hydrogen is the least electronegative non-metal, its oxidation number is+1 when bonded to a non-metal. In the case of metal hydrides, however, the oxidation number of hydrogen is−1, since it is more electronegative than the metal. The most electronegative element is fluorine, and oxygen is the next most electronegative element. Fluorine in combination with other elements always has an oxidation number of –1, since it always controls eight electrons as opposed to its seven valence electrons. In most cases, oxygen has an oxidation number of –2, because an oxygen atom bonded to other atoms gains control of two additional electrons. The common exception to this rule is peroxides. Examination of the electron-dot formula for hydrogen peroxide shows that each oxygen atom has gained control of one electron acquired from a hydrogen atom. The electron pair shared by the two oxygens, however, is split down the middle, since there is no difference in electronegativity between the two oxygen atoms. The result is that each oxygen atom controls seven electrons by having gained control of one additional electron, giving it an oxidation number of –1. Emphasize that the total of the oxidation numbers in compounds is zero.

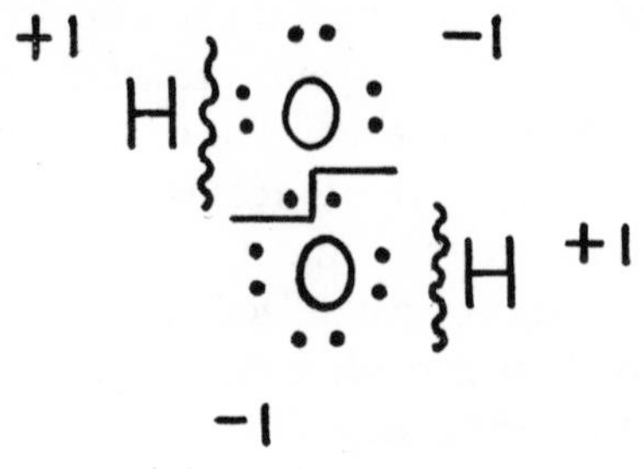

+1 H : Ö : −1

: Ö : H +1

−1

After discussing the examples already given, your students should be in a position to apply the following rules for assigning oxidation numbers:

(1) The oxidation number of a free element is zero.

(2) The oxidation number of hydrogen is +1 except in the case of metal hydrides, when it is −1.

(3) The oxidation number of oxygen is −2 except in the case of peroxides, when it is −1. Another exception is the case of OF_2, in which oxygen is +2.

(4) The total of the oxidation numbers in any specie is the charge of the specie. The total charge of compounds is zero, and the charge of an ion is equal to the total charge of the oxidation numbers of the elements making up the ion.

(5) The guiding principle in assigning oxidation numbers is based on the difference in electronegativity. The more electronegative atom controls the electrons shared with another atom.

Analyze several electron-dot formulas for various species:

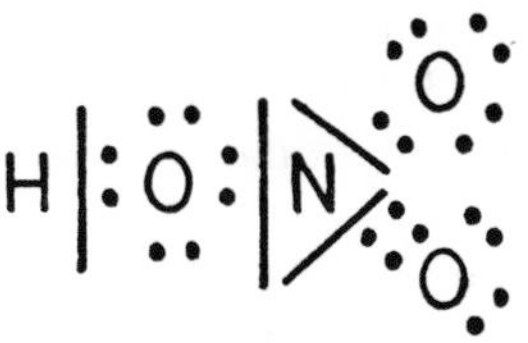

H +1, O −2, N +5

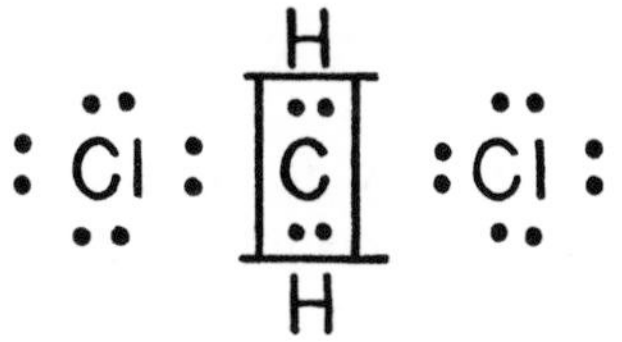

H +1, Cl −1, C 0

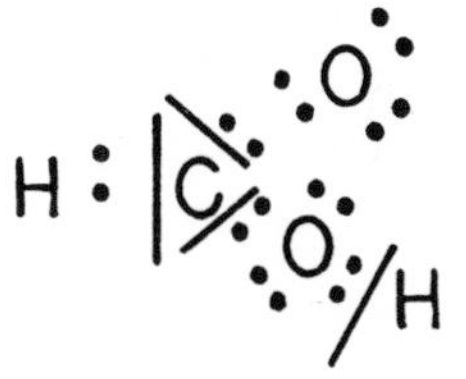

H +1, O −2, C +2

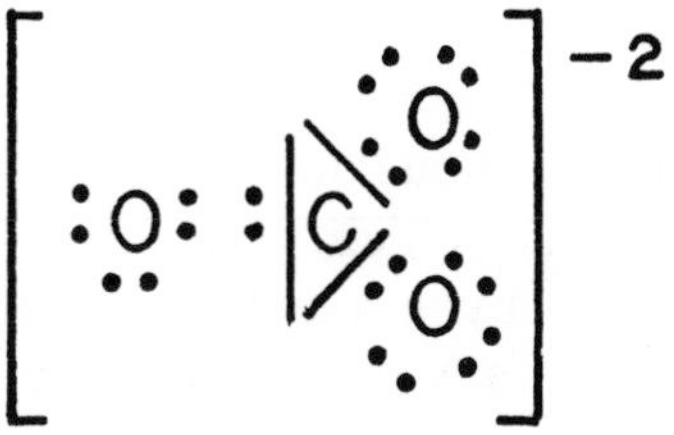

$[\ ]^{-2}$ C +4, O −2

The oxidation numbers of atoms can be determined from the formula by applying the rules mentioned above. Begin with examples, such as the following.

(1) Al_2O_3 Since O is –2, the total negative charge is –6. The total charge of the compound is zero, and so the total positive charge must be +6. The oxidation number of Al is +3.

(2) H_2SO_4 The total negative charge is –8 (each oxygen is–2). Let x represent the oxidation number of S. Each hydrogen is +1, so the charge of two hydrogens is +2. The total positive charge must be+8 to make the charge of the compound zero.

$$+2+x=+8$$
$$x=+6 \text{ (oxidation number of S)}$$

(3) $KMnO_4$ Four oxygens add up to –8, and the charge of K is +1. Let x represent the oxidation number of Mn. The total positive charge is +8, giving the compound a net charge of zero.

$$+1+x=+8$$
$$x=+7 \text{ (oxidation number of Mn)}$$

(4) PO_4^{-3} ion The total charge of the ion is–3, and the total charge of four oxygens is –8. Let x represent the oxidation number of P.

$$x+(-8)=-3$$
$$x=+5 \text{ (oxidation number of P)}$$

(5) CaH_2 This is a metal hydride. The oxidation number of Ca is +2 and two hydrogens add up to–2. The oxidation number of hydrogen is –1.

Give your students several other examples until they are able to apply the rules for assigning oxidation numbers. Remind your students that the oxidation number of an element in a compound is not necessarily its valence (see section 4.3). The oxidation number of carbon in CH_2Cl_2, for example, is zero, but the valence of carbon in this compound is 4. After your students have mastered the skill of determining oxidation numbers, they will be ready to tackle redox equations.

3. USE OF HALF-REACTIONS

Several methods for balancing redox equations are used, but the most common involve summing up half-reactions (which yields the net ionic equation) and balancing molecular equations by loss and gain of electrons. The key to the whole business is the idea that any redox reaction involves a transfer of electrons. Therefore, the number of electrons gained must equal the number of electrons lost.

Your students should develop the ability to write half-reactions by applying several simple rules. Most of the reactions which they will encounter proceed in aqueous solution that is (1) acidic or (2) neutral or basic. In many cases, oxygen is either added or removed from a specie, and water is either consumed or produced in the reaction. Give your students the following rules and then show them some examples of their application.

Acidic solution: Oxygen is removed by using H^+, producing H_2O. Oxygen is added by using H_2O, producing H^+. Hydrogen is added or removed as H^+.

Basic solution: Oxygen is removed by using H_2O, producing OH^-. Oxygen is added by using OH^-, producing H_2O. Hydrogen is removed by OH^-, producing H_2O.

Writing the half-reaction:

(1) Write the formula for the principal reactant and product.
(2) If oxygen or hydrogen is involved, apply the rules for acidic or basic solutions.
(3) Balance the equation in terms of atoms.
(4) Supply the necessary number of electrons to balance the charges.

Example 1 Write the half-reaction for the oxidation of Al metal to Al^{+3} ions.

Step 1: $Al = Al^{+3}$ (rule 1)
Step 2: $Al = Al^{+3} + 3e^-$ (rule 4)

Example 2 Write the half-reaction for the reduction of NO_3^- ion to NO gas in acid solution.

Step 1: $NO_3^- = NO$ (rule 1)
Step 2: $NO_3^- + H^+ = NO + H_2O$ (rule 2)
Step 3: $NO_3^- + 4H^+ = NO + 2H_2O$ (rule 3)
Step 4: $NO_3^- + 4H^+ + 3e^- = NO + 2H_2O$ (rule 4)

Example 3 Write the half-reaction for the oxidation of H_2S to free S in acid solution.

Step 1: $H_2S = S + 2H^+$ (rules 1 and 2 and 3)
Step 2: $H_2S = S + 2H^+ + 2e^-$ (rule 4)

Example 4 Write the half-reaction for the reduction of MnO_4^- ion to MnO_2 in basic solution.

Step 1: $MnO_4^- = MnO_2$ (rule 1)
Step 2: $MnO_4^- + H_2O = MnO_2 + OH^-$ (rule 2)
Step 3: $MnO_4^- + 2H_2O = Mn_2O + 4OH^-$ (rule 3)
Step 4: $MnO_4^- + 2H_2O + 3e^- = MnO_2 + 4OH^-$ (rule 4)

Example 5 Write the half-reaction for the oxidation of I^- ion to IO_3^- ion in basic solution.

Step 1: $I^- = IO_3^-$ (rule 1)
Step 2: $I^- + OH^- = IO_3^- + H_2O$ (rule 2)
Step 3: $I^- + 6OH^- = IO_3^- + 3H_2O$ (rule 3)
Step 4: $I^- + 6OH^- = IO_3^- + 3H_2O + 6e^-$ (rule 4)

Example 6 Write the half-reaction for the oxidation of I_2 to IO_3^- ion in acid solution.

Steps 1 and 2: $I_2 + H_2O = IO_3^- + H^+$ (rules 1 and 2)

Steps 3 and 4: $I_2 + 6H_2O = 2IO_3^- + 12H^+ + 10e^-$ (rules 3 and 4)

Give your students practice in writing half-reactions until they become proficient at playing this game. Here are a few they might try.

(1) SO_2 changed to SO_4^{-2} in acid solution.

$$SO_2 + 2H_2O = SO_4^{-2} + 4H^+ + 2e^-$$

(2) NO_3^- changed to NH_4^+ in acid solution.

$$NO_3^- + 10H^+ + 8e^- = NH_4^+ + 3H_2O$$

(3) SO_3^{-2} changed to SO_4^{-2} in basic solution.

$$SO_3^{-2} + 2OH^- = SO_4^{-2} + H_2O + 2e^-$$

(4) H_2O_2 changed to oxygen gas in acid solution.

$$H_2O_2 = O_2 + 2H^+ + 2e^-$$

(5) NH_3 is changed to nitrogen gas in basic solution.

$$2NH_3 + 6OH^- = N_2 + 6H_2O + 6e^-$$

(6) H_2O_2 acts as an oxidizing agent in basic solution.

$$H_2O_2 + 2e^- = 2OH^-$$

(Some texts give $HO_2^- + H_2O + 2e^- = 3OH^-$)

(7) $Cr_2O_7^{-2}$ is changed to Cr^{+3} ions in acid solution.

$$Cr_2O_7^{-2} + 14H^+ + 6e^- = 2Cr^{+3} + 7H_2O$$

(8) BiO_3^- ion is changed to Bi^{+3} ion in acid solution.

$$BiO_3^- + 6H^+ + 2e^- = Bi^{+3} + 3H_2O$$

4. BALANCING REDOX EQUATIONS

Emphasize that the key to balancing redox equations is the electron transfer: the number of electrons gained by the oxidizing agent must equal the number of electrons lost by the reducing agent. Start with molecular equations, since these may be more familiar to your students. The rules of the game are few but important.

(1) Write the formulas for the principal reactants and products.
(2) Spot the elements which undergo a change in oxidation number and write their oxidation numbers over the symbols.
(3) Indicate the number of electrons gained and lost by means of arrows or to one side (see examples).
(4) Determine the least common denominator for the number of electrons gained and lost and the coefficients needed to yield this number of electrons.
(5) Balance the principal reactants and products using the coefficients given by applying rule (4).
(6) Supply water where needed, then complete the balancing.

Emphasize that one must know the formulas for the reactants and products in order to write a balanced equation. Work out the following examples with your students.

Example 1 Ammonia is oxidized by oxygen gas, producing NO.

Step 1: $NH_3 + O_2 = NO + H_2O$ (rules 1 and 6)

Step 2: $\overset{-3}{N}H_3 + \overset{0}{O_2} = \overset{+2}{N}\overset{-2}{O} + H_2\overset{-2}{O}$ (rule 2)

Step 3:

(a) $\overset{-3}{N}H_3 + \overset{0}{O_2} = \overset{+2}{N}\overset{-2}{O} + H_2\overset{-2}{O}$ (rule 3)

(N to N: $-5e^-$; O_2 to O: $+4e^-$)

(b) $N^{-3} = N^{+2} + 5e^-$

$O_2 + 4e^- = 2O^{-2}$

Step 4: The least common denominator is 20. This means that we need four nitrogen atoms and five oxygen molecules (rule 4).

Step 5: $4NH_3 + 5O_2 = 4NO + 6H_2O$ (rules 5 and 6)

Example 2 Copper metal is oxidized to copper (II) nitrate by dilute nitric acid, producing NO.

Step 1: $Cu + HNO_3 = Cu(NO_3)_2 + NO$ (rule 1)

Step 2: $\overset{0}{Cu} + H\overset{+5}{N}O_3 = \overset{+2}{Cu}(NO_3)_2 + \overset{+2}{N}O$ (rule 2)

Step 3:

(a) $\overset{0}{Cu} + H\overset{+5}{N}O_3 = \overset{+2}{Cu}(NO_3)_2 + \overset{+2}{N}O$ (rule 3)

(Cu to Cu: $-2e^-$; N to N: $+3e^-$)

(b) $N^{+5} + 3e^- = N^{+2}$

$Cu^0 = Cu^{+2} + 2e^-$

Step 4: The least common denominator is 6. This means that we need three coppers and two nitrogens reduced to NO. (rule 4)

Step 5: $3Cu + 8HNO_3 = 3Cu(NO_3)_2 + 2NO + 4H_2O$ (rules 5 and 6)

Example 3 Phosphorus is oxidized to H_3PO_4 by nitric acid, which is reduced to NO in the process.

Step 1: $P + HNO_3 = H_3PO_4 + NO$ (rule 1)

Step 2: $\overset{0}{P} + H\overset{+5}{N}O_3 = H_3\overset{+5}{P}O_4 + \overset{+2}{N}O$ (rule 2)

Step 3:

(a) $\overset{0}{P} + H\overset{+5}{N}O_3 = H_3\overset{+5}{P}O_4 + \overset{+2}{N}O$ (rule 3)

(P to P: $-5e^-$; N to N: $+3e$)

(b) $P^0 = P^{+5} + 5e^-$

$N^{+5} + 3e^- = N^{+2}$

Step 4: The least common denominator is 15. Therefore we need three P's and five N's. (rule 4)

Step 5: $3P + 5HNO_3 = 3H_3PO_4 + 5NO$ (rule 5)

Step 6: $3P + 5HNO_3 + 2H_2O = 3H_3PO_4 + 5NO$ (rule 6)

Give your students plenty of practice on examples such as the following.

(1) H_2S is oxidized to free sulfur using dilute nitric acid, which is reduced to NO.

$$3H_2S + 2HNO_3 = 3S + 2NO + 4H_2O$$

(2) K_2SO_3 and $KMnO_4$ solutions react to produce MnO_2, K_2SO_4, KOH.

$$3K_2SO_3 + 2KMnO_4 + H_2O = 2MnO_2 + 3K_2SO_4 + 2KOH$$

(3) HNO_3 is decomposed thermally to yield NO_2 and O_2.

$$4HNO_3 = 4NO_2 + O_2 + 2H_2O$$

(4) Concentrated HNO_3 reacts with sulfur, producing NO_2 and H_2SO_4.

$$6HNO_3 + S = 6NO_2 + H_2SO_4 + 2H_2O$$

(5) I_2 and Cl_2 react in water, producing HIO_3 and HCl.

$$5Cl_2 + 6H_2O + I_2 = 2HIO_3 + 10HCl$$

(6) Concentrated H_2SO_4 reacts with KI crystals, producing K_2SO_4, H_2S, and I_2.

$$5H_2SO_4 + 8KI = 4K_2SO_4 + 4I_2 + 4H_2O$$

From a chemist's viewpoint, the more useful type of equation is the net ionic equation. Ionic redox equations are balanced quite easily by using half-reactions. Your students should learn to write these before attempting to balance the net ionic equations representing redox reactions. The net equation should balance electrically as well as atomically. Give your students the following rules and work out several illustrative examples.

(1) Write the half-reactions for the oxidation and reduction steps.
(2) Determine the least common denominator of electrons gained and lost, then multiply each half-reaction by the appropriate number to effect a balance of electrons transferred.
(3) Add the half-reactions.
(4) When necessary, simplify the sum of the half-reactions in order to obtain the net ionic equation.

Example 1 Aluminum metal reacts with acid, producing Al^{+3} and H_2.

Step 1: Write the half-reactions for the redox steps. (rule 1)

oxidation: $Al = Al^{+3} + 3e^-$

reduction: $2H^+ + 2e^- = H_2$

Step 2: The least common denominator is 6. Multiply the first equation by 2 and the second by 3. Add the equations. (rules 2 and 3)

$$2(Al = Al^{+3} + 3e^-)$$
$$3(2H^+ - 2e^- = H_2)$$
$$\overline{2Al + 6H^+ = 2Al^{+3} + 3H_2}$$

Example 2 MnO_4^- ions in acid solution react with SO_2 to produce SO_4^{-2} and Mn^{+2} ions.

Step 1: Write the half-reactions. (rule 1)

oxidation: $SO_2 + 2H_2O = SO_4^{-2} + 4H^+ + 2e^-$

reduction: $MnO_4^- + 8H^+ + 5e^- = Mn^{+2} + 4H_2O$

Step 2 The least common denominator is 10. Multiply the first equation by

5 and the second by 2. Add the equations. (rules 2 and 3)

$$5(SO_2 + 2H_2O = SO_4^{-2} + 4H^+ + 2e^-)$$
$$2(MnO_4^- + 8H^+ + 5e^- = Mn^{+2} + 4H_2O)$$
$$5SO_2 + 10H_2O + 2MnO_4^- + 16H^+ = 5SO_4^{-2} + 20H^+ + 2Mn^{+2} + 8H_2O$$

Step 3: Simplify by canceling excess H_2O and H^+. (rule 4)

$$5SO_2 + 2H_2O + 2MnO_4^- = 5SO_4^{-2} + 2Mn^{+2} + 4H^+$$

Example 3 H_2O_2 and $Cr_2O_7^{-2}$ yield O_2 and Cr^{+3} in acid solution.

Step 1: Write the half-reactions. (rule 1)

oxidation: $H_2O_2 = O_2 + 2H^+ + 2e^-$

reduction: $Cr_2O_7^{-2} + 14H^+ + 6e^- = 2Cr^{+3} + 7H_2O$

Step 2: The least common denominator is 6. Multiply the first equation by 3 and the second by 1. Add the half-reactions. (rules 2 and 3)

$$3(H_2O_2 = O_2 + 2H^+ + 2e^-)$$
$$1(Cr_2O_7^{-2} + 14H^+ + 6e^- = 2Cr^{+3} + 7H_2O)$$
$$3H_2O_2 + Cr_2O_7^{-2} + 14H^+ = 3O_2 + 2Cr^{+3} + 6H^+ + 7H_2O$$

Step 3: Simplify. (rule 4)

$$3H_2O_2 + Cr_2O_7^{-2} + 8H^+ = 3O_2 + 2Cr^{+3} + 7H_2O$$

Example 4 ClO^- and I^- ions in basic solution produce Cl^- and IO_3^- ions.

Write the half-reactions. The least common denominator is 6. Multiply the first equation by 3 and the second by 1. Add the half-reactions and simplify to obtain the net equation.

$$3(ClO^- + H_2O + 2e^- = Cl^- + 2OH^-)$$
$$1(I^- + 6OH^- = IO_3^- + 3H_2O + 6e^-)$$
$$3ClO^- + 3H_2O + 6OH^- + I^- = 3Cl^- + 6OH^- + IO_3^- + 3H_2O$$
$$3ClO^- + I^- = 3Cl^- + IO_3^-$$

Give your students several examples to work out by themselves. Remind them that the net equation should balance electronically.

(1) MnO_4^- and H_2O_2 produce Mn^{+2} and O_2 in acid solution.

$$2MnO_4^- + 5H_2O_2 + 6H^+ = Mn^{+2} + 5O_2 + 8H_2O$$

(2) $Bi(OH)_3$ and $Sn(OH)_3^-$ ions in basic solution produce Bi and $Sn(OH)_6^{-2}$ ions.

$$2Bi(OH)_3 + 3Sn(OH)_3^- + 3OH^- = 2Bi + 3Sn(OH)_6^{-2}$$

(3) Mn^{+2} and BiO_3^- ions in acid solution produce MnO_4^- and Bi^{+3}.

$$5BiO_3 + 2Mn^{+2} + 14H^+ = 5Bi^{+3} + 2MnO_4^- + 7H_2O$$

(4) Mn^{+2} and ClO_3^- ions in acid solution produce MnO_2 and ClO_2.

$$Mn^{+2} + 2ClO_3^- = MnO_2 + ClO_2$$

(5) VO_4^{-3} ions and SO_2 in acid solution produce V^{+2} and SO_4^{-2} ions.

$$2VO_4^{-3} + 3SO_2 + 4H^+ = 2V^{+2} + 3SO_4^{-2} + 2H_2O$$

(6) NO_3^- ions in basic solution are reduced to NH_4^+ by Al metal.

$$3NO_3^- + 8Al + 30H^+ = 8Al^{+3} + 3NH_4^+ + 9H_2O$$

5. HOW TO USE THE E° CONCEPT AND ITS RELATION TO EQUILIBRIUM

Your students should have some feeling for predicting the ease with which a metal loses electrons to form positive ions from their study of ionization energy (see section 3.7). The more active metals have lower ionization energy and should undergo oxidation more easily than the less active metals. Your students should be able to understand why the order of decreasing ionization energy for the alkali metals in Li > Na > K, etc. This order indicates that sodium is more active than lithium. Examination of the electromotive series (oxidation potentials) tells us that lithium is above sodium, however. This apparently contradictory order of reactivity is due to the experimental method by which oxidation potentials are measured. Ionization energy is measured in the gaseous state, but the oxidation potential is measured in aqueous solution. The higher the oxidation potential ($E°$ value), the more favored is the oxidation reaction. The $E°$ value is a measure of the tendency of an oxidation reaction to proceed. For alkali metals, this reaction is written

$$M = M^+ + e^-$$

What this equation does not show, however, is the fact that the metal ion is hydrated when the reaction is carried out in aqueous solution. Lithium ions, being considerably smaller than sodium ions, have a higher positive charge density and consequently have a greater attraction for water dipoles. The tendency of the ions to hydrate favors the reaction producing ions (hydration energy is released). The reaction producing hydrated lithium ions releases more free energy than that producing hydrated sodium ions, and so the $E°$ value for the oxidation of lithium in aqueous solution is greater than that for sodium (see sections 7.8 and 9.8).

In a sense, the potential energy of a body with respect to the earth is measured by its elevation above sea level. The oxidation potential (tendency to undergo oxidation) is referred to an arbitrary standard, too: the hydrogen electrode, which has a defined $E°$ value of exactly zero volts at 25° and 1 atmosphere pressure. Point out that the best oxidizing agents are the poorest reducing agents, and the best reducing agents are the poorest oxidizing agents.

Before examining the hydrogen electrode and the determination of oxidation potentials, however, develop the concept of cell voltage, using an electrochemical cell consisting of a copper electrode immersed in a 1 M CuSO solution and a silver electrode immersed in a 1 M $AgNO_3$ solution. An electrochemical cell (voltaic cell) consists of two electrodes of different oxidation potentials, an electrolytic solution, and an external circuit. The two beakers are connected by means of a salt bridge (such as $NaNO_3$ solution). Describe what is occurring at each electrode. In the case of copper, some of the copper

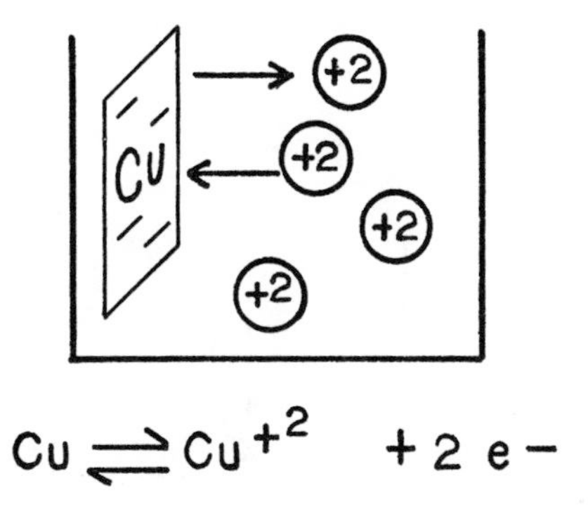

atoms lose electrons and enter the solution as copper ions. The electrons remain in the copper plate, giving it a slight negative charge. At the same time, some copper ions migrate toward the plate and accept electrons, forming copper atoms. At equilibrium, the two processes are proceeding at the same rate, and the concentrations of copper ions and electrons (charge density) have definite values. Consider the silver plate in equilibrium with silver ions in the solution. Here, too, we have some silver atoms losing electrons to produce silver ions, and some silver ions are accepting electrons, forming silver atoms. At equilibrium, there is a definite concentration of silver ions and electrons. Since silver has a lower tendency to become oxidized, however, the electron concentration on the silver plate is less than that on the copper plate.

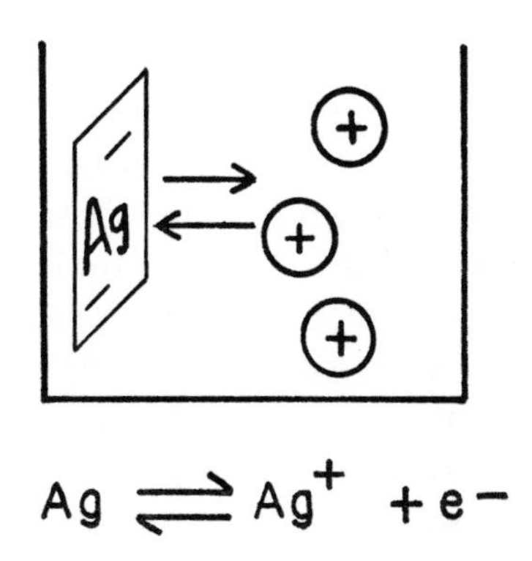

If the two plates are connected by means of a wire, a flow of electrons from the copper to the silver plate occurs, because the electron density on the copper plate is greater than that on the silver plate. Equilibrium is upset at both electrodes, and so the system undergoes a change.

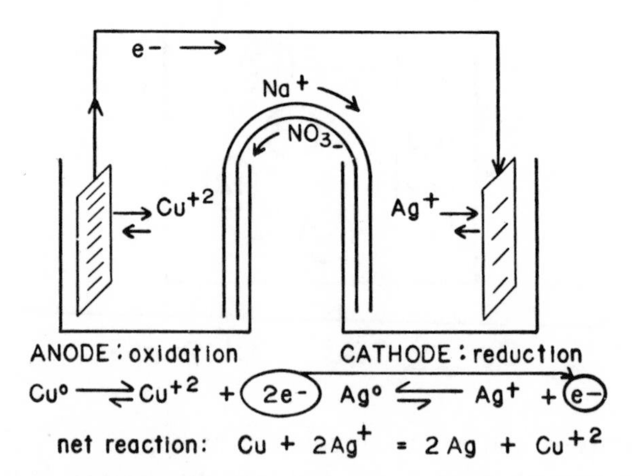

Since the electron concentration on the copper plate is decreasing, the net effect is to produce more electrons, accompanied by the formation of more copper ions (Le Chatelier's principle). Since the electron concentration on the silver plate increases, the balance is upset. Electrons must be consumed, along with silver ions, to produce silver metal. The net reaction is that copper goes into solution as copper ions, and silver ions are reduced to silver metal. A difference in potential exists between the two plates as long as the electron density on the copper plate is greater than that on the silver plate.

As more copper ions are produced, however, their concentration increases, increasing the rate of the reaction between copper ions and electrons. The electron density on the copper plate gradually decreases. As silver ions are consumed, however, the electron density on the silver plate gradually increases. Eventually the electron concentration on both plates becomes equal, and so no more difference in potential exists. The electrons stop flowing, and the system comes to equilibrium (no more change occurs).

The function of the salt bridge is to allow the ions to migrate in the solution. Point out that as positive copper ions are produced at the copper plate, a net positive charge begins to accumulate in the solution, preventing the electrons from leaving the plate (Coulomb's law). Likewise, as silver ions are reduced, a preponderance of nitrate ions gives the solution near the silver plate a negative charge, repelling any incoming electrons. The solutions must be kept electrically neutral. Negative ions (anions) are attracted by the accumulating copper ions and migrate toward the copper plate (anode). Positive ions (cations) are attracted toward the silver plate (cathode). Define the anode as the electrode at which oxidation occurs and the cathode at which reduction occurs. The general tendency is for cations to drift toward the cathode and away from the anode, while anions drift toward the anode and away from the cathode. The ion drift keeps the solution electrically neutral. An excellent CHEM Study film, "Electrochemical Cells," clearly illustrates and discusses the processes occurring during the operation of a cell.

Discussing the copper-silver cell should impress your students with the relationship between equilibrium, concentration, and cell voltage. At equilibrium, no more change occurs. The potential difference between the electrodes is zero, and so the free energy of the system is zero (conditions for equilibrium). Le Chatelier's principle can be used to predict the effect of changing the concentrations on the voltage of the cell. Review calculations involving $E°$ values with your students (see section 5.8). Point out that $E°$ values depend on concentration, not the amount of material involved.

oxidation:	$Cu = Cu^{+2} + 2e^-$	$-$ 0.34 volts
reduction:	$2(Ag^+ + e^- = Ag)$	+ 0.80
net reaction:	$2Ag^+ + Cu = Cu^{+2} + 2Ag$	+ 0.46 v

Having gained insight into the operation of a cell, your students should now be in a position to understand the concept of the hydrogen electrode. The CHEM Study film "Electrochemical Cells" shows a hydrogen electrode in operation, as well as the effect of changing the hydrogen ion concentration on the cell voltage. By definition, the $E°$ value for the electrode consisting of hydrogen gas (1 atmosphere pressure) in equilibrium with 1 M H^+ ion at 25° C on a finely-divided platinum surface is exactly zero volts. A cell can be constructed using this as one electrode and a metal (or other system) in equilibrium with 1 M ion concentration comprising the other electrode. The potential difference, therefore, is the $E°$ value for the half-reaction being compared to the hydrogen electrode. The direction of current flow determines which electrode is the anode and which is the cathode.

Show your students a diagram of the copper-copper ion electrode versus a hydrogen electrode.

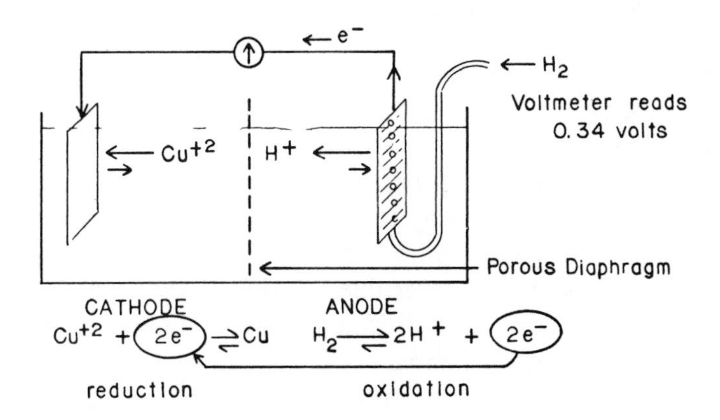

Since the spontaneous reaction has a voltage of +0.34 volts, reducing copper ions, the half-reaction shown has a positive $E°$ value.

$$Cu^{+2} + 2e^- = Cu \qquad +0.34 \text{ volts}$$

Reversing the equation to show oxidation of copper changes the sign of the voltage. The oxidation potential for copper, therefore, is − 0.34 volts, and the reduction potential is + 0.34 volts. Show your students a similar cell consisting of a zinc plate immersed in a 1 M zinc ion solution in place of the copper electrode. In this case, the current flows from the zinc (anode) to the hydrogen electrode (cathode), where reduction occurs. The oxidation potential of zinc is + 0.76 volts, and its reduction potential is − 0.76 volts.

Calculations involving $E°$ values, the determination of cell voltages, and the feasibility of redox reactions were discussed in section 5.8. Ask your students to predict, on the basis of the "activity series," whether or not silver will displace hydrogen from H_2S. Then show them the effect of concentration, pointing out that Ag_2S is so highly insoluble that the silver ion concentration in the system is extremely low, favoring the reaction

$$2Ag + H_2S = Ag_2S + H_2$$

Using the following oxidation potentials, determine the $E°$ value for the above reaction.

$$2Ag + H_2S_{(g)} = Ag_2S + 2H^+ + 2e^- \qquad + 0.036 \text{ volts}$$
$$2H^+ + 2e^- = H_2 \qquad 0.000$$
$$2Ag + H_2S = Ag_2S + H_2 \qquad + 0.036 \text{ volts}$$

Since the $E°$ value for the reaction is positive, it is feasible, although the reaction does not proceed extensively. Removal of hydrogen, however, favors the reaction proceeding to the right. It's little wonder that silver metal tarnishes when exposed to hydrogen sulfide or eggs, which release H_2S from the decomposition of methionine.

6. PREDICTING ELECTROCHEMICAL REACTIONS

The operation of electrochemical cells was discussed in the previous section, and the calculation of $E°$ values for cells was discussed in section 5.8. Several electrolysis cells were discussed in section 7.8. Distinguish between electrochemical cells (which produce energy) and electrolysis cells (which consume energy). In theory, any redox reaction can be made to operate as an electrochemical cell and the reverse reaction as an electrolysis cell.

A simple example of a reversible reaction is the lead storage battery. The electrodes consist of a lead dioxide plate (oxidation number of Pb is +4) and a lead plate (oxidation number of Pb is 0) which are immersed in sulfuric acid solution. As the cell operates, producing energy, lead sulfate is produced on both plates (oxidation number of Pb is +2).

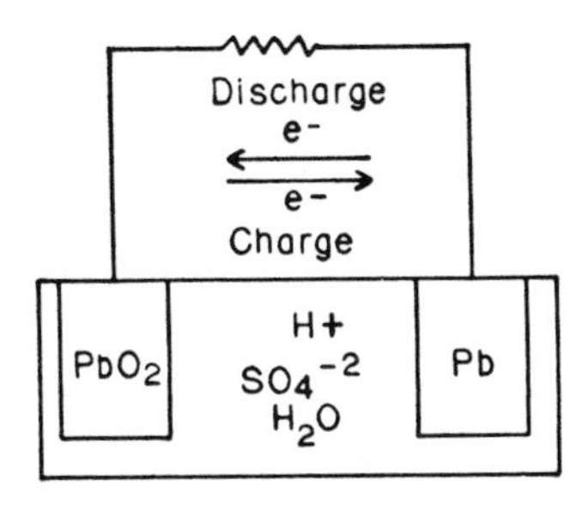

Discharge: Pb is anode, PbO_2 is cathode

Charge: Pb covered with $PbSO_4$ is cathode, PbO_2 covered with $PbSO_4$ is anode

Consider the oxidation potentials of the half-reactions involving lead, lead dioxide and sulfate ion in acid solution:

$$Pb + SO_4^{-2} = PbSO_4 + 2e^- \qquad +0.31 \text{ volts}$$
$$PbSO_4 + 2H_2O = PbO_2 + SO_4^{-2} + 4H^+ + 2e^- \qquad -1.69 \text{ volts}$$

The large negative value for the second half-reaction suggests that PbO_2 is an excellent oxidizing agent. Reversing the equation (writing it as a reduction) changes the sign of the $E°$ value, and we can calculate the standard voltage for the storage battery.

$$Pb + SO_4^{-2} = PbSO_4 + 2e^- \qquad +0.31 \text{ volts}$$
$$PbO_2 + SO_4^{-2} + 4H^+ + 2e^- = PbSO_4 + 2H_2O \qquad +1.69 \text{ volts}$$
$$\overline{Pb + PbO_2 + 4H^+ + 2SO_4^{-2} = 2PbSO_4 + 2H_2O \qquad +2.00 \text{ volts}}$$

As the cell operates, the concentrations of H^+ and SO_4^{-2} ions decrease (H_2SO_4 is used up), and the specific gravity of the electrolyte decreases. A hydrometer is a good method for determining the condition of the lead storage battery. The voltage also decreases as equilibrium is approached. Pumping the electrons "uphill" reverses their normal flow, and the battery is re-charged (electrolysis).

In principle, the reaction between hydrogen and oxygen, or any hydrocarbon plus oxygen, can be engineered into a fuel cell. The problem consists of separating the oxidation and reduction steps and transferring the electrons through an external circuit, thereby harnessing the free energy of the reaction.

Demonstrate that a current can be obtained from the reaction between an oxidizing and reducing agent by making a cell using acidified permanganate and iodide ions. Use a salt bridge, such as $NaNO_3$, as the electrolyte in the salt bridge, preventing mixing by means of cotton or glass wool plugs in the ends of U-tube. Use platinum electrodes. Point out that a difference in potential exists. Connect the electrodes by means of a wire and point out the brown color that develops around the anode, due to the formation of free iodine (in the form of I_3^- ion).

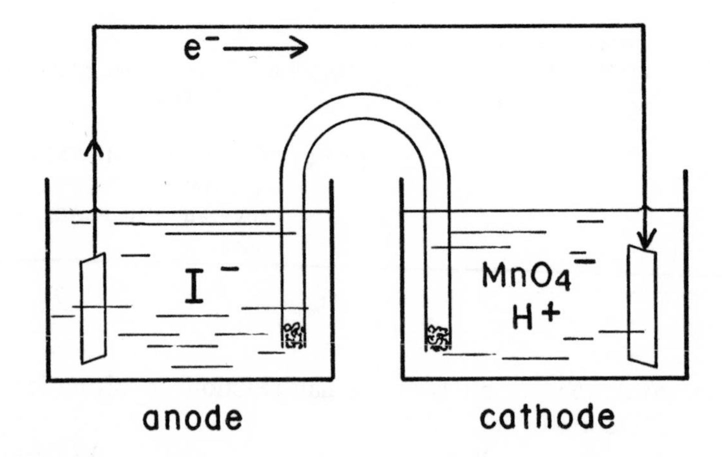

The steps involved are:

oxidation:	$5(2I^- = I_2 + 2e^-)$	$-$ 0.54 volts
reduction:	$2(MnO_4^- + 8H^+ + 5e^- = Mn^{+2} + 4H_2O)$	$+$ 1.51 volts
	$10I^- + 2MnO_4^- + 16H^+ = 5I_2 + 2Mn^{+2} + 8H_2O$	$+$ 0.97volts

If more than one electrode reaction is possible in an electrolysis cell the one having the higher $E°$ value is more likely to happen. The exceptions are caused by overvoltage (see section 7.8). A good illustration of this rule is the electrolytic refining of copper. Crude copper metal, containing traces of gold and silver, serves as the anode, and a thin piece of pure copper serves as the cathode. The electrodes are immersed in a solution of copper sulfate.

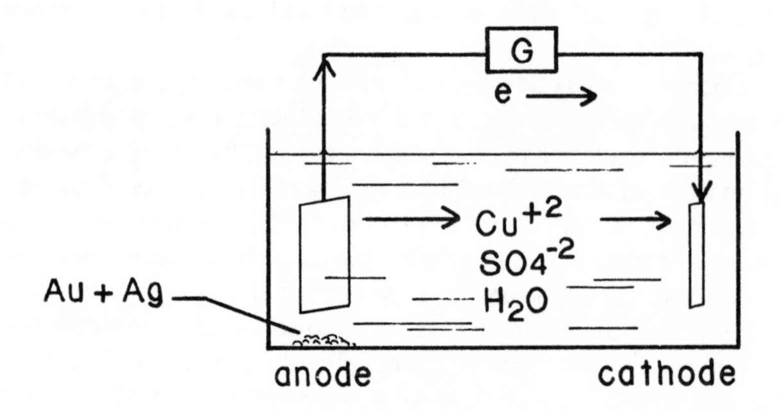

The possible oxidation reactions are:

$Cu = Cu^{+2} + 2e^-$	-0.34 volts
$Ag = Ag^+ + e^-$	-0.80 volts
$2H_2O = O_2 + 4H^+ + 4e^-$	-0.82 volts
$Au = Au^{+3} + 3e^-$	-1.50 volts

Copper metal is the most easily oxidized substance, and so the gold and silver metals fall to the bottom of the container, producing "anode sludge." If the voltage is not too high, the only oxidation reaction occurring will involve copper. Possible reduction reactions are:

$Cu^{+2} + 2e^- =$	Cu $+0.34$ volts
$2H_2O + 2e^- = H_2 + 2OH$	-0.41 volts

Copper is much more easily reduced than water, and so hydrogen is not produced at the cathode. Pure copper metal is deposited.

More applications of selective redox will be discussed in the next section. In general, water is discharged at the electrode in place of a stable cation (group I or II metal ions) or a stable anion (NO_3^-, F^-, SO_4^{-2}).

7. INTERPRETING THE CORROSION OF METALS

A popular theory which accounts for the corrosion of metals is based on the idea of a miniature voltaic cell. Carbon steel, for example, contains small crystals of carbon imbedded in iron. The carbon particles act as miniature cathodes, and the iron metal acts as an anode, giving up electrons which are transmitted through the carbon particles to water, which is reduced on the surface of the carbon particles. Whenever a mixture of different metals is exposed to an electrolytic solution, such as salt water, the more active metal becomes oxidized.

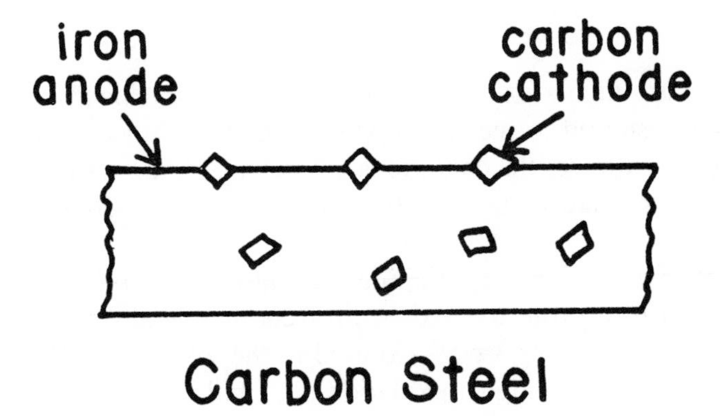

Iron and steel are very extensively used in many different applications. Since iron does not form a protective oxide coating, as does aluminum (iron rust does not stick to the metal), this metal must be protected from corrosion by either applying a coating, using a more active metal which acts as a sacrificial anode, or by alloying the iron with corrosion-resistant metals (stainless steel). The most obvious type of coating, paint, prevents the iron from making contact with an electrolytic solution. Discuss the principles of redox used in making galvanized iron and tin plating.

In making galvanized iron, a thin layer of zinc is formed on the surface of iron, which is dipped into molten zinc. Since zinc oxide sticks to the surface, the metal is protected from corrosion. If a scratch forms, however, iron is exposed to the action of an electrolytic solution. The requirements for a voltaic cell are present: two electrodes and an electrolytic solution.

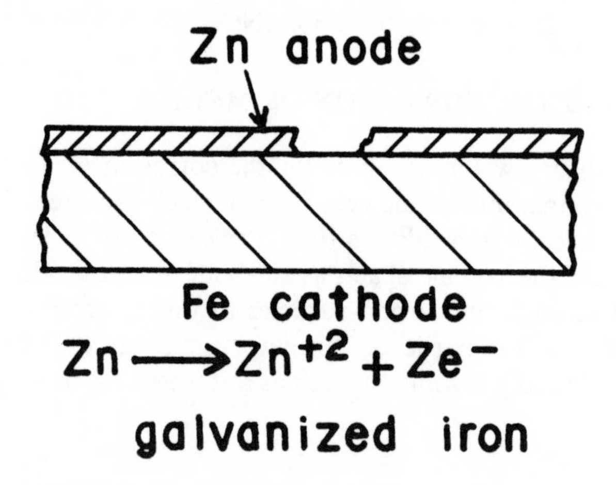

Since zinc has a higher oxidation potential than iron, zinc gives up electrons, which are transferred to the electrolyte via the iron. Since the iron is slightly negative (as a cathode, the conditions are reducing), it does not dissolve. The zinc coating gradually dissolves, but the iron remains protected as long as zinc is present.

Tin plate is produced by dipping iron into molten tin. The thin layer of tin (which forms a protective oxide) protects the metal from corrosion. If a scratch is made, however, iron is exposed to the solution, and a voltaic cell is set up. Since iron has a higher oxidation potential than tin, the iron dissolves (acts as anode), and the tin remains reduced (acts as cathode). The result is a pin hole in the tin can, which gradually disintegrates.

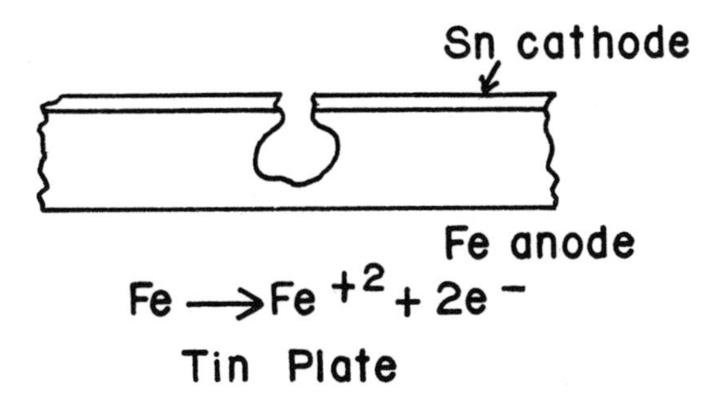

Tin Plate

Iron pipes buried under the ground can be protected by attaching a piece of magnesium to the pipe by means of a wire. Since magnesium has a higher oxidation potential than iron, it acts as the anode and gradually dissolves in the ground water (electrolytic solution), leaving the iron protected (iron acts as the cathode).

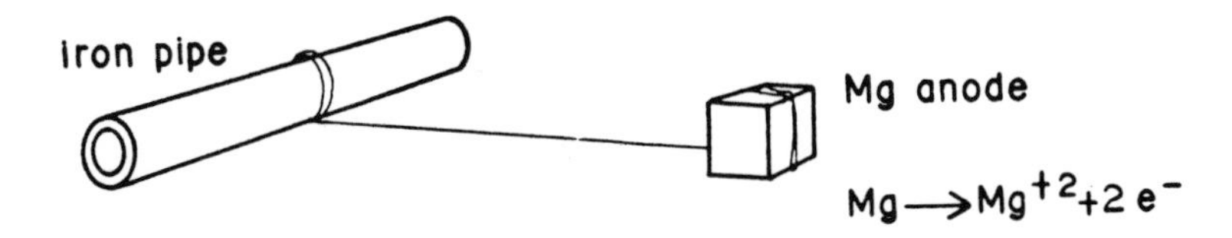

Other illustrations will be discussed in Chapter 13.

11

Teaching Organic Chemistry

1. EXPLAINING THE VARIETY AND PROPERTIES OF ORGANIC COMPOUNDS

All organic compounds contain carbon. Before Wohler synthesized urea in 1828, chemists believed that organic compounds had to originate in living matter (vitalistic theory), and this idea persisted for some time after Wohler's discovery. Tell your students that the number of possible organic compounds is virtually without limit, since carbon is able to bond with itself and other elements in countless permutations and combinations. Just as many different floor plans and styles of houses can be built from a pile of bricks, so many molecules can be built from a relatively small number of atoms. The most common elements that bond with carbon in forming organic compounds are hydrogen, oxygen, nitrogen, the halogens, sulfur, and phosphorus. A variety of metals also bond to carbon (tetraethyl lead, for example). Organic molecules range from the very simple, such as methane, to the highly complex biopolymers called proteins, which contain thousands of atoms. Chemists synthesize many new organic compounds each year during the course of various research projects. Our chief sources of organic compounds are petroleum and coal. These mixtures are subjected to distillation (destructive and fractional) to produce raw materials which chemists convert into products.

Emphasize that the vast majority of organic compounds are molecular, although some salts (usually salts of amines) exist. Only a small percentage of carbon compounds are soluble in water; so organic chemists usually work with non-aqueous solvents. Unlike reactions between inorganic ions in solution (which are very fast), organic reactions sometimes take hours to run their course. Very often more than one product results. Under one set of conditions the products often are different than under another set of conditions. Although the number of organic compounds is astronomical, chemists have found that classifying compounds on the basis of structure and functional groups simplifies the task of predicting their behavior. The field of organic chemistry cannot be developed in an introductory course, but your students should be given some appreciation of the general behavior of different classes of compounds, isomerism, and a few examples of the application of chemical principles to organic reactions. They should also be given examples of organic compounds and reactions essential to life. Give them examples of several common types of organic reactions, such as substitution, addition, polymerization (addition as well as condensation), hydrolysis of esters and peptides, and acid-base reactions. Don't spend too much time on nomenclature, but give them some examples of applying some of the rules for naming compounds. Show them examples of different types of isomerism, including optical and geometric isomerism. Remind your students that organic molecules are three dimensional. Organic chemists must think in three dimensions.

2. CLASSIFYING AND NAMING ORGANIC COMPOUNDS

Organic compounds can be considered as hydrocarbons or their derivatives, so begin with a discussion of alkanes (paraffins, or saturated hydrocarbons). These are non-polar and generally have little reactivity. The word *paraffin* describes this lack of reactivity. The names of simple paraffins are composed of a prefix, which denotes the number of carbon atoms, and the suffix *-ane,* which signifies that the compound contains no multiple bonds. Saturated means that the compound can hold no more atoms, as opposed to *unsaturated,* which means that a compound is able to add more atoms to itself by means of multiple (double or triple) bonds. Review sp^3 bonding with your students (see section 4.4), pointing out that single-bonded carbon atoms have a tetrahedral configuration. There is free rotation about a single bond.

Give your students the prefixes denoting the number of carbon atoms up to ten and add the suffix *-ane* to name the first ten normal (unbranched) alkanes. Show them the structural formulas, pointing out that the lines joining the atoms represent pairs of shared electrons. Since carbon has four valence electrons, it is able to share four pairs of electrons with other atoms. Therefore, each carbon atom normally has four "hands" which must be occupied. Point out that the chemist tries to write formulas as simply as possible. He does not write the formula for an organic compound as shown in most high school texts. Instead, he writes formulas as shown below. The atoms following each carbon atom are bonded to the carbon atom immediately preceding them.

Compound	*Number of C Atoms*	*Molecular Formula*	*Structural Formula*
methane	1	CH_4	$\begin{array}{ccc} & \mathrm{H} & \\ & \vert & \\ \mathrm{H}- & \mathrm{C} & -\mathrm{H} \\ & \vert & \\ & \mathrm{H} & \end{array}$ CH_4
ethane	2	C_2H_6	$\begin{array}{cccc} & \mathrm{H} & \mathrm{H} & \\ & \vert & \vert & \\ \mathrm{H}- & \mathrm{C}- & \mathrm{C} & -\mathrm{H} \\ & \vert & \vert & \\ & \mathrm{H} & \mathrm{H} & \end{array}$ CH_3CH_3
propane	3	C_3H_8	$\begin{array}{ccccc} & \mathrm{H} & \mathrm{H} & \mathrm{H} & \\ & \vert & \vert & \vert & \\ \mathrm{H}- & \mathrm{C}- & \mathrm{C}- & \mathrm{C} & -\mathrm{H} \\ & \vert & \vert & \vert & \\ & \mathrm{H} & \mathrm{H} & \mathrm{H} & \end{array}$ $CH_3CH_2CH_3$
butane	4	C_4H_{10}	$\begin{array}{cccccc} & \mathrm{H} & \mathrm{H} & \mathrm{H} & \mathrm{H} & \\ & \vert & \vert & \vert & \vert & \\ \mathrm{H}- & \mathrm{C}- & \mathrm{C}- & \mathrm{C}- & \mathrm{C} & -\mathrm{H} \\ & \vert & \vert & \vert & \vert & \\ & \mathrm{H} & \mathrm{H} & \mathrm{H} & \mathrm{H} & \end{array}$ $CH_3CH_2CH_2CH_3$
pentane	5	C_5H_{12}	$CH_3CH_2CH_2CH_2CH_3$ or $CH_3(CH_2)_3CH_3$
hexane	6	C_6H_{14}	$CH_3(CH_2)_4CH_3$
heptane	7	C_7H_{16}	$CH_3(CH_2)_5CH_3$
octane	8	C_8H_{18}	$CH_3(CH_2)_6CH_3$
nonane	9	C_9H_{20}	$CH_3(CH_2)_7CH_3$
decane	10	$C_{10}H_{22}$	$CH_3(CH_2)_8CH_3$

Emphasize, by means of ball and stick models, that there is no such thing as a "straight chain." The bond angles are 109° 28′, and the bonds are free to rotate. Point out that the prefixes from pentane are derived from the Greek numbers. Note that the formulas for the above compounds fit the general formula $C_nH_{(2n+2)}$. This is true for any non-cyclic alkane, whether it be straight chain or branched. Point out that the general formula is not sacred, however, since cyclic alkanes resemble the formula for alkenes, C_nH_{2n}.

Introduce the idea of *structural isomerism* and the rules for naming branched chain hydorcarbons. There are two possible butanes, which can be distinguished as normal butane and isobutane. When one encounters more complex compounds, however, systematic names are in order. The following rules will give your students some idea of what is meant by systematic nomenclature.

(1) Compound bears the name of the longest carbon chain.
(2) The longest chain is numbered from one end to the other, the direction being so chosen as to give the lowest numbers possible to the side chains.
(3) The numbers designating the carbon atoms in the chain are used to prefix the groups attached to the chains (street address).
(4) The prefix *n*– (meaning normal) designates an unbranched compound.
(5) If more than one *like* group is attached to the chain, the number of such groups is designated by the Greek number prefixes *di-*, *tri-*, *tetra-*, etc.
(6) Radicals derived from hydrocarbons end with *-yl*.

If your students think that this is cumbersome, show them the rules summarized in the Chemical Rubber Company's *Handbook of Chemistry and Physics*, which is only a summary of nomenclature rules. Show your students the following examples to illustrate the operation of the rules and the way chemists write structural formulas. Illustrate the structures of some of these compounds by means of ball and stick models.

$$\begin{array}{l} CH_3\underset{\displaystyle CH_3}{\underset{|}{C}}HCH_3 \end{array} \qquad \text{isobutane or 2-methylpropane}$$

$$\begin{array}{l} CH_3\underset{\displaystyle CH_3}{\underset{|}{C}}HCH_2CH_3 \end{array} \qquad \text{2-methylbutane (not 3-methylbutane)}$$

$$\begin{array}{l} CH_3CH_2CH_2CH_2\underset{\displaystyle C_2H_5}{\underset{|}{C}}HCH_2CH_3 \end{array} \qquad \text{3-ethylheptane}$$

$$CH_3{-}\overset{\displaystyle CH_3}{\overset{|}{\underset{\displaystyle CH_3}{\underset{|}{C}}}}{-}CH_2\,\underset{\displaystyle CH_3}{\underset{|}{C}}HCH_3 \qquad \text{2, 2, 4-trimethylpentane (isooctane)}$$

$$CH_3\underset{\displaystyle CH_3}{\underset{|}{C}}HCH_2{-}\overset{\displaystyle CH_3}{\overset{|}{\underset{\displaystyle C_2H_5}{\underset{|}{C}}}}{-}CH_2CH_3 \qquad \text{2, 4-dimethyl-4-ethylhexane}$$

Alkenes (olefins) are unsaturated hydrocarbons containing one or more double bonds. Review sp^2 bonding (see section 4.4), emphasizing the geometry involved and the restricted rotation about the double bond. Use models. The prefix part of the name denotes the number of carbon atoms, and the suffix *-ene* denotes a double bond, whose "street address" is given by a number. The number of double bonds is given by a Greek prefix coming before *-ene*. Several examples should be used to give your students some insight into how these compounds are named.

$CH_2 = CHCH_2CH_3$	butene-1	(or 1-butene)
$CH_3CH = CHCH_3$	butene-2	(or 2-butene)

$$\begin{array}{l} CH_3CH = \underset{\displaystyle CH_3}{\underset{|}{C}}—CH_2CH = CH_2 \end{array}$$ 4-methylhexadiene-1, 4

Alkynes (acetylenes) are unsaturated hydrocarbons containing at least one triple bond, denoted by the suffix *-yne*. The bonding here is *sp*, and the bond angle is 180° (see section 4.4). The same rules already mentioned apply to the naming of alkynes.

$CH_3C \equiv CCH_3$ butyne-2 (or 2-butyne)

$CH_3CH_2\underset{\displaystyle CH_3}{\underset{|}{C}}HC\equiv CH$ 2-methylpentyne-1

$CH_2 = CH\underset{\displaystyle C_2H_5}{\underset{|}{C}}HC \equiv CH$ 3-ethylpentene-1-yne-4

By this time your students should begin to appreciate the fact that all sorts of permutations and combinations are possible for carbon atoms, but they haven't seen anything yet. Introduce the idea of cyclic (ring) compounds. The possibilities are cyclic alkanes and alkenes, not to mention aromatic compounds which have properties somewhat different from non-aromatic compounds. There is also a host of heterocyclic compounds, which consist of rings containing other atoms beside carbon. Multiple-ring compounds are also quite common. Chemists usually do not show the carbon atoms in a cyclic compound by means of a symbol. The corners of the geometric figure represent carbon atoms. Names of cyclic hydrocarbons are usually prefixed by *cyclo-*.

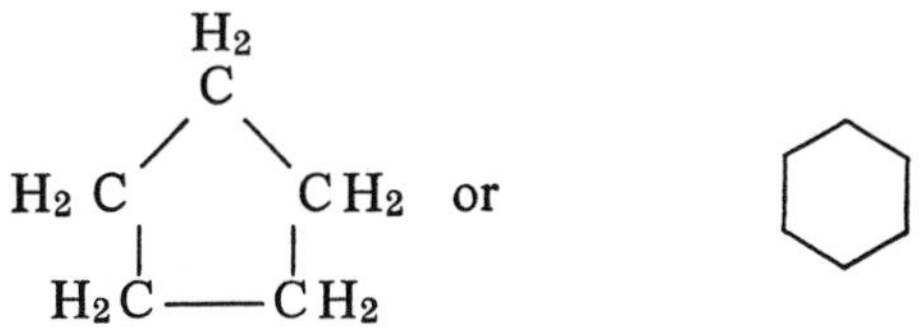

```
        H2
        C
      /   \
  H2 C     C H2   or    (hexagon)    cyclopentane
     |     |
   H2 C —— C H2
```

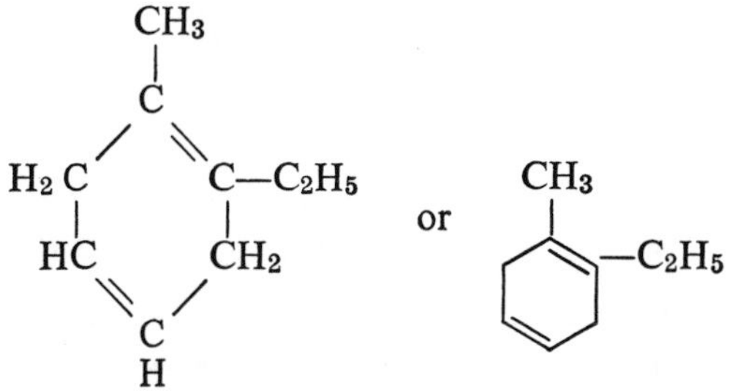

```
        CH3
         |
         C
       /   \\
  H2 C      C—C2H5          CH3
     |      |          or    |             1-methyl-2-ethylcyclo-
    HC      CH2          (ring)—C2H5       hexadiene-1,4
      \\   /
        C
        H
```

Make a model of cyclohexane and show your students that it is not planar. In fact, cyclohexane can assume the famous "boat" and "chair" forms. You might even stick a methyl group on cyclohexane and show the axial (directed away from the general plane of the ring) and equatorial configurations that are possible.

cyclohexane

equatorial

axial

chair form

boat form

simplified 3-dimensional representation of cyclohexane

Aromatic compounds (many have distinct but not unpleasant odors) consist of at least one ring which is planar and exhibits resonance. The classic example is benzene, which posed a problem for many years. August Kekule proposed his famous structural formula in 1865:

The Kekule structure implies resonance of alternating double bonds. The more modern interpretation is the assumption that the bonding of the carbon atoms is sp^2, in which the bond angle is 120° (the same as the angles in a hexagon), accounting for the planar structure of the benzene ring. Each unhybridized *p* orbital contains one pi electron, and these are responsible for the phenomenon we call resonance. These electrons are free to roam over the entire molecule and are not localized between two carbon atoms as would be the case in a double bond. Benzene does not contain "alternating double bonds" at all; the bond lengths and strengths are all the same and intermediate between those of single and double bonds. Point out that the planar geometry of the benzene ring permits the unhybridized *p* orbitals to be parallel to each other, permitting the free flow of the pi electrons around the ring. This explains why aromatic compounds do not behave like alkenes. The delocalization of pi electrons enhances the stability of the molecule.

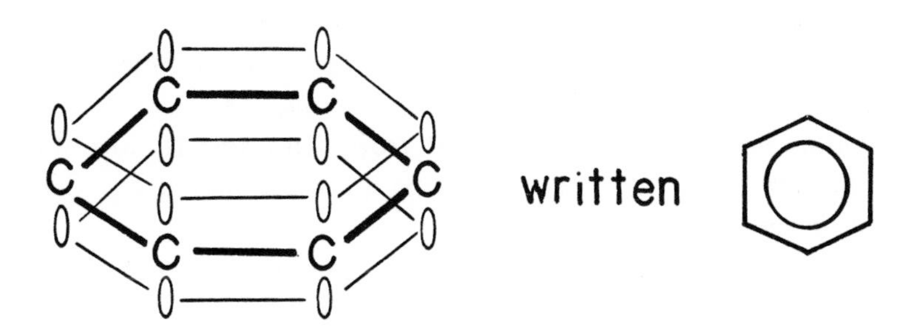

The orientation of substituents around the ring can be designated by the prefixes *ortho-* (*o-*), *meta-* (*m-*), and *para-* (*p-*) or by numbering the carbon atoms around the ring. Show your students some examples of aromatic hydrocarbons.

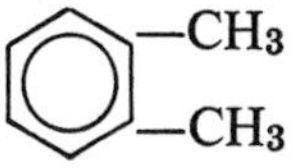

$-CH_3$
$-CH_3$ o-xylene (1, 2-dimethylbenzene)

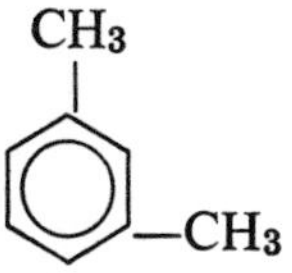

CH_3
$-CH_3$ m-xylene (1, 3-dimethylbenzene)

CH_3
CH_3 p-xylene (1, 4-dimethylbenzene)

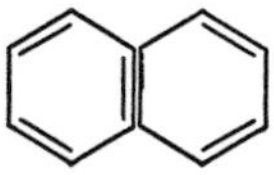

naphthalene

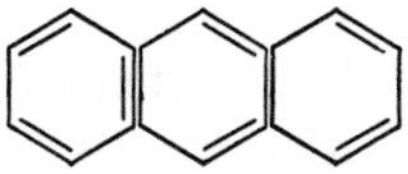

anthracene

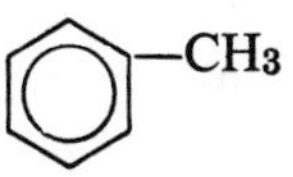

$-CH_3$ toluene

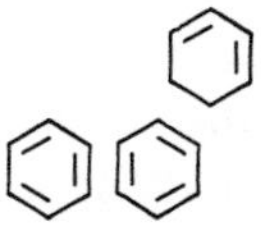

phenanthrene

Your students should begin to feel that there is a large variety of organic compounds possible. We now have two large groups of hydrocarbons: aliphatic and aromatic. This is only the beginning, however, because they haven't been introduced to the functional groups. Begin with the alcohols and ethers, which you should describe as derivatives of water. *R* represents an organic radical.

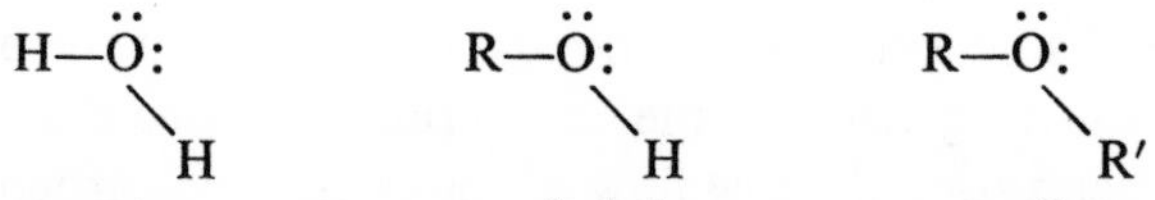

H—Ö: \\ H	R—Ö: \\ H	R—Ö: \\ R′
water	alcohol	ether

Just as water is a bent molecule (sp^3 bonding for oxygen), so are alcohols and ethers. More about their properties will be discussed later. The suffix *-ol* designates an -OH group of the alcohol, and ethers are named as oxides or just plain ethers. Distinguish between primary, secondary, and tertiary alcohols. In a primary alcohol, only one carbon atom is bonded to the one bearing the functional group. In a secondary alcohol, two carbon atoms are bonded to the one bearing the functional group. In a tertiary alcohol, three carbon atoms are bonded to the one bearing the functional group. Give your an students several examples.

Formula	Name	Other name
$CH_3CH_2CH_2CH_2OH$	butanol-1	(n-butanol, primary butanol)
$CH_3CH_2CHCH_3$ (with OH on the third carbon)	butanol-2	(secondary butanol)
CH_3CHCH_2OH (with CH_3 on the second carbon)	2-methylpropanol-1	(isobutanol)
CH_3—C—OH (with CH_3 above and below C)	2-methylpropanol-2	(tertiary butanol)
$CH_3CH—O—CH_2CH_3$ (with CH_3 on the CH)	isopropyl ethyl ether	(2-ethoxypropane)

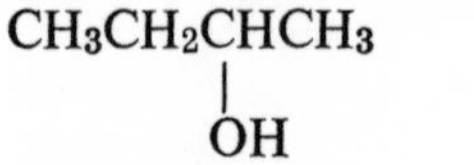

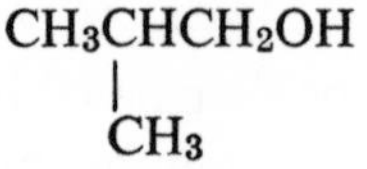

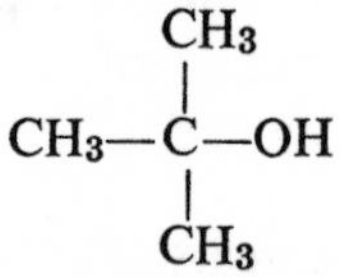

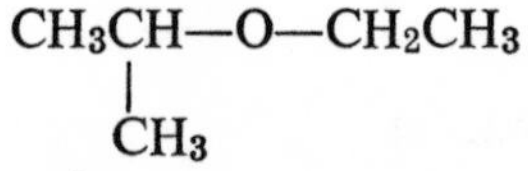

(benzene ring)—OH phenol, hydroxybenzene, carbolic acid

(benzene ring with CH_3 and OH on adjacent carbons) *o*-methylphenol, *o*-hydroxytoluene, 2-methylphenol, 2-hydroxytoluene, *o*-cresol

Another type of oxygen-containing compound contains the carbonyl group, C=O. Aldehydes contain this group on the end of a carbon chain, exemplified by the general formula RCH=O. Ketones contain the carbonyl group between two other carbon atoms: RCOR′. The systematic name for an aldehyde ends with *-al* and that for a ketone ends with *-one*. Here are a few examples.

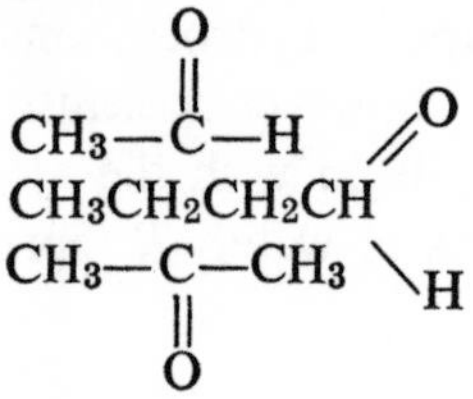

Formula	Name
$CH_3—C(=O)—H$	ethanal (acetaldehyde)
$CH_3CH_2CH_2CH(=O)$ (CH with //O and \\H)	butanal (butyraldehyde)
$CH_3—C(=O)—CH_3$	propanone, acetone, or dimethylketone

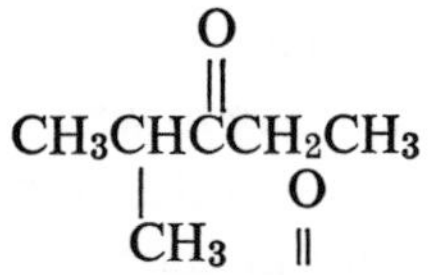

$$\underset{\substack{|\\CH_3}}{CH_3CH}\overset{\substack{O\\ \|}}{C}CH_2CH_3$$ 2-methylpentanone-3 or ethyl isopropyl ketone

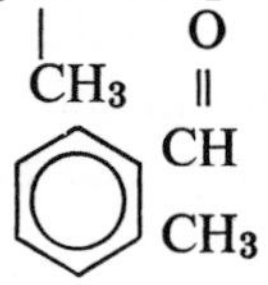

$C_6H_4(CHO)(CH_3)$ (benzene ring with $\overset{\substack{O\\ \|}}{CH}$ and CH_3 on adjacent positions) *o*-tolualdehyde or 2-methylbenzaldehyde

Some of the characteristics of the carbonyl group will be discussed later.

Carboxylic acids contain the carboxyl group, -COOH. The systematic name for an acid ends with *-oic acid.*

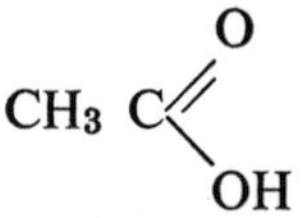

$$CH_3\,C\begin{matrix}\nearrow O\\ \searrow OH\end{matrix}$$ ethanoic acid (acetic acid)

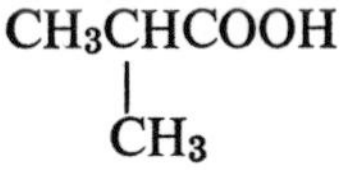

$$\underset{\substack{|\\CH_3}}{CH_3CH}COOH$$ 2-methylpropanoic acid (isobutyric acid)

$C_6H_4(COOH)(CH_3)$ (benzene ring with COOH and CH_3 on adjacent positions) 2-methylbenzoic acid (*o*-toluic acid)

The last common category of oxygen-containing organic compounds is esters, which are produced by an acid reacting with an alcohol, producing water as a by-product. Fats are glyceryl esters of fatty acids (aliphatic acids) which contain in the neighborhood of 14 to 18 carbon atoms. Oils are similar to fats, except that they are esters of unsaturated fatty acids. The formation of an ester and its hydrolysis can be diagrammed in this manner, although the "lasso" does not show the mechanism by which the ester is formed. It only shows which bonds are broken.

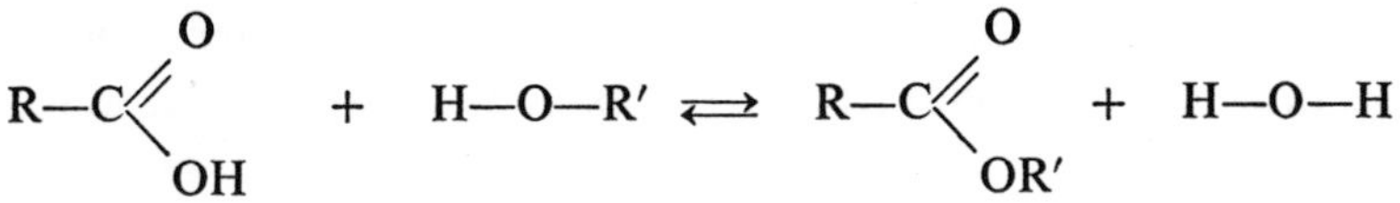

$$R{-}C\begin{matrix}\nearrow O\\ \searrow OH\end{matrix} \quad + \quad H{-}O{-}R' \rightleftarrows R{-}C\begin{matrix}\nearrow O\\ \searrow OR'\end{matrix} \quad + \quad H{-}O{-}H$$

Examples:

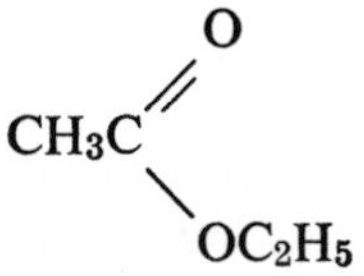

$$CH_3C\begin{matrix}\nearrow O\\ \searrow OC_2H_5\end{matrix}$$ ethyl acetate

$C_6H_5{-}COOCH_3$ (benzene ring) methyl benzoate (ethyl ester of benzoic acid)

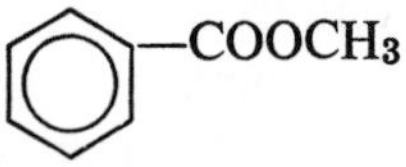

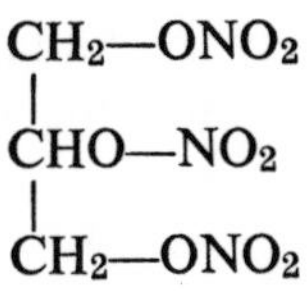

$$\begin{matrix}CH_2{-}ONO_2\\ |\\ CHO{-}NO_2\\ |\\ CH_2{-}ONO_2\end{matrix}$$ glyceryl trinitrate (nitroglycerine), or nitric acid ester of 1, 2, 3-trihydroxypropane (propanetriol-1, 2, 3, or glycerol)

One of the most important groups of compounds containing nitrogen is the amines, which are to ammonia what alcohols and ethers are to water. They are characterized by the basic nature of the nitrogen atom (unshared pair of electrons) and, as does ammonia, form salts (quaternary ammonium compounds). As in the case of alcohols, we can have primary, secondary, and tertiary amines. Give your students several examples.

$CH_3CH_2NH_2$ ethylamine (primary amine)

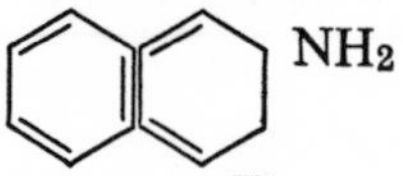

NH_2 2-naphthylamine

COOH, NH_2 (benzene ring)

o-aminobenzoic acid (anthranilic acid)

$$CH_3CH(CH_3){-}N(H){-}CH(CH_3)CH_3$$

diisoproplyamine (secondary amine)

$$(CH_3)_3N + CH_3I \longrightarrow (CH_3)_4\,N^+I^-$$

trimethylamine (tetirary amine) — methyl iodide — tetramethylammonium iodide (quaternary ammonium salt)

Some of the chemistry of amines will be discussed later.

There are many other types of compounds, including halides, nitro compounds, thiols and thioethers (sulfur in place of oxygen in alcohols and ethers), amides (analogs of esters, in which an amine reacts with a carboxylic acid), nitriles (organic cyanides), metal-organic compounds, and many others. By this time your students should have an idea of the tremendous variety of organic compounds, however, and it wouldn't prove much to give them all the other categories. Your time and theirs would be better spent relating chemical principles to several types of compounds and some general reactions.

3. INTERPRETING THE PROPERTIES OF COMPOUNDS FROM STRUCTURE AND ELECTRONIC EFFECTS

A good way to begin discussing the chemical properties of different compounds is to consider the oxidation states of the derivatives of methane. The oxidation number of carbon ranges from –4 in CH_4 to +4 in CO_2, and the alcohols, ethers, carbonyl compounds, and acids contain carbon having oxidation numbers between these extremes. Point out that methane contains the most chemical energy and carbon dioxide the least amount. In principle, one can oxidize a hydrocarbon stepwise to produce oxygen-containing compounds, and carbon dioxide represents the end of the line: the waste product in a series of oxidations.

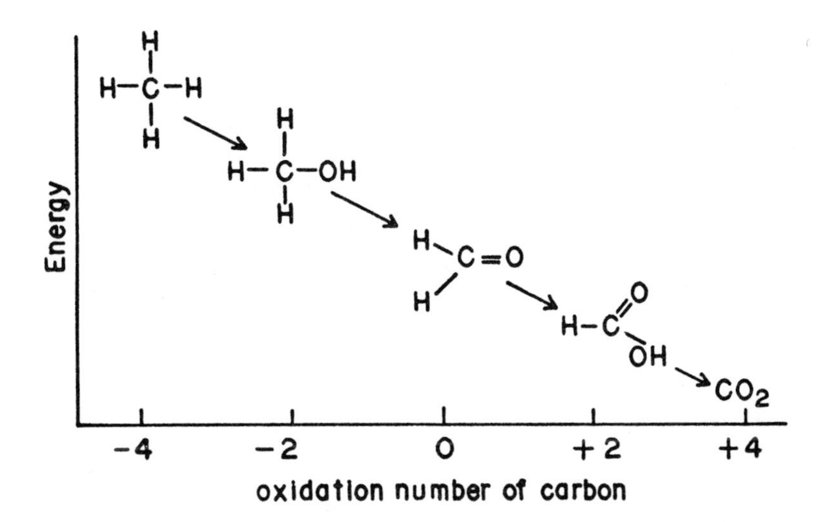

Paraffin hydrocarbons are not very reactive, and CO_2 is quite stable and does not react readily with other organic compounds. The compounds between these two extremes have reactive functional groups, however, and so chemists can make them react with other compounds to synthesize more complex molecules. Functional groups serve as "handles." Hydrocarbons generally have low melting and boiling points because they are non-polar (see section 4.5).

Alcohols behave like water in some ways. The hydroxy group can donate a proton and can hydrogen bond with itself and with water molecules. The reason the lower alcohols are readily soluble in water is because the hydrophilic -OH group hydrogen bonds with water. As the number of carbon atoms in the alcohol increases, however, the polar part of the molecule makes a smaller contribution than the non-polar hydrocarbon portion, and so the higher alcohols are not water soluble. The alcohols have considerably higher boiling points and melting points than molecules of similar complexity. Show your students some actual data and interpret it in terms of hydrogen bonding.

Compound	*Molec. Wt.*	*b. p. °C*	*Hydrogen Bonding*
$CH_3CH_2CH_3$	44	0	none
CH_3CH_2Cl	64.5	12	none
CH_3CH_2SH	62	35	very little, but molecule is polar
$CH_3—O—CH_3$	46	-23	none
$CH_3CH_2NH_2$	45	17	some
CH_3CH_2OH	46	79	extensive
$HOCH_2CH_2OH$	62	198	very extensive

Your more inquisitive students might be interested in reading L. Clapp's *The Chemistry of the OH Group* (Prentice-Hall, Inc.).

Alcohols donate protons less readily than water. This can be demonstrated qualitatively by observing the reaction between water and sodium, comparing this reaction to the ones between sodium and methanol (smooth evolution of hydrogen) and isopropanol (virtually no reaction at room temperature). The simplest explanation for this difference in acid strength is that methyl groups are "electron-releasing" groups. Compare the electron density around the oxygen atom in water, methanol, and isopropanol, using diagrams.

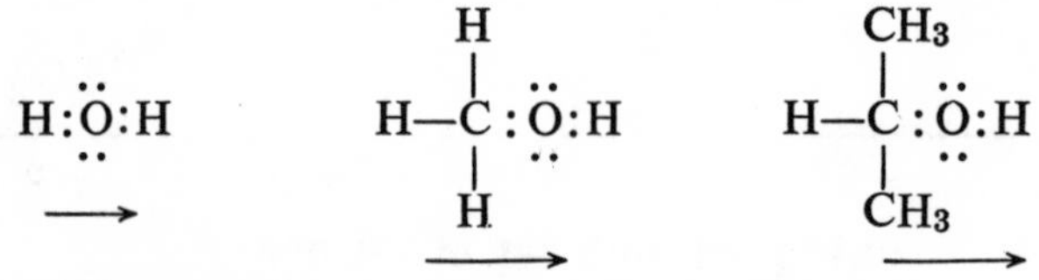

```
                    H               CH3
   ..               |   ..          |   ..
 H:O:H           H—C : O:H       H—C : O:H
   ..               |   ..          |   ..
  ——>               H               CH3
                  ——————>         ——————>
      electron drift
```

The more methyl groups present in the vicinity of the oxygen atom, the greater the drift of electrons toward the highly-electronegative oxygen atom. The higher the electron density around the oxygen, the more reluctant the hydrogen will be to leave as a proton (see section 7.4). The decreasing order of acid strength, therefore, is $HOH > CH_3OH > (CH_3)_2\,CHOH$.

Before proceeding to the carbonyl group, explore the addition reactions of carbon-carbon double bonds with your students. These bonds can "open up" and add two atoms or groups, one appearing on each of the carbon atoms. Review sp^2 bonding (see section 4.4), emphasizing that the bond angles around carbon are about 120° and that the bonded atoms about a double bond lie in the same plane. In the addition of bromine to ethene, for example, consider the polarization of the double bond. The two pi electrons can move toward one carbon atom, creating a pair of electrons and a negatively-charged site and leaving a deficiency of electrons and a positively-charged site on the other carbon atom. If necessary, review the Lewis acid-base concept (see section 7.6).

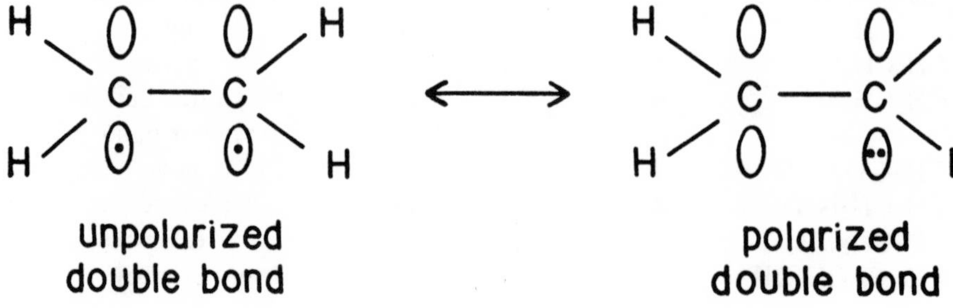

```
H   O   O   H                  H   O   O   H
 \         /                    \         /
  C ——— C          <——>          C ——— C
 /         \                    /         \
H   (•)  (•)  H                H   O   (••)  H

unpolarized                        polarized
double bond                        double bond
```

The carbon atom with the now-empty *p* orbital acts as a Lewis acid (electron pair acceptor), and the carbon atom which has acquired the additional electron in its *p* orbital acts as a Lewis base (electron pair donor). Bromine molecules can cleave in two ways: (1) bromonium (+) and bromide (−) ions are produced, or (2) bromine free radicals (atoms) are produced. Bromine is believed to add by means of an ionic mechanism, in which a bromonium ion is attracted toward the negatively-charged carbon atom, accepting the pair of electrons in a Lewis acid-base reaction. The bromide ion donates a pair of electrons to the positive carbon atom in a second Lewis acid-base reaction. The result is 1, 2-dibromoethane, in which the bonding of the carbon atoms is *sp*³ (tetrahedral).

$$:Br:Br \longrightarrow :Br:^{-} + :Br^{+}$$

$$H_2C{-}CH_2 \;(+)\;(-) \longrightarrow CH_2Br{-}CH_2Br$$

Evidence in support of this type of ionic mechanism is found by bubbling ethene gas through an aqueous solution of bromine and sodium chloride. A mixture of CH_2BrCH_2Br and CH_2BrCH_2Cl is obtained, indicating the involvement of ions in the process. Such addition reactions proceed more readily in a polar solvent, which favors the formation of ions and the polarization of the double bond.

When HBr adds to propene in a polar environment, the principal product is 2-bromopropane, although a small amount of 1-bromopropane is also obtained. This is predicted by Markownikov's rule, which states that the more negative portion of the substance being added goes to the carbon atom bearing the least number of hydrogen atoms. The reason for the predominance of one product over the other is the polarization of the double bond in the direction of the terminal carbon. Since the methyl group is electron releasing, the electron drift is in the direction away from the methyl group. This results in most of the hydrogen (+) ions accepting an electron pair from the terminal carbon atom and the bromide ion (−) donating a pair of electrons to the positive interior carbon atom, as shown top of next page.

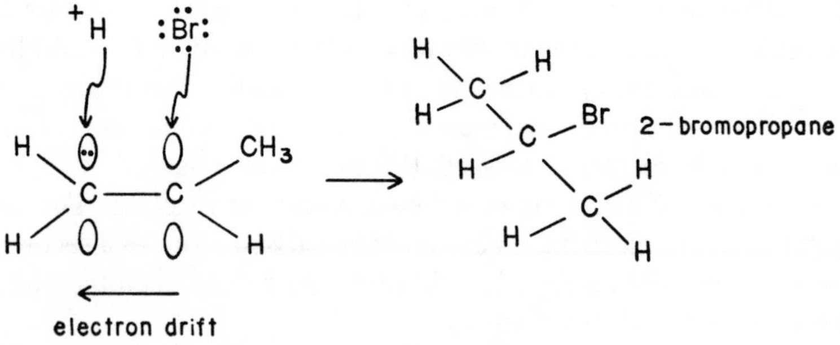

$$H_2C{=}CH{-}CH_3 + H^+ + :\ddot{Br}: \longrightarrow CH_3{-}CHBr{-}CH_3$$

electron drift

2-bromopropane

The distribution of electrons in organic molecules influences the course of reactions and the products obtained.

Polymerization means the joining together of many units to form a larger aggregate. Addition polymers are formed by a monomer (a single unit) adding to itself or to another monomer (producing mixed polymers) by means of a double bond. The simplest case is polyethylene, in which many ethylene (ethene) molecules add to each other to form long chains. Condensation polymers, on the other hand, are produced when monomers join together by splitting off small molecules, such as water or a simple alcohol. Nylon is an example of a condensation polymer, in which adipic acid and hexamethylene diamine condense to form long chains linked by an amide group. This is similar to the condensation of amino acids to form protein molecules.

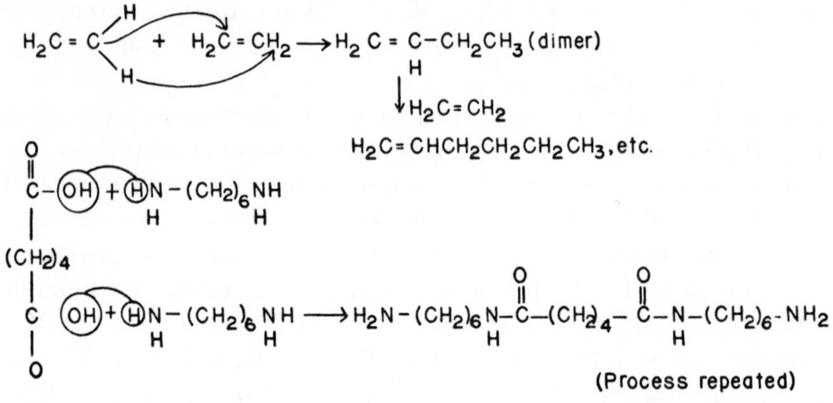

$$H_2C = CH_2 + H_2C = CH_2 \longrightarrow H_2C = CH{-}CH_2CH_3 \text{ (dimer)}$$

$$\downarrow H_2C = CH_2$$

$$H_2C = CHCH_2CH_2CH_2CH_3\text{, etc.}$$

$$HO{-}\overset{O}{\overset{\|}{C}}{-}(CH_2)_4{-}\overset{O}{\overset{\|}{C}}{-}OH + 2\,HNH{-}(CH_2)_6{-}NH_2 \longrightarrow H_2N{-}(CH_2)_6{-}NH{-}\overset{O}{\overset{\|}{C}}{-}(CH_2)_4{-}\overset{O}{\overset{\|}{C}}{-}NH{-}(CH_2)_6{-}NH_2$$

(Process repeated)

Point out that monomers used to make condensation polymers must have two functional groups which can link with other molecules.

The carbonyl group can undergo addition reactions quite readily, especially since the double bond is polarized toward the oxygen, leaving the carbon atom somewhat positive. Many substances, including HCN, H_2NNH_2 (hydrazine), H_2NOH (hydroxylamine), $NaHSO_3$, and organometallic compounds such as Grignard reagents (RMgBr, etc.), add to carbonyl groups. Aldehydes and ketones can also add to themselves. Most of these reactions are beyond the scope of an elementary course, however. Since the oxygen in the carbonyl group is highly electronegative, electrons tend to drift toward the oxygen atom, leaving the adjacent carbon atom somewhat positive. This, in turn, means that any hydrogen atom located on a carbon atom adjacent to a carbonyl group is slightly acidic. The carbonyl group is an electron-withdrawing group.

The hydrogen atom on a carboxyl group is acidic due to the presence of the carbonyl group. Other groups in an organic acid can influence the strength of the acid. Compare the strengths of formic acid, acetic acid, and chloroacetic acid. Formic acid is stronger than acetic acid, because the methyl group releases electrons toward the oxygen atom bearing the hydrogen. Since the electron density on the oxygen atom is higher in acetic acid than in formic acid, acetic acid donates protons less readily and is therefore a weaker acid. Since chlorine is highly electronegative, however, it attracts electrons, thereby reducing the electron density on the oxygen atom bearing the hydrogen. The result is that chloroacetic acid is stronger than acetic acid.

$$\begin{array}{ccc} & \text{O} & \\ & \| & \\ \text{H}- & \text{C} & -\ddot{\underset{..}{\text{O}}}:\text{H} \end{array} \qquad \begin{array}{cccc} & \text{H} & \text{C} & \\ & | & \| & \\ \text{H}- & \text{C}- & \text{C}- & \ddot{\underset{..}{\text{O}}}:\text{H} \\ & | & & \\ & \text{H} & & \end{array} \qquad \begin{array}{cccc} & \text{H} & \text{O} & \\ & | & \| & \\ \text{Cl}- & \text{C}- & \text{C}- & \ddot{\underset{..}{\text{O}}}:\text{H} \\ & | & & \\ & \text{H} & & \end{array}$$

$\longrightarrow$ electron drift $\qquad$ $\longleftarrow$ electron drift

Use the same type of argument to compare the relative base strengths of amines and that of ammonia. Methylamine is a stronger base than ammonia, since the methyl group releases electrons toward the nitrogen atom. Since the electron density on the nitrogen atom has been increased, it attracts protons to a greater extent.

$$\begin{array}{cc} & \text{H} \\ & | \\ \text{H}- & \text{N}: \\ & | \\ & \text{H} \end{array} \qquad\qquad \begin{array}{cc} & \text{H} \\ & | \\ \text{CH}_3- & \text{N}: \\ & | \\ & \text{H} \end{array}$$

$\longrightarrow$ $\qquad$ $\longrightarrow$ electron drift

The benzene ring (C_6H_5 group is called the phenyl group) is an electron-attracting group. Ask your students to compare the acid strength of phenol, C_6H_5OH, to that of water and the base strength of aniline, $C_6H_5NH_2$, to that of ammonia.

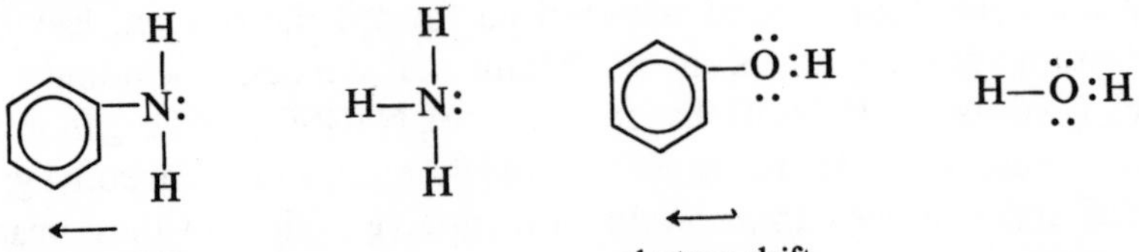

C_6H_5—N(H)(H):   H—N(H)(H): C_6H_5—Ö:H   H—Ö:H

electron drift   electron drift

Since the electron density on the oxygen atom has been reduced by the presence of the phenyl group, phenol is more acidic than water. Having electron-attracting substitutents on the benzene ring, such as nitro groups, reduces the electron density on the oxygen atom even more. It is little wonder, therefore, that picric acid (2, 4, 6-trinitrophenol) is a fairly strong acid. Aniline is a weaker base than ammonia because the electron density on the nitrogen atom is lower in aniline than in ammonia. Acetamide is a neutral compound, although it contains an amino group. The reason is that the carbonyl group effectively reduces the electron density on the nitrogen atom.

OH, O_2N, NO_2, NO_2 (picric acid)   H—C(H)(H)—C(=O)—N(H)(H): (acetamide)

electron drift

Discussing examples of molecular structure and electronic effects should awaken your students to the fact that the organic chemist must consider numerous factors when predicting the properties of compounds.

4. EXPLORING THE TYPES OF ISOMERISM

Introduce your students to the idea of isomerism by comparing atoms to building materials. Houses of different styles and floor plans may be built from the same pile of bricks. More than one compound may have the same molecular formula. Illustrate isomerism using a model of butane. Switch the place of a terminal carbon atom with a hydrogen atom on the second or third carbon atom in the chain and obtain isobutane. When developing the kinds of isomerism, include the five most common types: structural, geometric, positional, functional, and optical.

Structural isomerism refers to the basic carbon skeleton of molecules. Aliphatic hydrocarbons containing five carbon atoms could have several possible arrangements, such as

```
                                                    C
                                                    |
C—C—C—C—C              C—C—C—C                    C—C—C
                         |                          |
                         C                          C
```

Positional isomerism refers to the location of functional groups on a carbon skeleton. The hydroxy group may be located on different carbon atoms, leading to isomeric alcohols. The double bond in an alkene may be located between a different set of carbon atoms in another one. Show your students such examples as the ones below to get this idea across.

```
C—C—C—C—C—OH                 C—C—C—C=C
C—C—C—C—C                    C—C—C=C—C
      |
      OH
C—C—C—C—C
    |
    OH
```

Functional isomerism implies two or more compounds having the same molecular formula but different functional groups. Compounds having the molecular formula C_2H_6O, for example, include dimethyl ether (1) and ethanol (2). Compounds having the formula $C_3H_7NO_2$ could be nitropropane (3) or alanine (4), an amino acid.

```
CH3—O—CH3   (1)      CH3CH2CH2NO2  (3)
CH3CH2OH    (2)      CH3CHCOOH     (4)
                        |
                        NH2
```

Geometric isomerism is caused by lack of free rotation within a molecule. Free rotation is normally possible about a single bond, and you can show this by means of ball and stick models. Double bonds, however, inhibit rotation. Make a model of 1, 2-dichloroethene. Two possibilities exist: the chlorine atoms may be on the same side of the double bond (cis) or on opposite sides of the double bond (trans). This is similar to Rome's cis-Alpine and trans-Alpine Gaul. Perhaps the classic example of cis-trans isomerism is the case of maleic and fumaric acids. Maleic acid is easily dehydrated, yielding maleic anhydride. This is because the two hydroxy groups of the carboxyl groups come very close together and may interact. In fumaric acid, however, the carboxyl groups are on opposite sides of the double bond and do not interact to produce the anhydride.

```
H       H                H       Cl
 \     /                  \     /
  C=C                      C=C
 /     \                  /     \
Cl      Cl               Cl      H
```

cis-1, 2-dichloroethene   trans-1, 2-dichloroethene

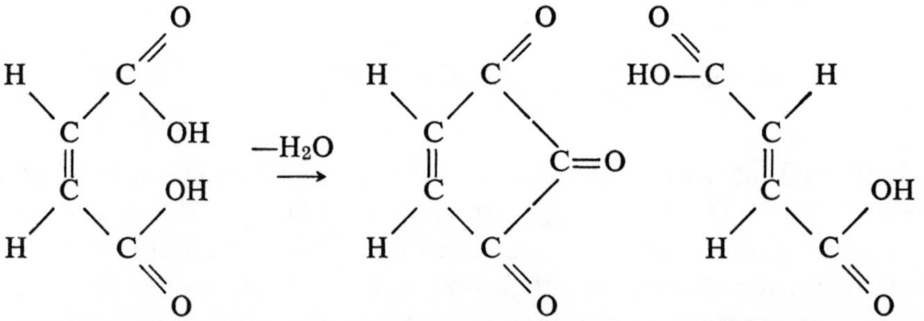

$-H_2O$

maleic acid → maleic anhydride

fumaric acid

The most subtle type of isomerism is optical. Using ball and stick models containing four different-colored balls around a single tetrahedral carbon atom, ask your students to distinguish any difference between possible arrangements. Superimpose one model on the other and see whether or not they are the same. Reverse the positions of any two colored balls on one of the models and see whether or not the two models may be superimposed. Compare these situations to a right and left hand: they are mirror images. Compare these models to one having two balls of the same color and develop the criterion for asymmetry. If you cannot pass a plane of symmetry through the molecule, right and left-handed forms are possible, and we have optical activity. Compounds which are optically active rotate the plane of polarized light either clockwise or counterclockwise. Chemists can measure the extent of rotation using a polarimeter. Show your students models of d and l-alanine. Optically active compounds contain one or more asymmetric centers. In general, a carbon atom bearing four different groups is asymmetric.

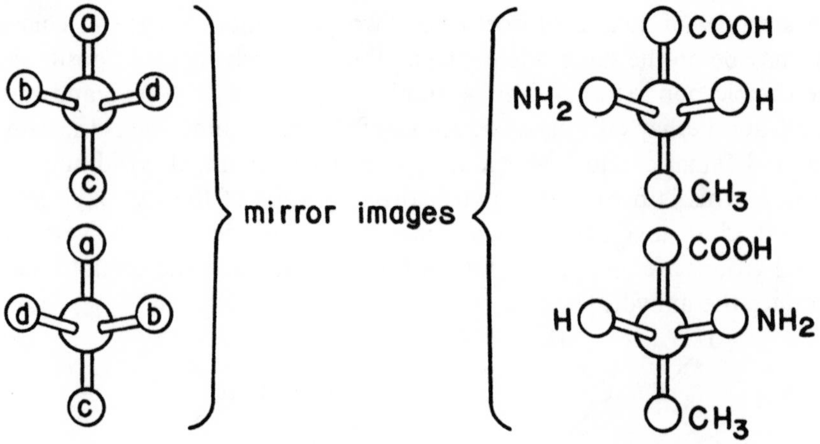

mirror images

d and l-alanine

Wrap up your discussion of isomerism by exploring all the possible structures having the molecular formula C_5H_{10}. Six alkenes and six cyclic alkanes, including four cyclopropanes, are possible.

$CH_3CH_2CH_2CH{=}CH_2$
pentene-1

$CH_3CH_2C(CH_3){=}CH_2$
2-methylbutene-1

$CH_3CH{=}C(CH_3)CH_3$
2-methylbutene-2

$CH_2{=}CHCH(CH_3)CH_3$
3-methylbutene-1

H(H)C=C(CH_2CH_3)(CH_3)   H(H_3C)C=C(CH_2CH_3)(H)
cis and trans-pentene-2

cyclopentane   methylcyclobutane (CH_3)

CH_3, CH_3 H_3C, CH_3
d-and l-trans-1, 1,2-dimethylcyclopropane

CH_3, CH_3 CH_3 CH_3
1, 1-dimethylcyclopropane   cis-1, 2-dimethylcyclopropane

Recommend Werner Herz's *The Shape of Carbon Compounds* (W. A. Benjamin, Inc.) to your students. This book discusses some of the fundamental ideas of organic chemistry in a way that most students can understand. Vander Werf's *Acids, Bases, and the Chemistry of the Covalent Bond* (Reinhold) presents many ideas of organic chemistry from the viewpoint of the Lewis acid-base concept.

5. EXPLORING A FEW ORGANIC REACTIONS

Organic reactions provide an excellent opportunity for illustrating the operation of chemical principles, such as moleuclar geometry, redox, acid-base reactions, kinetics, and equilibrium. Two mechanisms are involved in organic reactions: (1) ionic mechanisms (polar reactions) and (2) free radical mechanisms. Most reactions proceed by means of ions and involve Lewis acid-base reactions. Addition to double bonds was discussed in section 3. Discuss a few substitution reactions with your students.

An alkane may react with a halogen, such as chlorine, to produce a substitution product (alkyl halide) plus hydrogen halide. Such a reaction usually occurs in the gaseous state and proceeds by means of a free radical mechanism. We may write an equation for the substitution reaction between chlorine and ethane:

$$CH_3CH_3 + Cl_2 \longrightarrow CH_3CH_2Cl + HCl$$

Addition of chlorine to ethene, on the other hand, does not produce any HCl, and the resulting product contains all the chlorine:

$$H_2C = CH_2 + Cl_2 \longrightarrow CH_2ClCH_2Cl$$

The substitution reaction must be initiated by providing some external source of energy or a catalyst which will produce free radicals. A chlorine molecule can absorb light energy and split into two chlorine atoms (free radicals), which are very reactive. A chlorine atom then collides with an ethane molecule to produce an activated complex, which decomposes into an ethyl radical and HCl. The highly-reactive ethyl radical collides with another chlorine molecule, forming another activated complex. This complex decomposes into ethyl chloride and another chlorine atom, and the whole cycle begins again. This is an example of a chain reaction, and it proceeds very rapidly.

$$\text{energy} + Cl{:}Cl \longrightarrow Cl\cdot + Cl\cdot$$

$$Cl\cdot + CH_3CH_3 \longrightarrow [CH_3{-}\overset{H}{\underset{H}{C}}{-\!-\!-}H{-\!-\!-}Cl] \longrightarrow CH_3CH_2\cdot + HCl$$

$$CH_3CH_2\cdot + Cl_2 \longrightarrow [CH_3\overset{H}{\underset{H}{C}}{-\!-\!-}Cl{-\!-\!-}Cl] \longrightarrow CH_3CH_2Cl + Cl\cdot$$

Examine the oxidation state of the carbon atom which bears the chlorine. It has been oxidized from -3 to -1.

$$H_3C{:}\overset{H}{\underset{H}{\ddot{\underset{..}{C}}}}{:}H \quad ^{-3} \qquad\qquad H_3C{:}\overset{H}{\underset{H}{\ddot{\underset{..}{C}}}}{:}Cl \quad ^{-1}$$

Primary alkyl halides readily hydrolyze in the presence of OH^- ions to yield an alcohol. This reaction involves the displacement of chloride ion by hydroxide ion in a Lewis base-displacement reaction (see section 7.6). Point out that the oxidation number of the carbon atom bearing the hydroxy group did not change during the reaction.

$$HO{:} \curvearrowright \overset{CH_3}{\underset{H\ H\ Cl}{C}} \longrightarrow \left[HO{-\!-\!-}\overset{CH_3}{\underset{H\ H}{C}}{-\!-\!-}Cl\right]^- \longrightarrow \overset{CH_3}{\underset{HO\ H\ H}{C}} + {:}Cl^-$$

activated complex: CH_3 and H groups in plane perpendicular to HO—C—Cl bonds

The configuration around this carbon atom has been changed. If such a reaction is carried out on an optically-active halide and the attack is from the rear on the asymmetric carbon atom, there is an inversion of configuration; we go from d to l or from l to d. Such a reaction is a bimolecular nucleophilic substitution, or an S_N2 reaction. The rate is governed by the concentrations of two reacting species: the OH^- ion and the halide. The reaction is called a nucleophilic substitution because the attacking group (a pair of electrons) is seeking a positive center (nucleus).

Tertiary butyl bromide is readily hydrolyzed, but the chief product is isobutene. This is because a *t*-butyl carbonium ion (positive ion) is formed, and this ion eliminates a proton. The reason a tertiary carbonium ion is formed so readily is that the methyl groups occupy considerable space around the tetrahedral central carbon atom. The structure is less strained when the configuration is changed from sp^3 to sp^2 (planar, 120° bond angle). The carbonium ion can either accept a pair of electrons from a nucleophile or it can eliminate a proton. In the latter case, a double bond results.

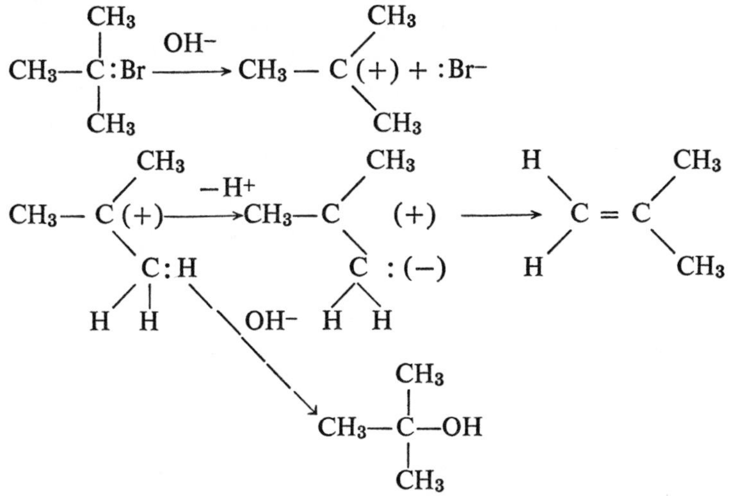

$$CH_3-\underset{CH_3}{\overset{CH_3}{\underset{|}{\overset{|}{C}}}}{:}Br \xrightarrow{OH^-} CH_3-C(+)\begin{matrix} /CH_3 \\ \backslash CH_3 \end{matrix} + {:}Br^-$$

$$CH_3-C(+)\begin{matrix} /CH_3 \\ \backslash C{:}H(H)(H) \end{matrix} \xrightarrow{-H^+} CH_3-C\begin{matrix} /CH_3 \\ \backslash \ddot{C}{:}(-)(H)(H) \end{matrix}(+) \longrightarrow \begin{matrix} H \\ H \end{matrix}\!\!>C=C<\!\!\begin{matrix} CH_3 \\ CH_3 \end{matrix}$$

$$\xrightarrow{OH^-} CH_3-\underset{CH_3}{\overset{CH_3}{\underset{|}{\overset{|}{C}}}}-OH$$

Ethanol can be dehydrated to produce either diethyl ether or ethene, depending upon the conditions for the reaction.

$$2CH_3CH_2OH \longrightarrow CH_3CH_2-O-CH_2CH_3 + H_2O$$

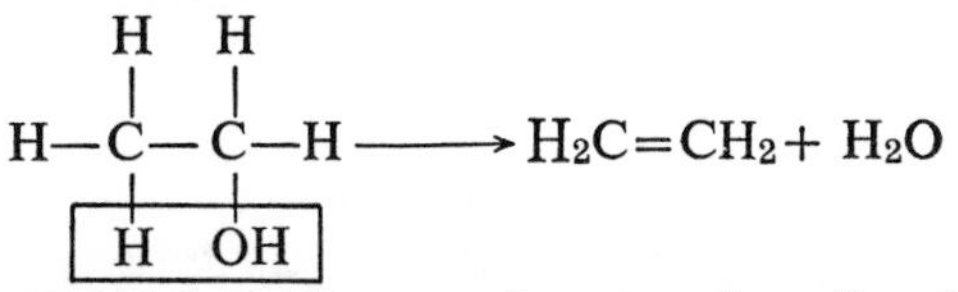

$$H-\underset{\boxed{H}}{\overset{H}{\underset{|}{\overset{|}{C}}}}-\underset{\boxed{OH}}{\overset{H}{\underset{|}{\overset{|}{C}}}}-H \longrightarrow H_2C{=}CH_2 + H_2O$$

The Friedel-Crafts reaction involves Lewis acid-base chemistry and electrophilic substitution on an aromatic ring. Electrophilic substitution involves the attack of a Lewis acid (electron-seeking) on a Lewis base (electron pair donor, or nucleophile). Consider the preparation of acetophenone (methyl phenyl ketone) from acetyl chloride and benzene.

$$CH_3C(=O)Cl + C_6H_6 \longrightarrow CH_3-\overset{O}{\overset{\|}{C}}-C_6H_5 + HCl$$

Anhydrous aluminum chloride (a Lewis acid, by virtue of an "open sextet") is used as a catalyst, accepting a chloride ion from acetyl chloride:

$$CH_3-C(=\ddot{O}:)\ddot{Cl}: + AlCl_3 \longrightarrow CH_3\overset{O}{\overset{\|}{C}}(+) + AlCl_4^-$$

One of the resonance forms of benzene can be written as shown, and the acetylium ion (a carbonium ion) forms a coordinate-covalent bond with the carbon bearing the pair of electrons. Elimination of a proton, which then reacts with $AlCl_4^-$ to produce HCl regenerating $AlCl_3$, leaves acetophenone. A second mole of $AlCl_3$ is needed in such a reaction, because the oxygen atom on the carbonyl group contains electron pairs which complex with $AlCl_3$. The product is isolated by hydrolyzing the complex, producing hydrated aluminum ions and chloride ions.

$$C_6H_6 \longleftrightarrow (+)H\,C_6H_5(-) + (+)\overset{O}{\overset{\|}{C}}CH_3 \longrightarrow (+)H(C_6H_5)\overset{}{C}(=O)CH_3 \xrightarrow{-H^+} C_6H_5-\overset{}{C}(=O)CH_3$$

Esterification is a reaction between an acid and an alcohol, and the reverse reaction is hydrolysis of the ester. The reaction producing the ester is usually catalyzed by an acid. Since the two possible reactions oppose each other, the esterification reaction cannot proceed to completion unless one of the products is removed from the equilibrium mixture. The reaction involves a Lewis base displacement reaction.

$$R-\overset{O}{\overset{\|}{C}}-OH + R'-\ddot{O}-H \rightleftharpoons \left[R-\overset{OH}{\overset{|}{C}}(-OH)-O-R'\right] \rightleftharpoons R-\overset{O}{\overset{\|}{C}}-OR' + H-\ddot{O}-H$$

Since the alcohol is a slightly stronger base than water, the forward reaction proceeds to a greater extent than the reverse one. Point out that the OH group of the acid is eliminated along with the H from the alcohol. Show your students the CHEM Study films "Mechanism of an Organic Reaction" and "Synthesis of an Organic Compound." These movies will give your students a greater insight into some of the principles and techniques of organic chemistry. More examples of organic reactions will be discussed in Chapter 13.

6. SOME COMPOUNDS OF BIOLOGICAL INTEREST

Since organic chemistry is so essential to life processes, take some time to discuss proteins, fats, carbohydrates, and a few other types of compounds. You should emphasize that nature is very particular about the geometry of the molecules which make up living organisms and are used by them. Left-handed amino acids (optically active) are incorporated into proteins, and optically active natural products of a particular configuration are found in living things. Only one optically-active isomer of certain drugs has any physiological activity, with rare exceptions. The other isomer is usually devoid of activity. An exception is 1-triiodotyhronine, which has the same effect in the body as 1-tetraiodothyronine (thyroxine, or thyroid hormone). The d isomer, on the other hand, does not have thyroid activity but has been found to reduce the concentration of cholesterol in the bloodstream.

Carbohydrates are compounds of carbon, hydrogen, and oxygen, in which the hydrogen-oxygen ratio is 2:1. Plants manufacture carbohydrates by means of the photosynthesis reaction, which produces simple sugars from carbon dioxide and water in the presence of the catalyst chlorophyll. This reaction is endothermic, deriving its energy from sunlight. The reverse reaction (oxidation of carbohydrates) is exothermic. Organisms oxidize carbohydrates in order to produce energy. Show your students the structures of glucose and fructose, the two monosaccharides which dimerize to produce sucrose.

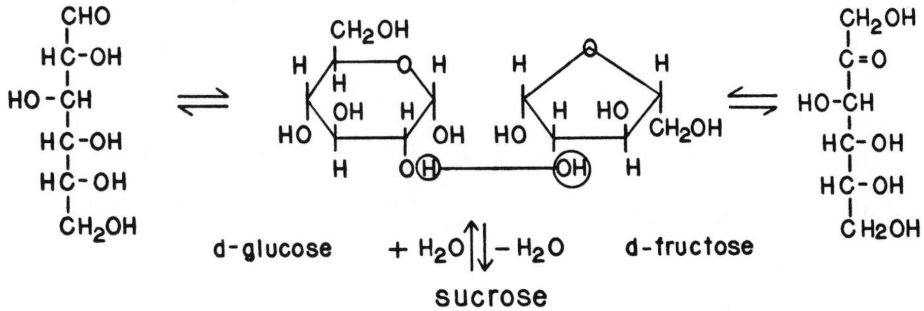

d-glucose $+ H_2O \uparrow\downarrow - H_2O$ d-fructose

sucrose

Ask your students to identify the asymmetric carbon atoms in the two simple sugars (glucose: the middle four; fructose: the middle three bearing OH groups). The ring structures (pyranose ring is composed of five carbons and one oxygen, furanose ring is composed of four carbons and one oxygen) are produced by the addition of an OH group to the keto or aldehyde carbonyl group. Point out that the formation of sucrose from the monosaccharides produces water as a by-product. The reverse reaction (hydrolysis) produces simple sugars.

$$\underset{\text{glucose}}{C_6H_{12}O_6} + \underset{\text{fructose}}{C_6H_{12}O_6} \rightleftharpoons \underset{\text{sucrose}}{C_{12}H_{22}O_{11}} + H_2O$$

Starch and cellulose, $(C_6H_{10}O_5)_x$, two polysaccharides produced by plants, differ essentially in the way the monosaccharide units are linked. The oxygen bridges in starch and cellulose differ in configuration.

$$x\,C_6H_{12}O_6 \rightleftharpoons (C_6H_{10}O_5)_x + x\,H_2O$$

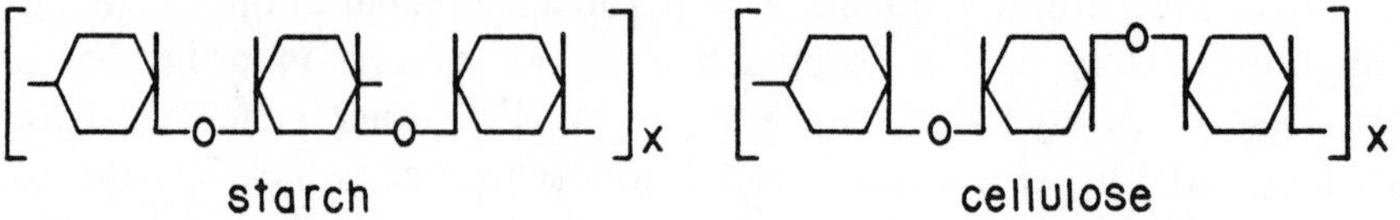

starch cellulose

Enzymes (catalysts) which enable a human to hydrolyze starch to simple sugars have no effect on cellulose. Humans cannot digest cellulose, but microorganisms found in the digestive tract of termites have a different set of enzymes which are able to hydrolyze cellulose to simple sugars. This is an example of the specificity of enzymes. The configuration in a compound is of utomst importance to living organisms.

Fats are glyceryl esters of fatty acids. Glyceryl tristearate, for example, is found in beef fat, which may be hydrolyzed to glycerol and stearic acid. The so-called "unsaturated fats" are similar to the saturated fats except for the presence of double bonds in the acid portion of the fatty ester. Oils are glycerol esters of unsaturated acids and may be hydrogenated to produce hard fats.

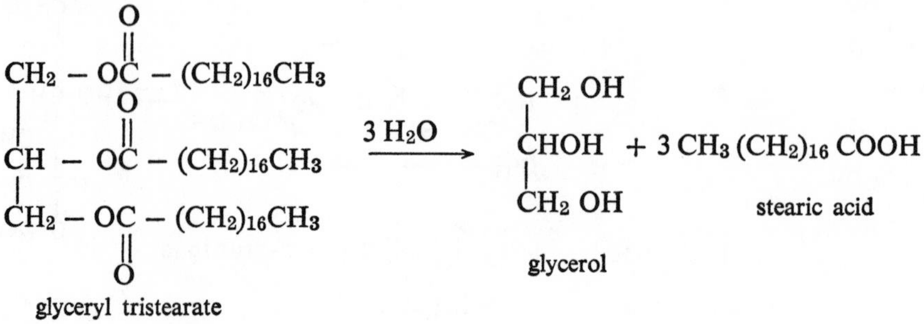

$$\begin{array}{l} CH_2-OC(=O)-(CH_2)_{16}CH_3 \\ | \\ CH-OC(=O)-(CH_2)_{16}CH_3 \\ | \\ CH_2-OC(=O)-(CH_2)_{16}CH_3 \end{array} \xrightarrow{3\,H_2O} \begin{array}{l} CH_2OH \\ | \\ CHOH \\ | \\ CH_2OH \end{array} + 3\,CH_3(CH_2)_{16}COOH$$

glyceryl tristearate glycerol stearic acid

Proteins are chains of amino acids linked together by the condensation of an amino group with an acid group, forming a peptide bond (amide). Digestion of proteins involves the hydrolysis of the peptide bonds to produce the individual amino acids, which are then used by the body to synthesize its own proteins having the order of amino acids dictated by the requirements of the organism. Since there are over twenty letters in the protein alphabet, the number of possible combinations is tremendously large.

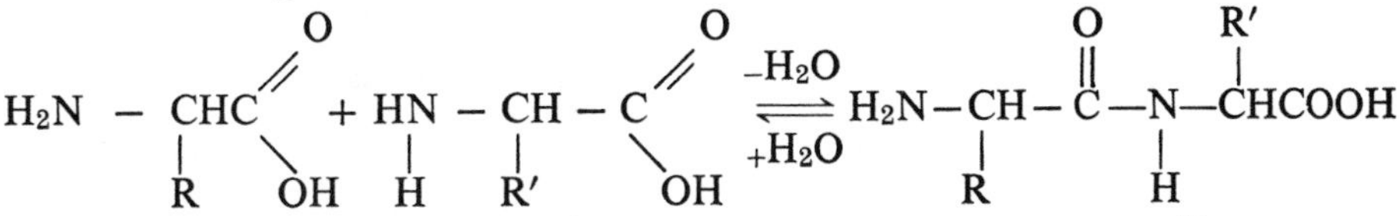

$$\underset{\text{amino acid 1}}{H_2N-\underset{R}{CH}-C(=O)OH} + \underset{\text{amino acid 2}}{\underset{H}{HN}-\underset{R'}{CH}-C(=O)OH} \underset{+H_2O}{\overset{-H_2O}{\rightleftharpoons}} \underset{\text{peptide}}{H_2N-\underset{R}{CH}-\overset{O}{\overset{\|}{C}}-\underset{H}{N}-\overset{R'}{CH}COOH}$$

Point out that the α carbon of each amino acid is asymmetric, leading to optical isomers. Naturally-occurring amino acids have the l configuration, and none of the d isomers are found in terrestrial organisms. The organic radical, R, ranges from hydrogen (glycine) to complex groups, such as the indole system in tryptophane.

H_2NCH_2COOH
glycine

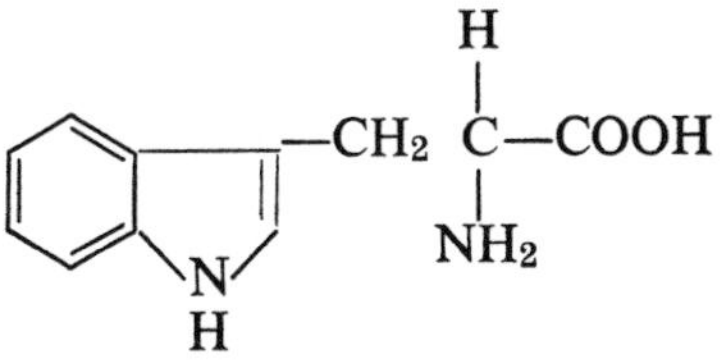

(indol-3-yl)$-CH_2-\underset{NH_2}{\overset{H}{C}}-COOH$
tryptophane

Other organic compounds used by organisms include vitamins and hormones, as well as DNA, RNA, and porphyrins found in red blood cells and chlorophyll. An interesting class of compounds found in many plants is the alkaloids. These compounds contain basic nitrogen atoms (amine functions), and so they were named alkaloids, meaning base-like. Most of these compounds are optically active and have physiological activity. Among some of the more potent alkaloid drugs are the opium alkaloids (morphine, codeine, etc.), the ergot group (from which LSD is derived), caffeine, nicotine, quinine, strychnine, and many others.

Make a model of nicotine, pointing out the planar nature and aromatic character of the pyridine ring, the asymmetric center, and the basic nitrogen atoms in the pyridine and pyrrolidine rings. Oxidation of this compound produces nicotinic acid, which is one of the B complex vitamins. Show your students the structural formulas for the steroid hormones testosterone (a male sex hormone) and estrone (a female sex hormone), pointing out the similarities and differences in structure. Such examples should not only make your students more aware of the great variety of organic compounds but will, hopefully, impress them with the fact that slight differences in the structure or configuration of molecules makes a profound difference in biochemical reactions and physiological activity. The CHEM Study film "Biochemistry and Molecular Structure" is worth showing, since it discusses enzyme action and the importance of structure of drugs in their action in living cells.

(O) →

N, N, CH_3

nicotine

COOH, N

nicotinic acid

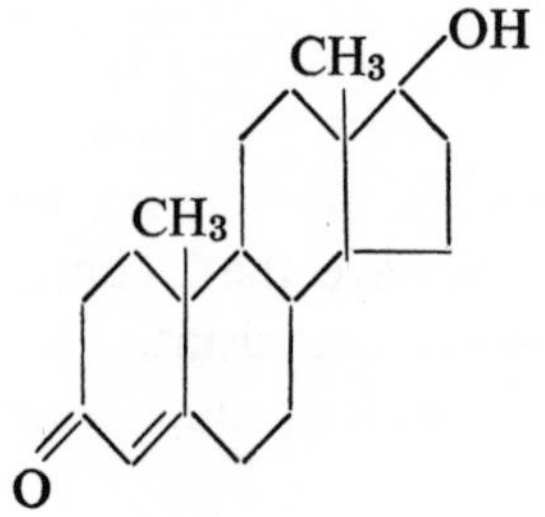

CH_3, OH, CH_3, O

testosterone

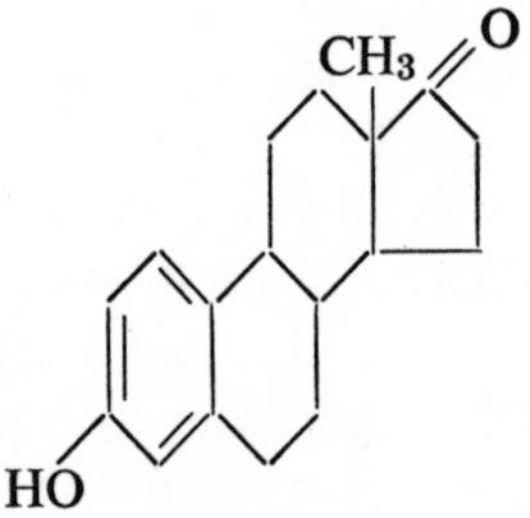

CH_3, O, HO

estrone

12

Explaining Nuclear Phenomena

1. EXPLAINING RADIOACTIVITY, α AND β DECAY

Radioactivity is the spontaneous elimination of particles and energy from an unstable nucleus. Use the analogy of an airliner that is overloaded and develops engine trouble. In order to remain ariborne, the crew throws out non-essentials, such as baggage and hijackers. The phenomenon was discovered by Henri Becquerel around 1896. He had been under the impression that uranium and its compounds stored solar radiation and then emitted it, as evidenced by the fogging of photographic plates. When he discovered that a plate wrapped in black paper became fogged after being near a uranium compound that had not been exposed to sunlight, he concluded that radiation was spontaneously emitted by uranium atoms.

Radioactive materials not only emit a penetrating radiation that fogs photographic plates, much as do X-rays, but they cause the ionization of air in the vicinity of the radioactive material. The ionized air discharges an electroscope. This instrument was usedby the Curies to isolate polonium and radium. More modern methods for detecting radioactivity were developed later and include the Geiger counter.

Three types of "rays" were discovered: α, β, and γ. Some of their properties were discovered by placing a radioactive material in a hole bored in a piece of lead, which serves as a shield for these rays. The beam emerging from the hole was allowed to pass through an electric field, and the ones which were bent strongly toward the positive plate were termed beta rays, since their nature was not known. These were later identified as fast-moving electrons by Becquerel, who performed an experiment similar to Thompson's (see

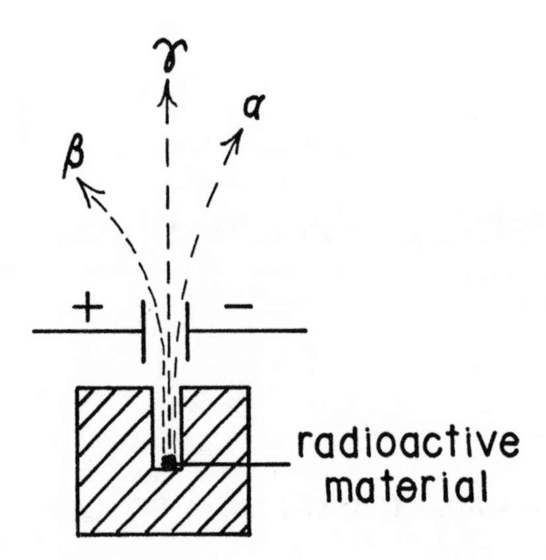

section. 3.2). Thompson had discovered that cathode rays, generated by moderate voltages, were elementary particles. Beta rays were found to be identical but much more energetic.

Since nuclear scientists usually deal with reactions of isolated atoms, they need a unit for expressing the energies of sub-atomic particles. The joule, defined as the energy acquired by a coulomb of charge accelerated by a potential difference of one volt, is too large for measuring the energies of particles on the atomic scale. The charge of a single electron is 1.60×10^{-19} coulombs, and so the energy acquired by an electron accelerated by a potential difference of one volt is 1.60×10^{-19} joule. A more convenient unit is the electron-volt, defined as the energy acquired when an electron (quantum of charge) is accelerated through a potential difference of one volt. Since many particles possess energies in the order of millions of electron-volts, however, the unit *million electron-volts* (Mev) is used.

Rutherford was aware of the presence of helium in radioactive minerals. He designed an experiment to trap α particles in a gas discharge tube by placing a radioactive material near a tube containing a thin glass window, through which the particles could travel. Some time later Rutherford passed electricity through the tube and observed the spectrum of helium, which proved to him that α particles were actually doubly-charged helium atoms. One property of α particles is that they cause zinc sulfide to fluoresce. Each time a single α particle strikes zinc sulfide, a small flash of light (scintillation) can be observed. This property enabled Rutherford to perform the α particle-scattering experiment which led to the concept of the nuclear atom (see section 3.3).

Considering the ejection of sub-atomic particles from the nuclei of unstable atoms, radioactivity should lead to transmutations. The most common varieties of radioactive disintegrations are α-decay and β-decay. When a nucleus ejects an α particle (2 protons + 2 neutrons), the nuclear charge (atomic number) of the new nucleus is two less than that of the original atom, and the mass number is reduced by four *amu*. Elimination of a negative elctron from a nculeus raises the nuclear charge of the resulting nucleus by one unit but does not change the mass number. This is due to the conversion of a neutron into a proton and a negative electron. A less common form of β-decay involves the elimination of a positive electron (positron), which produces a nucleus having a nuclear charge of one less than the original. Energy produced in the nuclear reaction is accounted for as the kinetic energy of the particles being eliminated and as γ radiation.

Show your students the steps involved when uranium 238 undergoes a series of radioactive decays, finally ending up as stable lead 206. An effective way to show the changes in nuclear charge and mass is to use a graph.

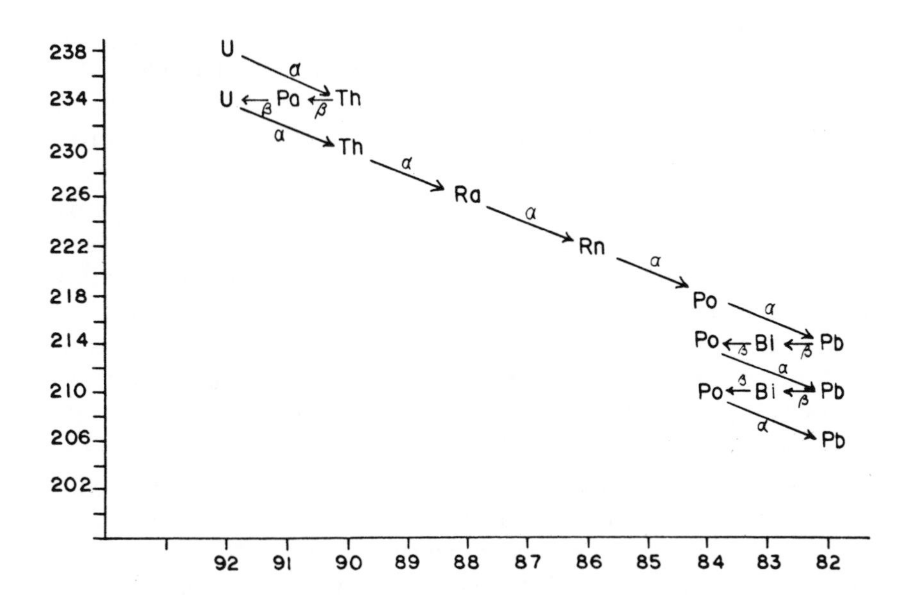

Show your students the change in nuclear composition when uranium 238 loses an α particle to produce thorium 234 and how thorium 234 loses a β particle to produce protactinium 234.

$$_{92}U^{238} \longrightarrow {}_{90}Th^{234} + {}_{2}\alpha^{4}$$
$$_{90}Th^{234} \longrightarrow {}_{91}Pa^{234} + {}_{-}\beta^{0}$$

The nuclear charge is represented by the subscript in front of the symbol, and the mass number is represented by the superscript following the symbol. Keep emphasizing that α-decay decreases the nuclear charge by two and the mass number by four units, while β -decay raises the nuclear charge by one unit but does not change the mass number. When a nculeus becomes stable, no more particles are emitted. Remind your students that radiation is harmful, causing undesired biochemical reactions. Mutations are believed to be caused by radiation as well as by cosmic rays.

2. EXPLAINING THE CONCEPTS OF HALF-LIFE, BINDING ENERGY, FISSION, FUSION

Introduce your students to the concept of the "nuclear well." Coulomb's law suggests that when like charges come very close together, the repulsive force becomes very large. The force varies inversely with the square of the distance. Why, then, do protons remain close together inside a nucleus? Coulomb's law holds only up to a certain limit. When particles having like charge approach each other within a distance approximating the radius of a nucleus, the repulsive force changes to an attractive force. The force which operates at very close range and holds nucleons (protons and neutrons) together is called nuclear force. Show your students an energy diagram for particles of the same charge approaching each other. Up to a certain distance of separation, the coulombic force of repulsion increases very rapidly (inversely with the square of the distance). When the particles come very close together, the nuclear force begins to attract them, and the energy decreases rapidly.

Nuclear scientists believe that nucleons which are close together in the nucleus attract each other strongly, but protons which are on opposite sides of the nucleus are far enough apart to repel each other. The reason neutrons are necessary for stability of a nucleus is that they provide attraction between close neighbors. The heavier nuclei must contain more neutrons than protons in order to minimize the repulsion between protons. Nuclei which contain an insufficient number or too many neutrons tend to be unstable (radioactive). Nuclei which have a large number of protons tend to be radioactive, regardless of how many neutrons are present.

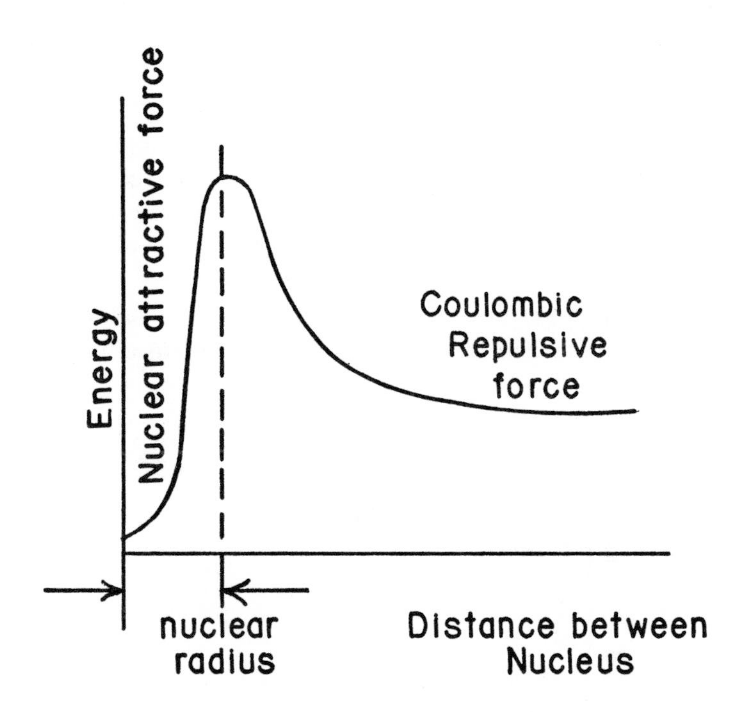

The fact that γ rays of different energies are emitted suggests that nucleons occupy different energy levels inside the nucleus. When nucleons fall to a lower energy level, they emit radiation, just as do excited electrons in an atom. The frequent occurrence of a particle elimination suggests that α particles represent a stable grouping of nucleons, providing more evidence for a nuclear ordering of energy levels.

Einstein's theory of relativity produced a relationship which has profound consequences on the energy processes in the universe: $e = mc^2$. Translated into English, the energy equivalent of a change of mass varies with the square of the velocity of light. Emphasize that this equation is similar to the kinetic energy equation, $KE = 1/2mv^2$. Since the velocity of light is 3×10^{10} cm/sec, one gram of mass is equivalent to 9×10^{20} ergs, or 9×10^{13} joules. Calculate the kilowatt hour equivalent as follows:

$$1 \text{ joule} = 1 \text{ watt second}$$

$$(9 \times 10^{13} \text{ watt sec}) \left(\frac{1 \text{ kw}}{10^3 \text{ watt}}\right) \left(\frac{1 \text{ hr}}{3600 \text{ sec}}\right) = 2.5 \times 10^7 \text{ kw hrs}$$

This means that if one gram of matter could be changed into energy, we would produce 25 million kilowatt hours of energy. This would keep ten hundred-watt light bulbs burning continuously for nearly three thousand years! At a cost of three cents per kilowatt hour, the value of this energy is about $750,000! Discuss the Einstein mass-energy equivalence before exploring binding energy and the energy obtained from nuclear reactions.

The mass of a proton is 1.0073 and that of a neutron is 1.0087 *amu.* The helium nucleus contains two of each and should have a total mass of 4.0320 *amu.* Since the actual mass of a helium atom is 4.0026, there seems to be a mass loss of 0.0294 *amu.* This mass defect represents the energy released when these four nucleons are assembled to form the helium nucleus and is called the binding energy. The greater the binding energy, the more stable the nucleus. Show your students a graph of binding energies for the naturally-occurring elements. This graph reveals that the most stable elements are the ones in the iron group.

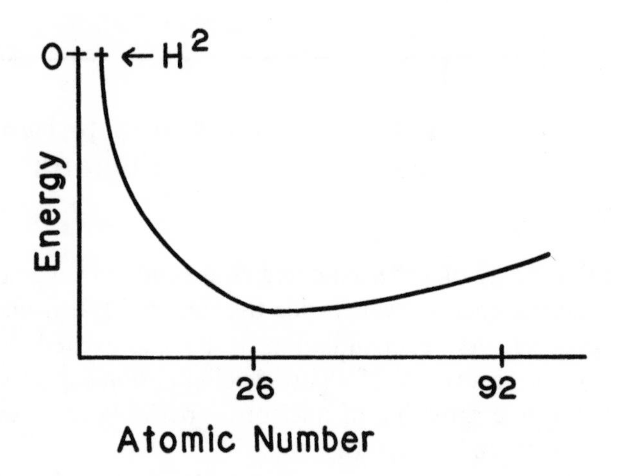

Considering the release of energy when nuclei are assembled suggests that nuclei of light elements could merge to form heavier ones (fusion) with the release of energy, and the heavier nuclei could split into smaller fragments (fission) with the release of energy. The hydrogen bomb involves the fusion of hydrogen or deuterium atoms to produce helium. Another combination is the fusion of lithium and hydrogen nuclei, producing helium. The technological problem is to overcome the repulsive forces as the nuclei approach each other. Emphasize that the approaching nuclei must have extremely high energies to overcome the coulombic repulsion. This is accomplished by using the energy from a fission reaction (an old-fashioned atom bomb). Fusion reactions do not begin until the temperature reaches several million degrees. The reaction between lithium and hydrogen nuclei, carried out by Cockroft and Walton in 1931, produces α particles as shown in the equation

$$_1H^1 + {_3Li^7} = {_2He^4} + {_2He^4} + 17.3 \text{ Mev}$$

Since 1 Mev $= 1.60 \times 10^{-13}$ joules (see section 1), the reaction between one hydrogen atom and one lithium atom would produce about 2.8×10^{-12} joules of energy. One mole of hydrogen and one mole of lithium atoms would produce about (6×10^{23}) (2.8×10^{-12}), or 1.7×10^{12} joules, or about 4 x 10^8 Kcal (1 cal $=$ 4.18 joules). Contrast this figure with the energy produced when one mole of water is produced by burning hydrogen in oxygen, which is about 60 kilocalories. The nuclear reaction produces nearly 10 million times more energy than the chemical one, on a molar basis.

Nuclear fission was first used for destructive purposes. Uranium has an isotope, mass 235, which undergoes fission by the addition of a neutron. The reaction was first observed in the laboratory by Hahn and Strassman in 1939. They observed that an isotope of barium, plus considerable energy, were produced when uranium was bombarded with neutrons. A neutron which does not have too much energy (slow moving) can be captured by a U-235 nucleus, which then splits into smaller nuclei with the emission of several neutrons and much energy. The neutrons thus produced can be captured by other uranium nuclei, leading to more fission and more neutrons. This indeed, is a chain reaction.

Nuclear fission is believed to be caused by a large nucleus being set into vibration by the capture of a neutron. When the nucleus becomes elongated, the repulsive force between protons increases rapidly, causing the nucleus to split violently into two approximately equal parts. Since the smaller nuclei do not require as many neutrons as half the number in the large nulceus, the unwanted neutrons are emitted. More about fission will be discussed in the next section.

Radioactive decay proceeds at a certain rate, depending upon the nature of the reaction involved. The process is not influenced by ordinary changes in temperature and is independent of pressure and the presence or absence of other materials. The rate of decay is measured in terms of *half-life*. The time required for half of the atoms of a radioactive material to disintegrate is called the half-life of that isotope. Show your students that the graph of number of atoms versus time is not a straight line. Compare the half-life curve to the distance a frog must jump to reach a wall if he jumps half way each time. He will approach the wall but never really reach it. Half-lives range from small fractions of a second to billions of years (see graph, next page).

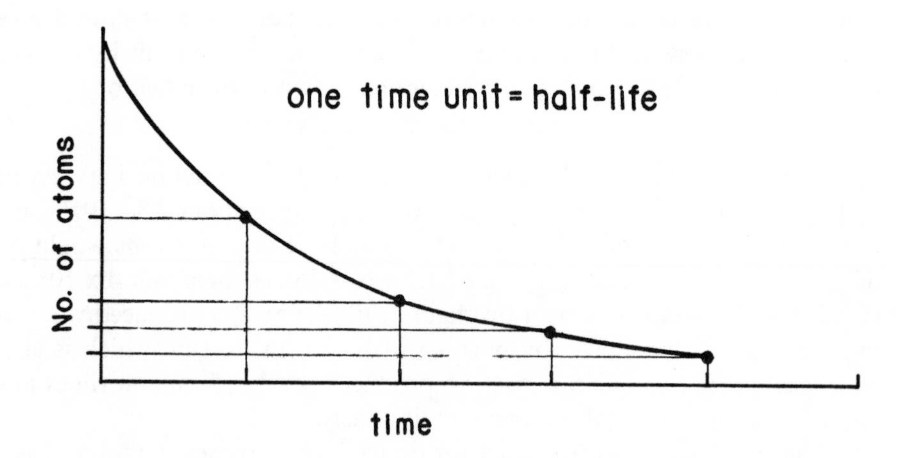

3. EXPLORING SOME APPLICATIONS OF NUCLEAR REACTIONS

The first artificial transmutation was accomplished by Rutherford in 1919, thus realizing the dream of the alchemists. After his famous α particle-scattering experiments (see section 3.3), Rutherford decided to explore the effect of α particles on light atoms, such as hydrogen. He reasoned that a collision between an α particle and a hydrogen nucleus would result in the lighter hydrogen nucleus being propelled at a very high speed (conservation of momentum). Therefore it should travel farther than an α particle. He constructed a box containing a fluorescent screen, whereby he could observe scintillations by means of a microscope whenever a charged particle (α particle or hydrogen nulceus) struck the screen. He found that α particles traveled about 25 cm in hydrogen but occasionally observed a particle that traveled as much as 100 cm from the source. He concluded that these must be hydrogen nuclei.

When he repeated this type of experiment using nitrogen, however, he found that the α particles only traveled about 7 cm from their source but found that an occasional particle traveled about 30 cm in nitrogen. He found these particles behaved like hydrogen nuclei and concluded that these must have been knocked out of the nitrogen nuclei by the α particles. The reaction he observed is shown in the equation

$$_7N^{14} + {}_2He^4 = {}_8O^{17} + {}_1H^1$$

Since Rutherford's time, scientists have been bombarding nuclei with particles of ever-increasing energy. One of the pioneers in this work was E. O.

Lawrence, who invented the cyclotron. This machine consists of a powerful magnet which causes charged particles to move in a circular path between the poles (charges are deflected perpendicular to a magnetic field). An alternating field is used to accelerate the charged particles resulting from hydrogen or deuterium being ionized in a circular path. The high energy ions are then allowed to strike a target. Modern particle accelerators, such as the Brookhaven National Laboratories synchotron (diameter about 840 feet) produces protons having energies of nearly 30 billion electron-volts. Numerous interesting nuclear reactions have been observed using such instruments as sources of "atomic bullets." Numerous isotopes have been produced by irradiating samples of elements in such machines.

Artificial radioactivity was discovered by Irene Curie and F. Joliot in 1934. Bombardment of magnesium with α particles resulted in the emission of neutrons and positrons. The neutrons were observed only while the magnesium was being bombarded, but the positrons were emitted for some time after the α particle treatment ceased. Apparently, radioactive silicon had been produced, which underwent β decay.

$$_{2}He^{4} + {}_{12}Mg^{24} = {}_{14}Si^{27} + {}_{0}n^{1}$$

$$_{14}Si^{27} = {}_{13}Al^{27} + {}_{+1}e^{0}$$

Since that time many artificial radioactive isotopes of most of the common elements have been made. Some of their uses will be discussed in section 5.

Nuclear reactions which are of most interest to mankind are those which produce energy which can be harnessed for peaceful uses. At the rate the human race is increasing its energy consumption, we will have to depend upon sources other than burning fossil fuels (which also lead to atmospheric pollution). Controlled nuclear fission is presently a reality, and a number of nuclear power plants are in operation. The big challenge in the field of nuclear energy, however, is controlled fusion: harnessing the source of energy used by stars.

The nuclear reactor, or atomic pile, was developed during World War II to produce plutonium. Natural uranium consists of about 0.7% uranium 235, the balance being uranium 238. Only the lighter isotope undergoes fission. The heavier one captures slow neutrons, producing plutonium by means of the following transformations:

$$_{92}U^{238} + {}_{0}n^{1} = {}_{92}U^{239}$$

$$_{92}U^{239} = {}_{93}Np^{239} + {}_{-1}e^{0}$$

$$_{93}Np^{239} = {}_{94}Pu^{239} + {}_{-1}e^{0}$$

Plutonium 239, like uranium 235, undergoes neutron capture and fission. Multiple neutron capture by plutonium 239 leads to americium 241, the next transuranium element.

Plutonium can be separated from uranium by chemical means, but uranium isotopes cannot be separated chemically. A large-scale application of Graham's law involves the separation of uranium isotopes. Uranium hexafluoride, a non-polar covalent compound (octahedral structure), is easily vaporized. Since the molecular weight of the compound containing the heavy isotope is slightly larger than the one containing the lighter isotope, the two kinds of molecules diffuse at slightly different rates. The mixture can be passed through a series of porous barriers, and the vapor containing the lighter isotope becomes concentrated at the end of the series of barriers.

The nuclear reactor consists of a large pile of hollow blocks made of graphite, which slows neutrons so they can be captured. Slugs of uranium are placed in the blocks. A stray neutron is captured by a uranium 235 nucleus, and the fission produces more neutrons. Some of these are captured by uranium 235 or plutonium. The net effect is that neutrons are buzzing around inside the reactor like a swarm of bees. Control rods made of a material that absorbs neutrons (cadmium or boron steel) serve to control the rate of reaction. Since much energy is released during the process, a cooling liquid, such as water, is circulated through the reactor to keep the temperature under control. The energy produced can be used to generate steam, which is used to generate electricity. Artificial isotopes can be produced by irradiating selected elements in the reactor. Some of these nuclei capture neutrons and produce isotopes. Since considerable harmful radiation is produced by a reactor, the device must be properly shielded in order to protect the operators.

The construction of a fission bomb requires that a critical mass of fissionable material be produced in order to sustain a chain reaction. A small mass of uranium 235, for example, contains atoms that fission, releasing fast neutrons. If insufficient material is present, most of these neutrons will be lost, and the fission process will not sustain itself. By bringing together small pieces of uranium, a mass of fissionable material exceeding the critical mass is produced, and the neutrons released are moderated, resulting in a good many captures and more fissions. The result is a chain reaction resulting in a tremendous explosion.

The ultimate in energy production would be the harnessing of thermonuclear reactions. The problem of fusing hydrogen nuclei consists of overcoming the tremendous repulsive force in order to bring the nuclei to the top of the nuclear "well" (see section 2) so that the protons can fuse, producing helium nuclei and positrons. Since much energy is required to cause fusion, the temperatures involved are much higher than the boiling point of any known material. Powerful magnetic and electric fields could be used to produce a plasma jet (nuclei) and force protons together, but the cost and size of the equipment might be prohibitive. Much more work must be done before controlled thermonuclear energy production becomes a reality, if ever.

4. INTERPRETING ENERGY SOURCES OF STARS

The production of stellar energy was a problem which baffled scientists for years. Ordinary chemical reactions, such as the burning of coal, could not account for the tremendous energy output or the long life of stars. With an understanding of atomic structure and nuclear processes, astronomers developed an understanding of the energy processes which keep stars going for billions of years.

The fundamental energy-producing process in the universe is the conversion of hydrogen to helium. Scientists believe that a star is born by a vast cloud of gas (mostly hydrogen) collapsing under gravitational influence. As the cloud collapses, potential energy is converted into heat energy, and the temperature of the gas cloud increases. As the cloud decreases in volume, the density increases, but since the temperature exceeds the critical temperature of the material, the liquid state is never reached. The temperature is too high to permit the existence of chemical compounds since no molecules are stable at temperatures of many thousands of degrees. Electrons are excited, and atoms become ionized. As the temperature reaches millions of degrees, hydrogen nuclei have sufficient energy to fuse, producing helium and positrons. Positrons and negative electrons fuse and annihilate each other, producing energy.

$$4\,{}_1H^1 = {}_2He^4 + 2\,{}_{+1}e^0 + \text{energy}$$
$${}_{+1}e^0 + {}_{-1}e^0 = \text{energy}$$

The conversion of hydrogen to helium actually occurs in several steps. Remind your students that multiple-body collisions are very rare (see section 8.4). The mechanism of hydrogen consumption by stars was solved by Hans Bethe around 1938. He postulated the proton chain and the carbon cycle. Since protons are very abundant, they collide frequently, producing dueterium and a positron. Deuterium nuclei fuse with protons to produce helium 3, which in turn fuses with itself to produce helium 4 and protons.

$${}_1H^1 + {}_1H^1 = {}_1H^2 + {}_{-1}e^0$$
$${}_1H^2 + {}_1H^1 = {}_2He^3$$
$${}_2He^3 + {}_2He^3 = {}_2He^4 + 2\,{}_1H^1$$

At higher temperatures other fusion reactions are possible, leading to the production of heavier nuclei. The reactions involved in the carbon cycle use carbon 12 as a catalyst (carbon is regenerated).

$${}_6C^{12} + {}_1H^1 = {}_7N^{13}$$
$${}_7N^{13} = {}_6C^{13} + {}_{+1}e^0$$
$${}_6C^{13} + {}_1H^1 = {}_7N^{14}$$
$${}_7N^{14} + {}_1H^1 = {}_8O^{15}$$
$${}_8O^{15} = {}_7N^{15} + {}_{+1}e^0$$
$${}_7N^{15} + {}_1H^1 = {}_6C^{12} + {}_2He^4$$

The overall result of these cycles is the conversion of hydrogen into helium plus energy. Other fusion reactions lead to the formation of heavier nuclei and hence the creation of the other elements found in the universe.

5. USE OF RADIOACTIVE ISOTOPES IN RESEARCH AND MEDICINE

The age of certain minerals can be estimated by chemical analysis. Rutherford proposed a method for dating igneous rocks containing uranium as far back as 1913. Using the half-lives of the elements produced from the radioactive decay of uranium 238 and realizing that the rate of a nuclear process is independent of the physical and chemical conditions existing on the earth, the ratio of lead 206 to uranium in a mineral can supply a clue to its age. Presumably, an igneous rock was produced from molten material during a volcanic eruption. Whatever uranium was incorporated into the rock at that time should remain indefinitely, being changed very slowly (half-life of uranium 238 is 4.5 billion years) into lead 206. The more lead 206 is present per unit of uranium in a uranium-bearing rock, the older the rock.

A method for estimating the age of materials containing carbon was worked out by Willard Libby around 1950. He also worked out a method for dating material containing hydrogen 3 (tritium). Remind your students that numerous processes occur in the atomosphere. The oxygen-carbon balance between plants and animals is only one of many reactions involving the atmosphere. Solar radiation and cosmic rays are responsible for numerous other processes occurring in the upper atomosphere. Cosmic rays, by virtue of their high energy, sometimes react with nuclei, causing the elimination of neutrons. When a high energy neutron collides with a nitrogen 14 nucleus, carbon 14, helium, and tritium are possible products which are actually produced in the upper atmosphere. The carbon 14 ends up in atomospheric carbon dioxide, and the tritium ends up in water vapor, which eventually falls as rain. Plants consume atmospheric carbon dioxide and thereby incorporate a small amount of radioactive carbon 14 in their make-up. A piece of charcoal found on the site of a prehistoric campfire or a piece of ancient wooden furniture found by archeologists should contain some carbon 14, whose half-life is 5700 years. By measuring the radioactivity of the sample, one can determine its age quite accurately. The older the object, the less carbon 14 remains, and the lower the radioactivity. Carbon 14 decays into nitrogen 14.

$$_{6}C^{14} = {}_{7}N^{14} + {}_{-1}e^{0}$$

Likewise, any water or water-derived artifact such as wine should contain some tritium whose half-life is 12.5 years. The older the sample, the lower the radioactivity due to tritium.

Isotopes can be used as tracers in chemical research and medicine. Many of these can be made by exposing samples of elements to neutron bombardment in a nuclear reactor or by the use of some other machine. A chemist can incorporate the desired isotope into a molecule and follow the path of the radioactive isotope by means of a Geiger counter. The path of radioactive iodine 131 can be followed to the thyroid gland, where it is incorporated into thyroxine. Since γ rays are produced by radioactive materials, treatment of cancers using cheaper materials than radium is possible. Radioactive cobalt is frequently used in cancer therapy. Carbon 14 can be incorporated into an organic molecule (used as a drug) at a certain position and the material can be traced through the body. The metabolism products can be followed by means of a Geiger counter. Isotopes which are not radioactive, such as deuterium (heavy hydrogen) and oxygen 18, are often used as tracers. Their presence can be detected by means of a mass spectrograph.

The use of isotopes as tracers is well illustrated in two CHEM Study films. The dynamic nature of equilibrium is illustrated using radioactive bromine and iodine in the film "Equilibrium," and the mechanism of the hydrolysis of an ester is worked out by following the path of oxygen 18 by means of a mass spectrograph in "Mechanism of an Organic Reaction." These films are worth showing to illustrate some of the principles and techniques used by scientists engaged in research. Isotopes have provided scientists with another tool for exploring chemical and biochemical processes.

13

Using Descriptive Chemistry

1. USE OF DEMONSTRATIONS AND LABORATORY EXPERIMENTS

The trend in chemical education has been toward the development of theory and principles and away from the traditional presentation of descriptive chemistry. This is somewhat unfortunate, since the students have less opportunity to become familiar with the basic chemistry of the elements and their compounds. It is possible to teach the principles and theory without sacrificing too much of the descriptive, however, provided the descriptive chemistry is used to illustrate the application of chemical principles. You can illustrate the principles by presenting suitable demonstrations and having your students perform experiments related to the underlying principles you are trying to teach.

The traditional chemistry course emphasized the occurrence, preparation, properties, and uses of chemical substances without stressing the underlying principles. Much of the course involved the memorization of facts, not the understanding of why substances behave the way they do. Some of the newer approaches tend to throw out the baby with the bath water, however, by neglecting a vital part of chemistry: first-hand knowledge of the behavior of chemical substances. When discussing a certain principle, such as acid-base chemistry, capitalize on the wealth of relatively simple reactions which can be used to illustrate the nature of acids and bases. Relate the principles of redox to the preparation of elements from their compounds or the chemistry of nitrogen. You can illustrate the ideas of rates of reaction and equilibrium using appropriate reactions. Periodicity can be illustrated in many ways, such as comparing some reactions of the elements in the nitrogen family.

Very often, several principles can be related to the same reaction. Once the students have gone through the basic principles of chemistry, many of which seem quite unrelated, they should have the opportunity to apply their knowledge. When they begin to apply the principles to actual situations, their understanding of chemistry should increase. They will begin to see that several basic ideas may apply in a given situation, and chemistry will become more meaningful.

2. RELATING PRINCIPLES TO PRACTICAL SITUATIONS

You can get considerable mileage from the chemistry of carbon dioxide and carbonates from either laboratory experiments or demonstrations. Use the formation of limestone caves as a springboard. Discuss carbonic acid as a diprortic acid, whose conjugate base is bicarbonate ion. Show your students that bicarbonate ion can act as either a proton acceptor or proton donor (amphiprotic). Generalize, stating that the conjugate base of a polyprotic acid can act as an acid in the presence of a stronger base or as a base in the presence of a stronger acid.

$$\underset{\text{stronger acid}}{HCO_3^-} + \underset{\text{stronger base}}{OH^-} \rightleftharpoons \underset{\text{weaker acid}}{H_2O} + \underset{\text{weaker base}}{CO_3^{-2}}$$

$$\underset{\text{stronger base}}{HCO_3^-} + \underset{\text{stronger acid}}{H_3O^+} \rightleftharpoons \underset{\text{carbonic acid is weaker acid}}{H_2O + CO_2} + \underset{\text{weaker base}}{H_2O}$$

Demonstrate the slight hydrolysis of aqueous sodium carbonate and sodium bicarbaonate by adding one drop of phenolphthalein to 0.1 molar Na_2CO_3 and to 0.1 molar $NaHCO_3$. Carbonate ion is a stronger base than bicarbonate ion, illustrating the general rule that the greater the negative charge on an anion in a series, the stronger the base. Relate this idea to the steps involved when carbonic acid donates protons:

$$H_2CO_3 \rightleftharpoons H^+ + HCO_3^-$$
$$HCO_3^- \rightleftharpoons H^+ + CO_3^{-2}$$

H_2CO_3 is a stronger aicd than HCO_3^-. Therefore HCO_3^- is a weaker base than CO_3^{-2}. Refer to section 7.3 for a discussion of aicd-vase theory.

Bubbling CO_2 through limewater produces a precipitate, which dissolves when more CO_2 reacts with the precipitate. Refer to the solubility rules regarding carbonates and bicarbonates: $CaCO_3$ is not soluble, but $Ca(HCO_3)_2$ is soluble in water. Explain the difference in solubility using Coulomb's law. Since the carbonate ion carries a double charge and bicarbonate only a single charge, there is a greater attraction between the calcium and carbonate ions than between the calcium and bicarbonate ions. The calcium and bicarbonate ions remain dispersed in the solution and do not precipitate. Use the Bronsted acid-base concept and Le Chatelier's principle to explain the precipitation of $CaCO_3$.

$$CO_2 + H_2O \rightleftharpoons H_2CO_3$$
$$H_2CO_3 + H_2O \rightleftharpoons H_3O^+ + HCO_3^-$$

Since the solution of limewater contains OH^- ions, hydronium ions are consumed, favoring the formation of more HCO^-_3 ions. These, in turn, donate protons to hydroxide ions, producing CO_3^{-2} ions. Since the solution becomes oversaturated with respect to $CaCO_3$, a precipitate is produced. Bubbling more CO_2 produces more carbonic acid, which donates protons to the carbonate ions, producing bicarbonate ions. Since the concentration of carbonate ion is reduced, the precipitate dissolves.

$$CaCO_3 + H_2CO_3 \rightleftharpoons Ca^{+2} + 2HCO_3^-$$

Bubbling CO_2 through a solution of $CaCl_2$ or $Ca(NO_3)_2$ produces no precipitate, since insufficient carbonate ions are produced. If you add some OH^- ions (in the form of aqueous NaOH) to a dilute solution containing calcium ions, bubbling CO_2 produces a precipitate of $CaCO_3$. Relate this to Le Chatelier's principle.

The general reaction of an acid salt decomposing into a normal salt plus the acid can be illustrated using bicarbonates. Heating $NaHCO_3$ produces Na_2CO_3, water, and carbon dioxide. When a solution of $Ca(HCO_3)_2$ is heated, CO_2 is produced, and the solution turns cloudy due to the formation of $CaCO_3$.

A useful rule relating the stability of salts to the activity of the metal ion can be illustrated using carbonates. When anhydrous Na_2CO_3 is heated, no CO_2 is produced, but when carbonates of the less active metals than those in Group I are heated, they decompose into the metal oxide and CO_2. The less active the metal, the more easily the carbonates decompose. This tendency can be explained, in part, by considering the size of the cation and what happens to the carbonate ion when it decomposes, using the Lewis acid-base concept and the effect of charge density. The carbonate ion is produced when an oxide ion donates a pair of electrons to carbon dioxide. Since the carbon-oxygen bond is polar (difference in electronegativity), the carbon atom is slightly positive. A resonance form of CO_2 involves the movement of a pair of electrons in one of the double bonds to the oxygen, leaving the carbon atom electron deficient. The carbon atom acts as a Lewis acid, accepting a pair of electrons from the oxide ion. This situation is discussed in section 7.6. Breaking up the carbonate ion requires the removal of an oxide ion (the reverse process). Since the alkali metal ions are large and singly charged, their charge density is too low to break up the carbonate ion by attracting an oxide ion. Therefore, alkali metal carbonates (except Li_2CO_3) do not decompose into the metal oxide and CO_2 upon heating.

Correlate the activity of the metal to the stability of nitrates (which yield metal oxide, NO_2, and oxygen), chlorates, oxides, and hydroxide. Sodium hydroxide does not decompose at the temperature of a Bunsen flame, but an aqueous precipitate of cupric hydroxide is converted to black CuO upon heating. Silver nitrate yields metallic silver on heating, and mercuric oxide yields mercury and oxygen. Silver hydroxide is so unstable that it breaks up into Ag_2O and water even at room temperature.

Nitrogen chemistry offers many opportunities for relating principles to practical situations. When magnesium turnings are heated in a crucible and exposed to air, MgO and Mg_3N_2 are produced. Point out that both compounds are essentially ionic. Magnesium oxide is basic because it contains the oxide ion. Magnesium nitride is extremely basic and reacts vigorously with water to produce ammonia.

$$Mg_3N_2 + 6H_2O = 3Mg(OH)_2 + 2NH_3$$

Analyze the reaction in terms of the stepwise reaction of strong bases removing protons from water.

$$\underset{\text{nitride ion}}{N^{-3}} \longrightarrow \underset{\text{imide ion}}{NH^{-2}} \longrightarrow \underset{\text{amide ion}}{NH_2^-} \longrightarrow \underset{\text{ammonia}}{NH_3}$$

strongest base ⟶ weakest base

Relate this to the leveling effect (see section 7.3).

Nitrogen is a very interesting element because its oxidation states range from −3 to +5. Make a table showing the oxidation states of nitrogen and an example of a compound for each state.

Oxidation State	*Examples*	
+5	HNO_3	nitric acid (nitrates)
+4	NO_2	nitrogen dioxide
+3	HNO_2	nitrous acid (nitrites)
+2	NO	nitric oxide
+1	N_2O	nitrous oxide
−0	N_2	nitrogen (free element)
−1	NH_2OH	hydroxylamine
−2	H_2NNH_2	hydrazine
−3	NH_3	ammonia (ammonium comounds.)

Point out that compounds having nitrogen in the higher oxidation states may be reduced, which implies that these compounds may act as oxidizing agents. Nitrogen in its lower oxidation states can be oxidized, and such compounds may act as reducing agents. The ones in the middle may go either way, depending upon the situation. Hydrazine can be oxidized by nitric acid, the products being nitrogen gas and water vapor. Considerable energy is produced, and this reaction is used to propel some rockets.

$$4H\overset{+5}{N}O_3 + 5H_2\overset{-2}{N}NH_2 = 7\overset{0}{N}_2 + 12\ H_2O$$

(5e⁻ gained by N of HNO_3; 4e⁻ lost by N of H_2NNH_2)

Prepare some 100% nitric acid (fuming nitric acid) in the laboratory, using a retort. Explain that the concentrated H_2SO_4 donates protons to the nitrate ions in the saltpeter. Since HNO_3 is a strong acid, nitrate ion is a weak base, and the reaction produces an equilibrium mixture containing H_2SO_4, HNO_3, and HSO_4^- ions. Heating the mixture drives off the volatile nitric acid, disturbing the balance. The reaction is driven to completion by removing HNO_3, leaving the bisulfate in the retort.

Demonstrate the oxidizing properties of fuming nitric acid by adding a pinch of powdered sulfur. The reaction produces brown NO_2 gas. Dilute the reaction mixture with water and test the solution for sulfate ions, using barium nitrate or barium chloride solution. Have your students formulate an equation for the reaction between nitric acid and sulfur.

$$S + 6HNO_3 = 6NO_2 + H_2SO_4 + 2H_2O$$

Place a wad of exselsior above some fuming nitric acid in a test tube and heat the tube. Nitric acid vapor ignites the exselsior. Nitrogen dioxide is first produced, but at a higher temperature the reduction product is nitrogen. Show the CHEM Study film "Nitric Acid," which discusses the role of nitric acid as an acid, a base, and an oxidizing agent. The discussion includes the relationship of $E°$ values, activation energy, and the principles of kinetics and equilibrium to the chemistry involved, as well as acid-base theory and the role of a catalyst.

The reduction of nitrate ion to ammonium ion can be effectively demonstrated by adding some magnesium turnings to very dilute nitric acid. After the reaction subsides (gas evolved), make the resulting solution basic with NaOH and warm, holding a piece of red litmus paper over the mixture. Ask your students what the products of the reaction are (Mg^{+2} and NH_4^+ ions) and have them write the net ionic equation for the reaction.

$$4\,(Mg = Mg^{+2} + 2e^-)$$
$$NO_3^- + 10H^+ + 8e^- = NH_4^+ + 4H_2O$$

$$4\,Mg + NO_3^- + 10H^+ = 4Mg^{+2} + NH_4^+ + 4H_2O$$

The preparation of free elements from their compounds is a fruitful field for relating the principles of redox. Give your students problems, such as, "What principle would you apply if you wanted to make free iodine from sodium iodide, and what would you use to carry out the reaction?" With a bit of coaxing, some of the students might recognize that the oxidation number of iodine must be changed from -1 to zero. A convenient oxidizing agent to use in the laboratory is MnO_2 and acid. Show them the CHEM Study film "Bromine—Element from the Sea," which does an excellent job relating the principles of redox and the use of $E°$ values to the practical problem of preparing bromine commercially. Ask your students to select a suitable oxidizing agent for the preparation of fluorine from a fluoride. The only oxidizing agent which can perform this job is the anode in an electrolysis reaction (refer to E° values). Emphasize that convenience is the critical factor in the laboratory and economics are vital for industrial processes.

Another interesting preparation is that of elemental phosphorus from calcium phosphate. This compound can be visualized as a Lewis complex of a base (calcium oxide) and an acid (phosphorus pentoxide). The trick here is to liberate the phosphorus oxide and reduce it to free phosphorus, tying up the calcium oxide with another non-metal oxide to produce a molten salt. Silica (SiO_2) serves as a flux, producing a fused salt, $CaSiO_3$ (slag) which can be poured out of the reactor. Carbon is a cheap reducing agent, and the reaction must be carried out in an inert atmosphere. An electric furnace provides the necessary heat, and the phosphorus vapor (P_4) distills out of the reaction mixture.

Metals can be prepared by reduction, since they generally occur as positive ions in their ores. There is little value to be gained from discussing industrial processes in detail, but the relationship of the chemical principles to the problem is of interest and should be stressed. An interesting series of chemical reactions occurs in the metallurgy of copper, which often occurs in combination with sulfur as Cu_2S (chalcocite), $CuFeS_2$ (chalcopyrite), or Cu_3FeS_3 (bornite). After separation from mineral impurities, the concentrated ore is partially roasted (heated in the presence of air), producing SO_2 and metal oxides. Roasting involves oxidation of the sulfur from -2 to $+4$ by oxygen. The roasting process is stopped when about two moles of Cu_2O and one mole of Cu_2S are present in the mixture. Silica and any metal oxides (iron oxide) form a slag which is drained from the reaction mixture. The copper oxide and copper sulfide react to produce more SO_2 and impure copper (blister copper). The sulfur dioxide can be recovered and oxidized to sulfuric acid, and the crude copper is refined electrolytically. The cell consists of copper sulfate solution as the electrolyte, and the anode is crude copper containing precious metal impurities (gold and silver). Ask your students which of these metals is most easily oxidized. By maintaining a low voltage the copper is selectively oxidized, and the gold and silver fall to the bottom of the tank and can be profitably recovered. Pure copper is deposited at the cathode.

The preparation of aluminum metal from crude bauxite involves acid-base chemistry and redox. Pure alumina (Al_2O_3) must be separated from other metal oxides, such as iron and titanium oxides. Since aluminum is amphoteric, Al_2O_3 can be selectively dissolved in strong base (OH^- ions). The solution is separated from the unwanted impurities, and Al_2O_3 is precipitated by lowering the pH slightly. In the Hall process the solvent for infusible Al_2O_3 is cryolite, Na_3AlF_6, which has a relatively low melting point. The melt contains Na^+, Al^{+3}, O^{-2}, and AlF_6^{-3} ions (AlF_6^{-6} is a complex of Al^+ and F^- ions). Since oxide ion is more easily oxidized than fluoride ion, oxygen gas is liberated at the anode (graphite), producing CO and CO_2. Since the aluminum ions are more easily reduced than sodium ions, metallic aluminum is produced at the cathode.

Contrary to what the traditional texts advocate, the preparation of limewater is very simple. Don't go through the involved process of heating stale calcium oxide, slaking the lime, settling and decanting. Just add a small amount of calcium hydride to water and let the hydrogen escape. The resulting solution contains calcium and hydroxide ions. If you don't have calcium hydride (available from Ventron Corporation, Beverly, Mass.), cheat by mixing dilute NaOH with dilute Ca^{+2} solution (as nitrate or chloride). What you really want is a solution of calcium and hydroxide ions, and the others are merely spectators and don't interfere with the carbonate chemistry. Likewise, when preparing ammonia gas, don't asphyxiate yourself and others by mixing slaked lime and ammonium sulfate as advocated by the traditionalists. Since the solubility of a gas decreases as the temperature increases (entropy factor), heat 28% aqueous ammonia solution and collect the gas. Relate the principles involved in these preparations to your students who might get in on your secrets.

3. GETTING MILEAGE FROM THE PERIODIC TABLE

Discuss the trends from metal to non-metal going from left to right in a period. The factors which determine acidic or basic character of the hydrides and hydroxy compounds were discussed in Chapter 7 (refer to section 7.5 for periodic variations and section 7.4 for the causes of acidic or basic behavior). As a general rule, the metal hydrides tend to be ionic and are therefore very basic. The non-metal hydrides tend to be more acidic as the electronegativity of the element increases going across the table. Metal hydroxides tend to be basic, producing metal ions and hydroxide ions, but non-metal hydroxides tend to be acidic. The acidity increases going from left to right in a period. Sodium hydroxide is basic, aluminum hydroxide is amphoteric, chlorine hydroxide (hypochlorous acid) is acidic. The acid-base properties of oxides also changes from very basic (ionic oxides) on the left to acidic (covalent) on the right of the periodic table. Acidity of an oxide or hydroxy compound tends to increase as the oxidation number of the element increases. Sulfur dioxide and sulfurous acid are less acidic than sulfur trioxide and sulfuric acid. Manganese in the + 2 oxidation state produces a typical metal cation, but in the + 7 oxidation state, manganese is part of an anion (permanganate ion). Permanganic acid is not only a strong oxidizing agent, but it is also a fairly strong acid.

Discuss some of the chemical properties of the members of the nitrogen family, illustrating these properties by means of simple reactions. The trend going from nitrogen to bismuth is from non-metallic to metallic. Correlate this trend to the decreasing ionization energy and electronegativity of the elements. Add a pinch of phosphorus pentachloride to a small amount of water. This material undergoes complete hydrolysis in two steps, first producing liquid phosphorus oxychloride and then phosphoric acid, as well as HCl.

$$PCl_5 + H_2O = POCl_3 + 2HCl$$
$$POCl_3 + 3\,H_2O = H_3PO_4 + 3\,HCl$$
$$\overline{PCl_5 + 4\,H_2O = H_3PO_4 + 5\,HCl}$$

Arsenic trichloride solution must contain a fairly high concentration of acid to suppress the hydrolysis reaction, and antimony trichloride must also contain some (but not as much) acid to suppress the reaction.

$$SbCl_3 + H_2O = SbOCl + 2\,HCl$$

Correlate the suppression of hydrolysis using acid with Le Chatelier's principle. Dilution of the acid solution of $SbCl_3$ produces a precipitate of SbOCl, which is redissolved by adding hydrochloric acid. Bismuth nitrate solution needs less acid to suppress hydrolysis. The trend is from a completely covalent compound to one having more salt-like character (i.e., from non-metallic to metallic).

Discuss the acid-base character of the oxides of nitrogen through bismuth. Nitrogen pentoxide is the anhydride of a very strong acid, HNO_3. Phosphorus pentoxide is the anhydride of a moderately strong acid, H_3PO_4. By the time you get to arsenic oxide, the acid strength decreases (arsenic and arsenious acids are weak), and arsenic trioxide is amphoteric. Demonstrate this by warming a pinch of As_2O_3 with (1) NaOH solution, (2) water, (3) hydrochloric acid. The reactions in (1) and (3) may be formulated

$$(1)\ As_2O_3 + 2OH^- = H_2O + 2AsO_2^-$$
$$(H_3AsO_3 = HAsO_2 + H_2O)$$
$$(2)\ As_2O_3 + 6H^+ = 2\,As^{+3} + 3\,H_2O$$

Arsenic behaves like a metal, producing cations in acid solution.

Follow this up by preparing the sulfides of arsenic, antimony, and bismuth. Add a few drops of saturated thioacetamide solution (thioacetamide hydrolyzes to produce H_2S) or bubble H_2S gas into a solution of Na_3AsO_4 which has been acidified with concentrated HCl. A yellow precipitate of As_2S_5 is produced upon heating. Thioacetamide or H_2S added to solutions of $SbCl_3$ (containing HCl) and $Bi\,(NO_3)_3$ stabilized with HNO_3 produce maroon and dark brown precipitates of Sb_2S_3 and Bi_2S_3, respectively. Extra H_2S might have to be used in the case of $Bi(NO_3)_3$, since some of the H_2S will be oxidized to free sulfur by the nitric acid. These reactions producing sulfides are typical of metal ions.

Antimony hydroxide and bismuth hydroxide behave differently in the presence of excess hydroxide ion. Addition of extra OH^- ions to a precipitate of $Sb(OH)_3$ dissolves the precipitate, producing $Sb(OH)_4^-$ ion. Addition of excess OH^- ions to $Bi(OH)_3$ does not dissolve the precipitate, however. Bismuth is more metallic than the amphoteric antimony ion. Gradual addition of acid to $Sb(OH)_4^-$ ion solution first precipitates $Sb(OH)_3$, which dissolves in excess acid, producing Sb^{+3} ions.

You can show the trend of more non-metallic to less non-metallic in the halogen series by taking advantage of simple redox reactions. Refer to the oxidation potentials of the halide ions. Fluoride ion can be oxidized only by an anode, and iodide ion is the most easily oxidized in the series. The hydrogen halides are similar; they are gases which fume in moist air (except for HF, which boils at room temperature), very soluble in water, strong acids. Add a few drops of concentrated H_2SO_4 to a pinch of NaCl in a test tube. The reaction produces colorless HCl gas, which fumes in moist air (blow gently across the mouth of the test tube). Addition of H_2SO_4 to a pinch of NaBr produces HBr, which fumes in moist air, and some free bromine. Bromide ion reduces H_2SO_4 to SO_2. Addition of H_2SO_4 to NaI produces some HI (fumes in moist air) as well as free iodine (purple-brown color) and the odor of rotten eggs (H_2S). Iodide ion is a stronger reducing agent than bromide ion. The reactions producing the free halogens may be formulated

$$8\,NaI + 5\,H_2SO_4 = 4\,I_2 + H_2S + 4\,Na_2SO_4 + 4\,H_2O$$
$$2\,NaBr + 2\,H_2SO_4 = Br_2 + SO_2 + Na_2SO_4 + 2H_2O$$

In order to prepare HBr or HI, one must use non-oxidizing conditions. One possible method for preparing HI is to hydrolyze PI_3. Put some red phosphorus in a test tube, add a little bit of water, then add some iodine crystals. The reaction soon begins. Attach a delivery tube and hold the end of it just above the surface of water in a beaker, pointing out the "oily" appearance as the gas dissolves. Lowering the end of the delivery tube below the surface of the water causes water to be sucked back rapidly into the generator tube, since HI is extremely soluble in water. Test the HI solution for acidity and for iodide ion, using chlorine water and carbon tetrachloride. Iodine oxidizes the phosphorus and is reduced.

$$2\,P + 3\,I_2 + 6\,H_2O = 2\,H_3PO_3 + 6\,HI$$

A rather intriguing reaction consists of adding a small portion of 0.1 molar NaI solution to a dilute solution of NaBr, producing a mixture of Br^- and I^- ions. Add enough carbon tetrachloride to produce enough lower layer to reveal the presence of free halogen. Add chlorine water in small portions, shaking vigorously between each addition. The first color to appear in the carbon tetrachloride is purple (free iodine). On adding more chlorine water, the color changes from purple to orange, revealing the presence of free bromine. Since iodide ion is more easily oxidized than bromide ion, the purple color appears first. Further addition of chlorine causes the oxidation of free iodine to iodate ion (colorless and not soluble in CCl_4). Then the bromide ion is oxidized to free bromine. Addition of sodium sulfite (reducing agent) in small portions discharges the orange color (bromine reduced to bromide ion) and the reappearance of the purple color (iodate is reduced to free iodine. Addition of more sulfite reduces the purple iodine to colorless iodide ion. This sequence of reactions may be formulated as follows.

$$2\,I^- + Cl_2 = 2\,Cl^- + I_2 \text{ (purple)}$$
$$I_2 + 6\,H_2O + 5\,Cl_2 = 10\,Cl^- + 2\,IO_3^- + 12\,H^+ \text{ (colorless)}$$
$$2\,Br^- + Cl_2 = 2Cl^- + Br_2 \text{ (orange)}$$
$$Br_2 + SO_3^{-2} + H_2O = SO_4^{-2} + 2Br^- + 2H^+ \text{ (colorless)}$$
$$2\,IO_3^- + 5\,SO_3^{-2} + 2\,H^+ = 5\,SO_4^{-2} + I_2 + H_2O \text{ (purple)}$$
$$I_2 + H_2O + SO_3^{-2} = SO_4^{-2} + 2\,I^- + 2\,H^+ \text{ (colorless)}$$

This series of reactions demonstrates that iodide is more easily oxidized than bromide ion. Iodine is readily oxidized to iodate, but excess chlorine water does not oxidize bromine to bromate. Bromine has a higher electron affinity, electronegativity, and ionization energy than iodine. Bromine is more non-metallic than iodine.

4. SOME EXAMPLES OF CREATIVE CHEMISTRY

For better or for worse, the science of chemistry has enabled man to make many things which have raised his material standard of living. If you feel like engaging in a philosophical discussion, introduce the premise that every invention has two sides: the potential for good, and the potential for evil. Science itself is ethically neutral. Man uses the power of knowledge according to his own desires. Man can create, or he can destroy. Perhaps the most dramatic illustration of this premise is atomic energy. Man has the capability of blowing himself into oblivion, or he can use the secret of the atom to benefit himself. Unfortunately, war has historically produced more advances of knowledge in a short time than periods of peace. To illustrate this, the fixation of nitrogen and the synthesis of rubber are good examples.

Consider Germany prior to World War I. In order to wage war against the Allies, the Central Powers had to have an unlimited supply of nitric acid for making high explosives. The only known method for producing nitric acid at the turn of the century was the distillation of nitric acid from a mixture of Chile saltpeter and sulfuric acid. Since Great Britain ruled the seas, it was unlikely that Germany could import much sodium nitrate from South America. The German chemists came to the rescue, however, and used air as a source of nitrogen. Fritz Haber had discovered a process for synthesizing ammonia from its constituent elements, and Wilhelm Ostwald had discovered a process for the catalytic oxidation of ammonia to nitric oxide, which was further oxidized and converted to nitric acid. Once the Germans had their supply of high explosives, they could conceivably engage in warfare.

World War II posed another problem. Mobile armies roll on rubber, which was available from Southeast Asia and South America. Since Germany would be blockaded from access to these sources, it was imperative that she have an unlimited access to the product from domestic sources. Coal, air, and water were plentiful in Central Europe. The technological problem was to convert the carbon contained in coal into the monomer for rubber. Hydrogenation of coal to hydrocarbons by the Fischer-Tropsch process had given Germany synthetic petroleum with which to run the war machine. Synthetic rubbers could be produced by polymerization of butadiene, chloroprene, and various other unsaturated monomers. The Germans, led by Reppe, developed the technology of acetylene chemistry. Limestone and coke can be converted to calcium carbide in an electric furnace, and the calcium carbide, upon treatment with water, yields acetylene. This reactive compound can be converted into all kinds of intermediates by addition reactions.

$$CaCO_3 \longrightarrow CaO + CO_2$$

$$CaO + 3\,C \longrightarrow CaC_2 + CO$$

$$CaC_2 + 2\,H_2O \longrightarrow HC \equiv CH + Ca(OH)_2$$

Addition of water:

$$CH \equiv CH + H_2O \longrightarrow \underset{\text{vinyl alcohol}}{[CH_2{=}CHOH]} \longrightarrow \underset{\text{acetaldehyde}}{CH_3CH{=}O}$$

$$CH_3CH{=}O \longrightarrow CH_3COOH$$

Addition to itself:

$$3\,CH \equiv CH \longrightarrow C_6H_6 \text{ (benzene)}$$

$$2\,CH \equiv CH \longrightarrow CH_2 = CHC \equiv CH \text{ (vinylacetylene)}$$

$$CH_2 = CHC \equiv CH + HCl \longrightarrow CH_2 = CH\underset{\substack{| \\ Cl}}{C} = CH_2 \text{ (chloroprene)}$$

Butadiene synthesis:

$$CH_3\,CH = O + CH_3CH = O \longrightarrow CH_3\,\underset{\substack{| \\ OH}}{C}HCH_2\,CH = O \longrightarrow \text{(aldol)}$$

$$CH_3\,\underset{\substack{| \\ OH}}{C}HCH_2\,CH_2\,OH \longrightarrow CH_2 = CH_2 = CHCH = CH_2 \text{ (butadiene)}$$

Acetylene is also a source of vinyl acetate, from which polyvinyl acetate may be produced. Acetylene adds acetic acid.

$$CH \equiv CH + CH_3C{\substack{\nearrow O \\ \searrow OH}} \longrightarrow CH_3C{\substack{\nearrow O \\ \searrow O{-}CH{=}CH_2}}$$

Petroleum is an important source of organic chemicals. One of the principal starting materials obtained from petroleum processing is ethylene (ethene), which can add to itself to produce polyethylene. Addition of water produces ethyl alcohol.

$$CH_2 = CH_2 + HOH \longrightarrow CH_3\,CH_2\,OH$$

Oxidation of ethyl alcohol yields acetaldehyde, and further oxidation yields acetic acid. Chemists have been able to synthesize many complex molecules from simple starting materials.

An interesting but not well-known bit of chemical magic is the racemization of left-handed amphetamine, which has no physiological activity. The drug which is active is the right-handed molecule, and the left-handed isomer is useless as a drug. Instead of throwing away the inactive form, a process was developed which enabled the manufacturer to convert some of the left-handed material into a mixture of right and left-handed molecules, from which the right-handed variety could be isolated. Amphetamine is manufactured by pyrolizing a mixture of phenylacetic acid and acetic acid to yield phenylacetone (benzyl methyl ketone).

$$C_6H_5COOH + CH_3COOH \longrightarrow C_6H_5CH_2\underset{\underset{\displaystyle O}{\|}}{C}CH_3$$

The ketone is converted to the amine.

$$C_6H_5CH_2\overset{\overset{\displaystyle O}{\|}}{C}CH_3 \longrightarrow C_6H_5CH_2 - \overset{\overset{\displaystyle H}{|}}{\underset{\underset{\displaystyle NH_2}{|}}{C}}-CH_3 \quad \text{(mixture of d and l isomers)}$$

The mixture of the two optical isomers is resolved by selective precipitation of the d-tartaric acid salt of d-amphetamine, from which the desired isomer is obtained. The l isomer is heated with a catalyst, which causes the temporary elimination of hydrogen and the establishment of a $C=N$ double bond. The optical activity is destroyed. Hydrogen then adds across this double bond, producing a mixture of the two optical isomers. This mixture is recycled in the process. The end result is that the undesired isomer is converted to the desired one, eliminating waste.

An interesting aspect of research is the quest for new drugs. Much must still be learned before medicinal chemists and biochemists can predict the type and extent of activity a particular molecule will have in the body, but progress is being made. Sulfanilamide had been synthesized by Gelmo in 1908, but it was not until much later that its value as a drug was discovered. In 1934, Domagk announced that a substance called Prontosil cured numerous bacterial infections in laboratory animals. In 1935, Trefouels and Fourneau found that Prontosil broke down into the actual active chemical, *p*-aminobenzenesulfonamide. This was the beginning of the development of sulfa drugs.

Show your students the synthetic route to the drug sulfathiazole, starting with aniline, vinyl acetate, and thiourea. This may give them some idea of what chemical synthesis involves. Follow this up by showing them the CHEM Study film "Biochemistry and Molecular Structure," which reveals the merging of several disciplines in attacking research problems.

$$C_6H_5NH_2 \xrightarrow{Ac_2O} C_6H_5NHCOCH_3 \quad \text{(acetanilide)}$$

Aniline is acetylated in order to protect the amine group in the subsequent steps. It is later removed by hydrolysis.

$$C_6H_5NHCOCH_3 \xrightarrow[\text{(chlorosulfonic acid)}]{HOSO_2Cl} p\text{-}CH_3CONHC_6H_4SO_2Cl$$

p-acetylamino-benzenesulfonyl chloride

condensed with 2-aminothiazole

$$CH_3C(=O)OCH=CH_2 \xrightarrow{Cl_2} CH_3C(=O)OCHClCH_2Cl \xrightarrow{H_2O} ClCH_2C(=O)H$$

vinyl acetate — chloroacetaldehyde

$$H_2N{-}C(NH_2){=}S \longleftrightarrow HN{=}C(NH_2){-}SH \; + \; O{=}C(H){-}CH_2{-}Cl \longrightarrow H_2N{-}C\text{(thiazole ring: } {-}N{=}CH{-}CH{=}\text{, } {-}S{-}\text{)}$$

Thiourea — 2-aminothiazole

$$CH_3CONH{-}C_6H_4{-}SO_2Cl + H_2N{-}(C_3H_2NS) \longrightarrow CH_3CONH{-}C_6H_4{-}SO_2NH{-}(C_3H_2NS)$$

putting two parts of molecule together

$$\xrightarrow{\text{hydrolysis}} H_2N{-}C_6H_4{-}SO_2NH{-}(C_3H_2NS)$$

Point out that the molecular manipulation performed does not change the basic sulfanilamide portion of the molecule. Molecular modifications of certain drugs sometimes enhance their activity, change their rate and duration of effect, or aid in their metabolism, thereby decreasing their toxicity. Scientists believe that since sulfanilamide is similar in structure to *p*-aminobenzoic acid, bacteria ingest the drug but are unable to metabolize it. This leads to their death.

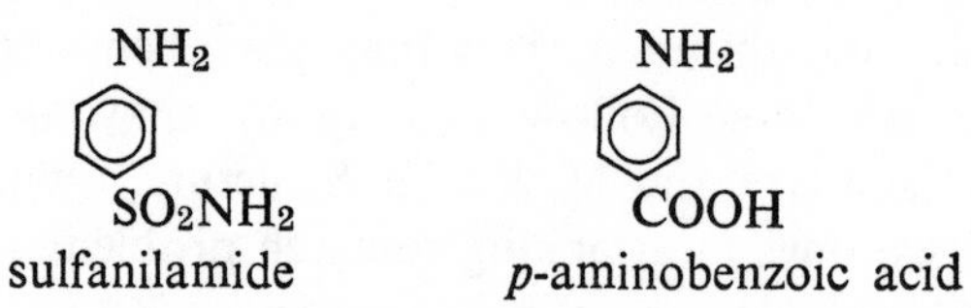

Many other examples of creative chemistry are available and can be used effectively to show your students the profound effect that chemistry has on our lives. The synthesis of nylon (see section 11.3) is man's attempt to do better than the silkworm. Leaded gasoline provides an example of a practical application of the periodic table. Tetraethyl lead, made by treating a sodium-lead alloy with ethyl chloride, was found to be a good anti-knock fluid. The only trouble was that lead and lead oxide fouled up test engines. The culprit had to be eliminated. Point out the positions of lead and bromine on the periodic table and ask your students to predict the relative electronegativities of lead and bromine. Hopefully they will conclude that since the difference is not very large, lead bromide should be easily vaporized. Ethylene dibromide (addition of bromine to ethene) is mixed with lead tetraethyl, and during the combustion process in the engine, lead and bromine combine. The compound is vaporized, escaping in the exhaust.

5. HOW TO STRIKE A BALANCE BETWEEN DESCRIPTIVE CHEMISTRY AND CHEMICAL PRINCIPLES

One of the big catch words in today's society is *relevance*. Young people are criticizing the educational institutions from universities on down and accusing them of not being relevant or providing a meaningful experience. The square generation does not speak a language the kids can understand. You, as a chemistry teacher, should try to relate chemistry to the experience of your students in a way they can understand. If you keep your course on a theoretical level and only discuss the principles of chemistry, many of your students will lose interest. Show them, in everyday terms, how the principles apply to situations they can appreciate.

When discussing the competition for protons between two bases having different strengths, compare the situation to the choice a red-blooded American young man makes between walking down the street with a voluptuous girl (Raquel Welch) or a skinny one (Twiggy). The proton is attracted to the stronger base, just as most normal men are attracted to the lucious beauty. The same type of example can be used in redox. Electrons are attracted by the better oxidizing agent. Develop your own examples to illustrate the operation of abstract principles. Use of dramatic effects and a flair for showmanship can liven up a course and often stimulate students.

You can talk all you want about principles, but these will not mean very much to most students unless they can be seen in operation. Good demonstrations and well-chosen laboratory experiments are an absolute necessity if you wish to present a meaningful and interesting course. Cookbook stuff doesn't serve much of a purpose except in a home economics class. It is almost self-evident that a chemistry student must have first-hand contact with chemicals and be familiar with some properties of common substances. Don't just have the students learn descriptive chemistry for the sake of becoming familiar with substances, however. Capitalize on the properties of these things by relating them to the principles you are trying so hard to teach and have the kids understand.

Diamond is extremely hard, high melting, and does not conduct electricity, but graphite is soft and conducts. Don't stop there! Relate these properties to the type of bonding in the carbon crystals. Diamond is slightly denser than graphite. The heats of combustion of the two forms are: graphite —94.03 Kcal/mole, diamond—94.48 Kcal/mole. So what? This information is virtually meaningless unless you consider the ramifications. Diamond is thermodynamically more stable than graphite, the difference in energy being about 450 cal/mole. Why doesn't diamond spontaneously turn into graphite? The energy barrier for the change is high. One can make diamonds from graphite by supplying the necessary activation energy and encouraging the formation of the material occupying the smaller volume by using very high pressure (apply Le Chatelier's principle). Diamonds can be made synthetically by using tremendously high pressure and a high temperature. A simple case like the allotropy of carbon can provide an opportunity to illustrate the principles of bonding, thermodynamics, kinetics, and equilibrium.

A burning candle provides a rich field for applying chemical principles. Showing the film "The Science of Fire" (Association Films, Inc., 600 Grand Avenue, Ridgefield, N.J. 07657) might be a good way to begin your course. It takes a scientific look at a candle and shows some close-ups of a burning candle, revealing the flow of molten wax into the wick. Explain the formation of soot as the result of thermal breakdown of the complex molecules into simpler ones, including elementary carbon. Relate the thermal decomposition of candle wax to the processes occurring during the destructive distillation of coal or wood. You can introduce the idea that reactions require the reactants meeting in order to interact (collision theory). An intimate mixture provides more contact between reactants and a faster reaction. Gas mixtures react very rapidly, since the amount of contact between reactants is so great. You could even follow up the burning candle discussion with a brief look at the phlogiston theory and how Lavoisier's twelve-day experiment gave him the clue that burning consists of a reaction between oxygen and a burning material rather than the escape of phlogiston into "dephlogisticated air." Stress that theories are useful only as long as they can account for the facts and predict phenomena successfully.

At some point, demonstrate an ammonia fountain. Add a pinch of congo red and a few drops of dilute HCl to the water. Relate the acid-base properties of ammonia and its high solubility in water to the polar structure and an unshared pair of electrons. Hydrogen chloride behaves in a similar fashion (except that it is an acid), but HCl fumes in moist air. Account for this property by reminding your students that HCl reacts with water to produce ions, which become hydrated. The strong attraction of H_3O^+ and Cl^- ions for the polar water molecules leads to the formation of droplets of hydrochloric acid. Ammonia and water don't react extensively, however, and no droplets of "ammonium hydroxide" result. Ammonia and hydrogen chloride gases react to form ammonium and chloride ions, which attract each other strongly and produce tiny crystals (semi-colloidal) of ammonium chloride. This accounts for the smoke that is seen when these gases are mixed. Simple phenomena can often provide a springboard for discussing the operation of chemical principles.

If you want a three-ring circus involving redox, equilibrium, buffering, and solubility phenomena, demonstrate or have your students oxidize chromium III ions to dichromate with PbO_2. Add about one gram of lead dioxide to about half a large test tube of 0.1 molar Cr^{+3} ion solution (in the form of the nitrate or sulfate). Add a few milliters of dilute nitric acid to suppress the formation of chromate ions (which would precipitate $PbCrO_4$). Boil the mixture for several minutes, pointing out that since there is a heterogeneous system, the reaction occurring between solid PbO_2 and the ions is slow (small surface area of contact). Decant some of the orange solution containing Pb^{+2} and $Cr_2O_7^{-2}$ ions in acid solution to another test tube and add some sodium acetate (buffer). Lead chromate should precipitate. Point out that lead is in the carbon family and has an oxidation state of $+4$, which can be reduced to $+ 2$ by gaining electrons. Lead dioxide is a good oxidizing agent and is used as such in a lead storage battery. An equilibrium exists between chromate and dichromate ions. Reducing the acidity (acetate ion is basic) results in more chromate ions being produced, and the solubility product of lead chromate is exceeded. The solution becomes oversaturated with respect to lead chromate, resulting in its precipitation.

$$3\,(PbO_2 + 4H^+ + 2\,e^- = Pb^{+2} + 2H_2O) + 1.69 \text{ volts}$$
$$2\,Cr^{+3} + 7\,H_2O = Cr_2O_7^{-2} + 14\,H^+ + 6\,e^- - 1.33$$
$$\overline{3\,PbO_2 + 2\,Cr^{+3} + H_2O = 3\,Pb^{+}{}_{2} + Cr_2O_7^{-2} + 2\,H^+ + 0.36 \text{ v}}$$
$$Cr_2O_7^{-2} + H_2O \rightleftharpoons 2\,CrO_4^{-2} + 2\,H^+$$
$$\quad OAc^- \longrightarrow HOAc$$
$$Pb^{+2} + CrO_4^{-2} \rightleftharpoons PbCrO_4$$

Since chemistry is an experimental science, the laboratory work should be an important part of the course. Performing experiments not only involves the students with the feeling of chemistry, but also gives them some of the descriptive chemistry they might not otherwise encounter in class. Exercising judgment in selecting equipment and quantities, making measurements and collecting data is forced upon the students, provided the laboratory program allows freedom of choice. A good experiment involves the student, makes him observe and think, and relates principles to actual situations. Although well-performed demonstrations have their place in the classroom or lecture, there is no substitute for student involvement in the laboratory situation. After all, the laboratory is the heart of the science of chemistry.

A good laboratory program should strike a balance between quantitative and qualitative experiments. Have your students prepare oxygen gas and have them burn some metals and non-metals in oxygen, testing the oxides with litmus. Have them determine the formula for a hydrate or a sulfide experimentally. Determination of the molecular weight of oxygen gas and the equivalent weight of a metal, the solubility of a salt, the heat of solution, molecular weight by freezing point depression, and the titration of sodium carbonate with HCl using different indicators are good quantitative experiments which involve principles and provide the students with experience in determining quantitative results. Experiments illustrating ionic reactions, equilibrium, acid-base concepts, redox reactions, and the chemistry of nitrogen, sulfur, and the halogens are very worthwhile. Ask them questions relating the principles to the experiments and relate the theory to the facts.

A good way to end the year is to have your students identify several unknown salts, applying the principles of qualitative analysis. Most students find this type of work interesting and challenging. It serves as a good review of principles, including solubility rules, acid-base chemistry, ionic equilibrium, and redox. Have your students carry out the reactions involved in the separation and identification of the ions in the HCl group (Ag^+, Pb^{+2}, Hg^{+2}) and devise a scheme for separating the mixture and identifying the ions. Give them an unknown mixture. Olmsted's *Enrichment Experiments in Basic Chemistry* (Hayden Publishing Company, New York, 1966) describes a number of experiments relating descriptive chemistry to principles as well as a scheme for identifying unknown samples of salts.

You will find it impossible to include all the material discussed in this book in a one year chemistry course. Some of it may be too sophisticated for your students to grasp in a short time. Hopefully, you will be able to use some of the examples given to good advantage and will develop many of your own. Introduce chemical principles in terms your students can understand and relate them to practical situations by means of demonstrations, laboratory experiments, and examples from the world in which they live. The principles are the skeleton and the descriptive material the flesh. The body of chemistry needs both. You, the teacher, must supply the breath of life.

Index

A

A priori, 18
Absolute error, 20
Acceleration, 25
Accuracy, 20
Acid-base concepts, 129-149
Acids, Bases, and the Chemistry of the Covalent Bond, 143, 229
Activation energy, 152-155
Addition reactions, 222
Adsorption, 126
Alcohols, 217-219
Aldehydes, 218
Alkaloids, 235
Alkanes, 212
Alkenes, 214, 215
Aliphatic hydrocarbons, 217
Americium, 241, 245
Amides, 220
Amines, 220
Anode, 146
Aromatic compounds, 215, 216, 217
Aromatic hydrocarbons, 217
Arrhenius, 129, 130, 131, 132, 141
Atom:
  atomic radius, 62
  aufbau principle, 60
Atom (*cont.*)
  Avogadro's number, 50
  Becquerel, 53, 237
  Bohr, Niels, 56, 58
  Broglie, 57, 58
  Chadwick, 55
  "Chemical Families," 65
  Coulomb's law, 61
  Dalton, 49, 50, 53
  Democritus, 49
  development of structure, 53-54
  diersible, 53
  Dobereiner, 64
  dual nature of electromagnetic radiation, 57
  Einstein, 57
  electrolysis, laws, 53
  electrolytes, 53
  electromagnetic spectrum, 57
  electromagnetic waves, 57
  electron affinity, 61
  electron spin, 59
  electronegativity, 61
  electronic distribution, 59
  Faraday, Michael, 53, 132
  Geiger, 53
  Heisenberg, 58
  Hund's rule, 60

Atom (*cont.*)
"Hydrogen Atom as viewed by Quantum Mechanics (Advanced Version)," 59
ionization energy, 55, 61
isotopes, 54-55
fission, 54, 55
fusion, 54, 55
ions, 53
line spectra, 58
magnetic and spin properties of electrons, 59
mass spectrograph, 51
Maxwell, 57
Mendeleeff, Dmitri, 64
metals, properties, 66-67
Meyer, Lothar, 64
Millikan, Robert, 52
model, 50-52
Moseley, Henry, 65
neutrons, 55
non-electrolytes, 53
non-metals, properties, 66-67
orbital, 58
paramagnetism, 59
Pauli's exclusion principle, 60
periodic law, development, 64-66
periodic properties, 62, 66-67
photoelectric effect, 53, 55, 57
photons, 57
Planck, Max, 57
protons, 55
Prout, William, 55
quantum mechanics and quantum atom, 56
radioactivity, 53, 54-55
Rutherford, 53, 54, 55, 238, 239, 244, 248
shapes and orientations of orbitals, 61
Soddy, Frederick, 50
Stern and Gerlach, 59
structure and periodic law, 49-67
thermoionic, effect, 55
Thompson, J. J., 51, 53, 237, 238
wave mechanics, 58
weight, 49-50, 95-97

Atom (*cont.*)
X-ray spectra, 65-66
Zeeman effect, 59
Atomic pile, 245
Atomic structure, 29
Attractive forces:
common types, 85
conductivity, 84
correlated using Coulomb's law, 83
covalent crystals, 85
"Crystals and Their Structure," 85
dipole-dipole, 85
increase with complexity of molecules, 83
ion-dipole, 85
ion-ion, 85
ionic compounds, 83
metals, 84-85
non-polar molecules, 83, 85
polar molecules, 83
Vander Waals, 41, 42, 85
Aufbau principle, 60
Avogadro's hypothesis, 33, 36, 37, 39-40, 104-106
Avogadro's number, 40, 50

B

Becquerel, 53, 237
Bethe, Hans, 247
Bimolecular nucleophilic substitution, 231
Binding energy, 242
"Biochemistry and Molecular Structure," 236
Bohr, Niels, 56, 58
Boiling point elevation, 123
Bomb, fission, 246
Bonding:
acetylene, 81
ammonia, 80
assigning oxidation numbers, 76
attractive forces, 83-85
(*see also* Attractive forces)
carbon, 78

Bonding (*cont.*)
carbon dioxide molecule, 82
charge density, 87-89
chlorine molecule, 75, 76
coordinate-covalent, 73-74
covalent, 72, 73, 74
electronegativity scale, 75-77
ethylene, 80
formaldehyde, 77
hybridization of orbitals, 77-82
hydration energy, 87-89
hydrogen, 87-89
hydrogen chloride molecule, 73, 75, 77
hydrogen sulfide, 80
"inert" elements, 71
ionic, 71
ionic compound, 72
ionic radius, 87-89
lattice energy, 87-89
metal combined with non-metal, 72
molecular geometry, 77-82
molecular orbital theory, 74
negative ion larger than neutral atom, 71
oxidation numbers, 75-77
Pauling, Linus, 75
polarity of molecules, 82
positive ion smaller than neutral atom, 71
predicting types, 75-77
resonance and charge density, 85-87
carbonate ion, 86
delocalization of electrons, 85
melting points, 86-87
ozone, 85
sodium chloride, 76
type, 77-82
valence, 69-70
(*see also* Valence)
valence bond theory, 74
water, 79
Born-Haber cycle, 71, 182-185
Boyle, Robert, 27
Boyle's law, 33, 37, 161
Bronsted acid-base concept, 132-136, 141
Brookhaven National Laboratories synchotron, 245
Brownian motion, 33, 127
Burning, nature, 18
Butanes, 213

C

Calculations:
atomic and molecular weights, 95-97
Avogadro's hypothesis, 104-106
Cannizzaro's principle, 95, 96
correcting pressure for gases collected over water, 107-108
Dalton's law, 105, 107
Dulong and Petit's law, 95
Dumas method, 96
electrochemistry, 108-110
empirical formulas, 98-100
equilibrium constants, 110-113
equivalents, 93-95
Gay Lussac's law, 105
general gas equalion, 104-106
molar and normal solutions, 102-104
oxidation potential concept, 108-110
per cent composition, 98
pH, 110-113
Raoult's law, 97
stoichiometry, 100-102
teaching using mole concept, 91-113
Victor Meyer method, 96
Campbell, J. Arthur, 158, 160
Cancer therapy, 249
Cannizzaro, 37, 95, 96
Carbohydrates, 233
Carbon cycle, 247
Carboxylic acids, 219
"Catalysis," 154
Cathode, 146
Cellulose, 234
Chadwick, James, 55
Changes, physical and chemical, 28
Charge density, 23, 85-89

Charge of ions, 29
Charles' laws, 33
Chemical bonding, 29
Chemical changes, 28
Chemical energy, 172-175, 178
"Chemical Families," 27, 65
Chemistry of OH Group, 222
Clapp, L., 222
Coal, 211
Cobalt, radioactive, 249
Cockroft, 243
Coefficients, 30
Colligative properties of solutions, 122-125
Collision theory, 152-155
Colloids:
  adsorption, 126
  distinct from solutions and suspensions, 125-126
  light-scattering, 126-127
Combination, 31
"Combining capacity," 29
Compounds, 26-28, 29, 69-89 (*see also* Bonding)
Concentration, 22-23
Concepts, 18
Conceptual definitions, 18
Conservation of matter, 30
Coordinate-covalent, 73-74
Corrosion of metals, 207-209
Cosmic rays, 248
Coulomb's law, 23, 61-64, 71, 131, 171, 172
Covalent, 72, 73, 74
Creative chemistry, 260-264
Crystallization, 120-121
"Crystals and Their Structures," 43, 127
Curie, Irene, 245
Curies, 237
Cyclic alkanes, 213, 215
Cyclic alkenes, 215
Cyclic hydrocarbons, 215
Cyclic (ring) compounds, 215
Cyclohexane, 215
Cyclotron, 245

D

Dalton, 29, 49, 50, 53
Dalton's law, 33, 36, 37, 105, 107
Debye, 131
Decay, rate, 243
Decomposition, 31-32
Deductive reasoning, 18
Definitions, 18
Delocalization of electrons, 85
Democritus, 49
Demonstrations, 251-252
Descriptive chemistry, 251-268
Dimensional analysis, 18-20, 102-104
Displacement, 32
Distribution curve, 34
DNA, 235
Dobereiner, 64
Dueterium, 247, 249
Dulong and Petit's law, 95
Dumas method, 96

E

E° concept, 200-204
Ebullition, 45
Einstein, 57, 241, 242
"Electric Interactions in Chemistry," 23
Electrochemical reactions, 204-207
Electrochemistry, 108-110
Electrode reactions, 146-148
Electrolysis, 53
Electrolysis cells, 146-148
Electrolytes, 53, 125
Electromagnetic spectrum, 57
Electromagnetic waves, 57
Electron affinity, 61, 71
Electron-dot formulas, 70
Electron spin, 59
Electron transfer, 196
Electron-volt, 238
Electronegativity, 61, 71
Electronegativity scale, 75-77
Electrophilic substitution, 231
Electroscope, 237

Elements, 26
Empirical formulas, 30, 98-100
Endothermic processes, 26
Energy:
  binding, 242
  calculations, 178-180
  chemical, 172-175
  coordinates, 152-155
  diagrams and Born-Haber cycle, 182-185
  entropy, 175-178
  free, 175-178, 180-182, 185-188
  heat content, 175-178
  stellar, 247-248
  varieties, 171-172
Enrichment Experiments in Basic Chemistry, 162
Enthalpy, 26
Entropy, 26, 175-178
Enzymes, 234
Equations, 30-32
Equilibrium:
  constants, 110-113
  E° concept, 200-204
  free energy, 186-188
  ionic, 162-166
  non-ionic, 166-169
  recognize and explain, 151-152
  writing constants, 159-160, 161-162
Equivalents, explaining concepts, 93-95
Error:
  absolute, 20
  analysis, 20
  calculating, 20-22
  relative, 20
Ester, 249
Esterification, 232
Esters, 219
Ethers, 217-218
Exclusion principle, 60
Exothermic processes, 26
Experiments, 251-252

F

Factor-label method, 18
Faraday, Michael, 53, 132
"Father of Chemistry," 27
Fats, 219, 234
Fission, 54, 55, 242-243, 245
Force, 25, 33
Formulas, 29-30
Free energy, 175-178, 180-182, 185-188
Free radical mechanisms, 229
Freezing point depression, 123
Friedel-Crafts reaction, 231
Functional isomerism, 227
Fusion, 54, 55, 242-243, 245

G

Geiger counter, 237, 249
Gas equation, general, 40-41
Gas laws, 33-37
"Gas Pressure and Molecular Collisions," 33, 38
"Gases and How They Combine," 36
Gases:
  collected over water, 107-108
  in liquids, 121-122
  real and ideal, 41-42
Gaussian distribution curve, 34
Gay-Lussac's law, 33, 36, 37, 105
Geiger, 53
General gas equation, 40, 104-106
Geometric isomerism, 227
Gerlach, 59
Graham's law, 33, 35, 37, 246
Guess, 17
Guldberg, 159

H

Haber Process, 168
Hahn, 243
Half-life, 243
Half-reactions, 194-196
Halides, 220
Handbook of Chemistry and Physics, 214
Heat content, 175-178

Heisenberg, 58
Helium, 238
Henry's law, 121
Herz, Werner, 229
Hess, G. H., 175, 182
Heterocyclic compounds, 215
Heterogeneous, 26
Homogeneous, 26
Hormones, 235
Huckel, 131
Hund's rule, 60
Hybridization of orbitals, 77-82
Hydration, 116
Hydration energy, 87-89
Hydrocarbons, 217
"Hydrogen Atom as Viewed by Quantum Mechanics (Advanced Version)," 59
Hydrogen bonding, 87-89
Hydrolysis of ester, 232
Hypothesis, 17

I

"Ideal gas equation," 40, 104-106
Igneous rocks, 248
Inductive reasoning, 17, 18
Inertia, 25
Ionic bonding, 70, 71, 72
Ionic equations, 31, 143-146
Ionic redox equations, 198
Ionic equilibrium, 162-166
Ionic mechanisms, 229
Ionic radius, 87-89
Ionization:
  constants, 148-149, 160
  energy, 55, 71
  theory, 129-149
Ions, 53
Isobutane, 213
Isomerism:
  functional, 227
  geometric, 227
  optical, 228
  positional, 227
Isomerism (*cont.*)
  structural, 226
  types listed, 226
Isomers, 30
Isotopes, 54, 55

J

Joliot, F., 245
Joule, 238

K

Kekule, 216
"Kernel," 70
Ketones, 218
Kilowatt hour equivalent, 241
Kinetic energy, 33
Kinetic-molecular theory, 33-47
Kinetics and equilibrium, 151-169

L

Laboratory, 251-252
Lattice energy, 87-89
Lavoisier, 18
Law, 17
Lawrence, E. O., 244-245
Le Chatelier's principle, 46, 121, 148, 161, 162, 165, 177
Length, 19
Lewis, 18
Lewis acid-base concept, 141-143
Lewis electron-dot formulas, 70
Libby, William, 248
Light-scattering, 126-127
Line spectra, 58
Lowry, 132

M

Markownikov's rule, 223
Mass, 19, 25

Mass action, 159-160
Mass-energy equivalence, 242
Mass spectrograph, 51
Matter, different kinds, 26
Matter, states:
  Avogadro's hypothesis, 33, 36, 37, 39-40
  gas laws, 33-37
  general gas equation, 40-41
  kinetic-molecular theory, 33-47
  liquid and solids, 42-44
    changes in state, 43-44
    physical properties, 42-43
  real and ideal gases, 41-42
  temperature, 37-39
  vapor pressure, 44-47
Maxwell, 57
Maxwell-Boltzmann distribution curve, 34
Measurement, 18, 20
"Mechanism of the Organic Reaction," 233, 249
Medicine, 248-249
Melting points, ionic compounds, 86-87
Mendeleeff, 64, 65
Metal-organic compounds, 220
Metals:
  corrosion, 207-209
  periodic properties, 66-67
Metathesis, 32
Method, scientific, 17-18
Mev, 238
Meyer, 64, 96
Millikan, Robert, 52
Million electron-volts, 238
Mixtures, 26-28
Model, 17
Molar solutions, 102-104
Molarity, 102
Mole concept, 29, 91-93
Molecular equations, 196
Molecular formulas, 30, 31
Molecular geometry, 77-82
"Molecular Motions," 43
Molecular orbital theory, 74
Molecular weights, 95-97
Momentum, 33
Moseley, Henry, 65
Motion, Newton's law, 25
Multiple-ring compounds, 215

N

Nernst equation, 182
Net ionic equation, 198
Neutrons, 55
Newton, 25
Nitriles, 220
Nitro compounds, 220
Nomenclature, 213-214
Non-aromatic compounds, 215
Non-electrolytes, 53, 125
Non-ionic equilibrium, 166-169
Non-metals, periodic properties, 66-67
Normal solutions, 102-104
Nuclear phenomena:
  Bethe, Hans, 247
  binding energy, 242
  carbon cycle, 247
  Cockroft and Walton, 243
  conversion of hydrogen to helium, 247
  dueterium, 247, 249
  Einstein, 241, 242
  energy sources of stars, 247-248
  fission, 242-243, 245
  fusion, 242-243, 245
  Hahn and Strassman, 243
  half-life, 243
  kilowatt hour equivalent, 241
  lithium and hydrogen nuclei, 243
  mass-energy equivalence, 242
  nuclear force, 240
  "nuclear well," 240, 246
  particles of same charge, 240
  positron, 247
  proton chain, 247
  radioactive isotopes, 248-249
    cancer therapy, 249
    cobalt, 249
    cosmic rays, 248
    dating igneous rocks, 248

Nuclear phenomena (*cont.*)
radioactive isotopes (*cont.*)
dating materials containing carbon, 248
dating materials containing hydrogen 3, 248
dynamic nature of equilibrium, 249
hydrolysis of ester, 249
Libby, William, 248
solar radiation, 248
tracers, 248, 249
radioactivity, 237-240
Becquerel, Henri, 237
Curies, 237, 245
detecting, 237
electron-volt, 238
electroscope, 237
fast moving electrons, 237
Geiger counter, 237, 249
helium in radioactive minerals, 238
ionized air, 237
joule, 238
million electron-volts, 238
polonium, 237
radium, 237
Rutherford, 238, 244, 248
three types of rays, 237
transmutations, 239
undesired biochemical reactions, 240, 246
rate of decay, 243
reactions, 244-246
americium, 241, 245
artificial radioactivity, 245
atomic pile, 245
Brookhaven National Laboratories synchotron, 245
controlled nuclear fission, 245
controlled nuclear fusion, 245
cyclotron, 245
first artificial transmutation, 244
fission bomb, 246
Graham's law, 246
Joliot, 245
Lawrence, E. O., 244-245
modern particle accelerators, 245
nuclear reactor, 245
Nuclear phenomena (*cont.*)
artificial radioactivity (*cont.*)
peaceful uses of energy, 245
plutonium, 245-246
separation of uranium isotopes, 246
thermonuclear, 246
relativity, 241
star is born, 247
uranium, 243
"Nuclear well," 240, 246
Nucleophilic substitution, 231

O

Oils, 219
Olmsted, 162
Operational definitions, 18
Optical isomerism, 228
Orbitals, 59-61, 77-82
Organic compounds:
Acids, Bases, and the Chemistry of the Covalent Bond, 229
addition reactions, 222
chemistry of OH Group, 222
chief sources, 211
classifying and naming, 212-220
alcohols, 217-219
aldehydes, 218
aliphatic hydrocarbons, 217
alkanes, 212
alkenes, 214, 215
amides, 220
amines, 220
aromatic, 215, 216, 217
aromatic hydrocarbons, 217
bond angles, 213
butanes, 213
carbonyl group, 218
carboxylic acids, 219
corners of geometric figures, 215
cyclic alkanes, 213
cyclic alkenes, 215
cyclic hydrocarbons, 215
cyclic (ring) compounds, 215
cyclohexane, 215

Organic compounds (*cont.*)
classifying and naming (*cont.*)
esters, 219
ethers, 217-218
fats, 219
halides, 220
Handbook of Chemistry and Physics, 214
heterocyclic, 215
hydrocarbons, 217
isobutane, 213
Kekule structural formula, 216
ketones, 218
metal-organic, 220
multiple-ring, 215
naming branched chain hydrocarbons, 213
nitriles, 220
nitro, 220
no "straight chain," 213
nomenclature, 213-214
non-aromatic, 215
number of double bonds, 214
oils, 219
orientation of substituents around ring, 217
paraffin, 212
permutations and combinations, 215
prefixes denoting number of carbon atoms, 212
prefixes from pentane, 213
saturated, 212
structural formulas, 212
structural isomerism, 213
thioethers, 220
thiols, 220
unsaturated, 212
writing formulas simply, 212-213
coal, 211
isomerism, 226-229
(*see also* Isomerism)
majority are molecular, 211
Markownikov's rule, 223
non-aqueous solvents, 211
number, 211, 212

Organic compounds (*cont.*)
of biological interest, 233-236
alkaloids, 235
"Biochemistry and Molecular Structure," 236
carbohydrates, 233
cellulose, 234
DNA, 235
enzymes, 234
fats, 234
hormones, 235
porphyrins, 235
proteins, 235
RNA, 235
starch, 234
"unsaturated fats," 234
organic reactions, 229-233
(*see also* Organic reactions)
petroleum, 211
polymerization, 224
properties interpreted from structure and electronic effects, 220-226
Shape of Carbon Compounds, 229
some salts, 211
synthesized, 211
urea, 211
vitalistic theory, 211
Wohler, 211
esterification, 232
free radical mechanisms, 229
Friedel-Crafts, 231
hydrolysis of ester, 232
ionic mechanisms, 229
"Mechanism of the Organic Reaction," 233, 249
substitution, 230-231
bimolecular nucleophilic, 231
elctrophilic, 231
"Synthesis of an Organic Compound," 233
Organizational energy, 26
Osmotic pressure, 124
Ostwald Process, 168
Overvoltage, 147
Oxidation number, 69, 75-77, 190, 192-194
(*see also* Oxidation-reduction)

Oxidation potential concept, 108-110
Oxidation-reduction:
  balancing redox equations, 196-199
    electron transfer, 196
    half-reactions, 198
    ionic redox equations, 198
    molecular equations, 196
    net ionic equation, 198
    reactants and products, 197
  E° concept, 200-204
  "Electrochemical Cells," 203
  half-reactions, 194-196
  oxidation number, 190, 192-194
    assigning, 193
    defined, 190
    determining from formula, 192-194
    free element, 192, 193
    hydrogen, 192, 193
    oxygen, 192, 193
    peroxides, 192
    total in any specie, 192, 193
  redox, 189-192

P

Paraffin, 212
Paramagnetism, 59
Particle accelerators, 245
Pauli, 60
Pauling, Linus, 75
Per cent, 20
Per cent compositions, 98
Periodic law, 64-66
Periodic properties, 62, 66-67
Periodic table, 257-260
Periodicity, 140-141
Petit, 95
Petroleum, 211
pH, 110-113, 148-149
Phlogiston theory, 18
Photoelectric effect, 53, 55, 57
Photons, 57
Physical changes, 28
Planck, Max, 57
Plutonium, 245-246
Polonium, 237
Polymerization, 224
Porphyrins, 235
Positional isomerism, 227
Positron, 247
Powers of ten, 19
Practical situations, relating principles, 252-257
Pressure, 33
Primary alcohol, 218
Primary amines, 220
Principles:
  descriptive chemistry and chemical principles, 264-268
  relate to practical situations, 252-257
Products, 197
Properties:
  colloids, 125-127
    (*see also* Colloids)
  electrolytes, 129-132
  compound, 69-89
    (*see also* Bonding)
  liquids and solids, 42-44
  organic compounds, 220-226
  solutions, 115-126
    (*see also* Solutions)
Proteins, 235
Proton chain, 247
Protons, 55
Prout, William, 55

Q

Qualitative, 17
Quantitative, 17-18
Quantum atom, 56-59
Quantum mechanics, 56-59

R

Radioactive decomposition, 54
Radioactivity, 53, 54-55
    (*see also* Nuclear phenomena)

Radium, 237
Raoult's law, 97, 132
Rate-concentration dependence, 23-24
Rate laws, determining experimentally, 155-158
Rates of reactions, 151
Rays, three types, 237
Reactants, 197
Reasoning, 18
Redox, developing the concept, 189-192
Redox equations, 31, 196-199
Relative error, 20
Relativity theory, 241
Research, 248-249
Resonance, 85-87
RNA, 235
Rounding off numbers, 19
Rutherford, 53, 54, 55, 238, 239, 244, 248
"Rutherford Atom," 54

S

Saturated, defined, 212
Saturated solutions, 119-120
Scientific method, 17-18
Scientific notation, 19
Scintillation, 238
Secondary alcohol, 218
Secondary amines, 220
Shape of Carbon Compounds, 229
"Shapes and Polarities of Molecules," 118
Shielding effect, 62
Significant figures, 19
Soddy, Frederick, 50
Solar radiation, 248
Solubility and solubility curves, 120-121
Solubility product, 160
Solute, 116-118
Solute particles, 118
Solutions:
  colligative properties, 122-125
    boiling point elevation, 123
    freezing point depression, 123-124
Solutions (*cont.*)
  colligative properties (*cont.*)
    osmotic pressure, 124-125
    vapor pressure lowering, 122
  crystallization, 120-121
  distinct from colloids and suspensions, 125-126
  electrolytes, 125, 129-132
  "Equilibrium," 119
  factors influencing solubility, 116-118
    effect of temperature, 118
    nature of solute and solvent, 116-118
    size of solute particles, 118
    stirring and mixing, 118
  gases in liquids, 121-122
  general properties, 115-116
  Henry's law, 121
  hydration, 116
  molar and normal, 102-104
  non-electrolytes, 125
  "Shapes and Polarities of Molecules," 118
  solubility, 120-121
  solubility curves, 120-121
  solvation, 116
  unsaturated, saturated, supersaturated, 119-120
Solvation, 116
Solvent, 116-118
Starch, 234
Stellar energy, 247-248
Stern, 59
Stoichiometry, 100-102
"Straight chain," 213
Strassman, 243
Stratton, 178
Strong, 178
Structural isomerism, 213, 226
Subatomic particles, 29
Sublimation, 46
Substitution reaction, 230-231
Supersaturated solutions, 119-120
Suspensions, 125-126
Synchotron, 245
"Synthesis of an Organic Compound," 233

T

Temperature, 37-39
Temperature-pressure-volume relationship, 33
Thermoionic effect, 55
Thermonuclear reactions, 246
Thioethers, 220
Thiols, 220
Thompson, J. J., 51, 53, 237, 238
Transmutations, 239, 244
Tyndall effect, 127

U

Unsaturated, defined, 212
"Unsaturated fats," 234
Unsaturated solutions, 119-120
Uranium, 243
Urea, 211

V

Valence:
- bond theory, 74
- defined, 69
- equivalence, 70
- historically, 69
- hydrogen atoms, 69
- Lewis electron-dot formulas, 70
- positive and negative, 70

Valence (*cont.*)
- sum of positive and negative, 70
- table, 69, 70

Validity, 20
Vander Waals, 41, 42, 85
Vander Werf, 143, 229
Vapor pressure, 44-47, 122
Velocity, 25
Victor Meyer method, 96
Vitalistic theory, 211
Vitamins, 235

W

Waage, 159
Walton, 243
Wave mechanics, 58
Wohler, 211
Why Do Chemical Reactions Occur, 158, 160
Word equations, 30

X

X-ray diffraction, 43
X-ray spectra, 65

Z

Zeeman effect, 59